# BEER, BED
## AND
# BREAKFAST

# BEER, BED
## AND
# BREAKFAST

### Edited by Roger Protz

Robson Books

in association with the Campaign for Real Ale

Designed by Harold King

*Maps by David Perrott*

Cover picture of the Falkland Arms, Great Tew, Oxon, courtesy of John Milligan

First published in Great Britain in 1988 by Robson Books Ltd., Bolsover House, 5–6 Clipstone Street, London W1P 7EB.

**British Library Cataloguing in Publication Data**

Beer, bed and breakfast.—2nd ed.
  1. Great Britain. Inns — Directories
  I. Protz, Roger II. Campaign for Real Ale
  647'.9441

ISBN 0-86051-482-X
ISBN 0-86051-510-9 Pbk

Typeset by Action Typesetting Limited, Gloucester
Printed by Billing & Sons Ltd, Worcester

# CONTENTS

# INTRODUCTION

*There is nothing which has yet been contrived by man, by which so much happiness is produced as by a good tavern or inn.*

Boswell's *Life of Dr Johnson*

Slowly but surely we are rediscovering what the good doctor took for granted two hundred years ago: that inns and taverns·are splendid places in which to drink, dine and rest awhile. The modern 'public house', a Victorian term unknown to Johnson, has tended to play down the eat-and-rest tradition of its predecessors. For generations, the pub was where you went for a pint. If you were hungry, you went to a restaurant; if you were tired and away from home, you went to a hotel.

The first edition of this guide was produced in the hope that it would help rekindle both a desire in travellers to stay in pubs and in publicans to provide accommodation where none existed. That edition found a ready market and has prompted this second one, thoroughly revised and with many new entries. Buyers and users have sent many recommendations for pubs worthy of inclusion and, in a few cases, worthy not only of exclusion but of removal from the face of civilisation. Publicans not in the first edition have lobbied for consideration; those who put down their marker the first time round have responded warmly and encouragingly to edition two. Cynics who say 'Well they would, wouldn't they?' ignore the fact that the average publican is as much unlike his cartoon stereotype (unshaven and unwelcoming) as the average CAMRA member is to his (barrel-belly and wholemeal beard).

Publicans are enthusiasts and their enthusiasm goes well beyond the simple venal one of the ring of the cash register. They are fond of their pubs and want you to share their pleasure. They are proud of their beer and, increasingly, of the food and accommodation they provide. A publican in Nottinghamshire neatly caught the knock-on effect of a good ale house that also offers bed and breakfast in a letter to the guide: 'My visitors have realised that if the beer is OK then the rest will be of good standard.'

*Beer, Bed and Breakfast* is produced for people who enjoy staying in pubs, whether they are on holiday, on business or just travelling. The fact that a second edition has become necessary means that more and more such people prefer the homely atmosphere and personal welcome of a pub to the 'Sorry, what was your room number?' approach of large hotels with wall-to-wall jacuzzis, 'mini-bars' that cost an arm and both legs, and staff who manage the considerable facial feat of curling their lips and looking down their noses at one and the same time.

Pubs are also wonderfully good value: within these pages you will find splendid hostelries in fine towns or beautiful countryside where you can eat and sleep well for around £10 a head. There are some entries where you will pay considerably more and the decision whether to stay in them will depend as much on your attitude to what constitutes a pub as your ability to pay. Many pubs include the word 'hotel' in their names and are within their rights to do so although they remain public houses where the bars, not reception foyers and restaurants, predominate.

Such places make up the bulk of entries in the guide but there are several that are essentially hotels but which include within their walls one or more bars or lounges with a good 'pubby' atmosphere. Purists many object but such establishments may be more amenable to families than a town or rural pub confined by its size to just a public bar and lounge where children cannot enter. To exclude all such hotels would not only reduce the number of entries but would wipe out large areas of Scotland where, away from the Borders, the pub does not exist. Scottish bars are places for serious drinking and accommodation is confined to hotels. In the Home Counties, where pub accommodation is limited as a result of the rise of the chain hotel, the tendency is to turn pubs into 'semi-hotels' and to price accordingly. We leave it to readers to decide, say, in St Albans, whether they want the genuine, simple pub B&B of the Lower Red Lion or the more expensive offerings of the White Hart and Black Lion with their separate restaurants and lounges. Feedback is welcomed.

Some of the glaring gaps in the first edition have been filled. There are many new entries in Scotland, Yorkshire, Wales and East Anglia. The Home Counties remain difficult terrain. The hotel chains, many of them part of the 'leisure empires' that used to be simple brewing companies, have forced publicans either to stop offering accommodation or to ape the hotels with plastic food and beer and upwardly-mobile prices. London and other major cities remain disaster areas as far as pub accommodation is concerned but if you use the new and improved maps in this edition it is possible to stay in a pub within striking distance of most major conurbations.

Bradford, a city that is serious about attracting visitors on business and pleasure, is not only maintaining and restoring buildings that are an important part of the North's industrial and archaeological heritage but also offers a good choice of pub accommodation. Other towns and cities please do likewise, especially in the south-east. We can do no more than repeat our appeal in the first edition for publicans in the Home Counties to avoid the flash and the fancy and to offer facilities for visitors that are the opposite of the tawdry package hotel rather than its insipid lookalike.

## How entries are chosen

The strength of the guide is the strength of CAMRA, the Campaign for Real Ale. Some 19,000 members provide a vast data base of nationwide pub information. From that base they have chosen a select number for this guide, augmented by the recommendations of users of the first edition and those found and visited by the editor. CAMRA members literally climb every mountain in their eagerness to maintain and update their information on pubs. They do so in their spare time and holidays without any form of recompense, not even travel expenses. As always I owe them an enormous debt for their enthusiasm. Wherever possible, information supplied by both CAMRA members and readers is checked with publicans to ensure that prices, facilities and beers are as up to date as possible.

CAMRA members cannot find every outlet. Readers are invited and encouraged to submit new entries by using the forms at the back of this edition. If you can improve on the description of an existing outlet your wise words will be welcomed, for some CAMRA members and publicans lose their usual loquaciousness when confronted by a blank sheet of paper. Needless to say, we are also anxious to hear of any entries that fall short of acceptable standards.

## Prices

Prices for rooms are, in the main, 1987 ones as few licensees were willing to project ahead to the spring of 1988. The prices shown, however, do give a good indication of the type of pub and range of facilities offered. It is advisable always to check prices as well as availability of accommodation before leaving home. Wherever possible we give the price for both single and double rooms or the price per person if using a double. Most pubs have now adopted the sensible practice of charging on a room basis rather than per person: if an entry says '£16 single, £28 double' they will be room prices. We try to make it clear when rooms are charged on a per person basis, i.e. 'double £15 per person'.

## Children

There is still a widespread belief that children cannot stay in pubs. They can and, as this guide makes clear, many pubs positively welcome children and set aside family rooms and outdoor play areas for their use.

The legal position is as follows: persons under 18 cannot be served in bars dispensing alcohol and children under 16 cannot be served in pub dining rooms. But pubs and hotels with residential licences can admit children to bedrooms, dining rooms and residents' lounges. Even when a full residential licence does not operate, an increasing number of publicans provide family facilities away from bars. We list all known outlets that allow children to stay, have family rooms or lounges, and provide reduced rates for children. It is important to check that a chosen pub does still accept children: a change of licensee could vary the situation. Readers who regularly take children to pubs or who would like to do so are urged to buy CAMRA's companion guide *Pubs for Families* advertised on page 222 in this edition. It lists pubs that have family rooms, gardens and play areas, dining rooms with children's menus and high chairs, and rooms for feeding and changing babies.

## Licensing hours

England and Wales may at long last be liberated from the hangover of the Defence of the Realm Act introduced in World War One to stop munitions workers from over-indulgence. A bill before parliament is expected to become law in 1988 and will allow pubs to open all day from Monday to Saturday. There will be no compulsion for licensees to open from 11am to 11pm, however, and the likely outcome is that publicans will fashion their hours to suit their trade. Visitors may find during the lifetime of this guide that pubs in tourist and holiday areas will remain open during the afternoon when there is a demand.

An amendment in 1987 to existing law allows pubs with separate dining areas to serve alcohol with meals during the afternoon, good news for visitors who arrive at a pub outside 'permitted hours' in urgent need of sustenance.

Scotland has had the benefit of afternoon and late night opening for a decade now and many of the pubs and hotels in the guide will offer food and drink all day long, including Sundays. A few areas of Wales are still 'dry' on Sunday and it is worth checking before setting out for a stay in a Welsh pub. But in general pubs throughout Britain that have residential licences have considerable freedom to dispense food and drink outside permitted hours to people who book accommodation.

## Food

We give details of lunch and dinner menus when these are supplied by either CAMRA inspectors or licensees. The guide, in spite of its title, receives little information about breakfasts. We are anxious to know more about the quality and range of breakfasts offered as they are an important element of the price of accommodation. Please send us information about good breakfasts and also indicate what you, the consumers, look for. How many people actually want a 'traditional English cooked breakfast' and prefer a choice that offers a range of cereals and bread and rolls, fish (bring back the kipper!) and coffee — ground not 'keg'— as well as tea? We are keen to award accolades for good breakfasts in the next edition and your nominations are keenly anticipated.

## Real ale

Real ale, also known as traditional draught beer or cask-conditioned beer, is a definition of a British beer style that is accepted by the Oxford English Dictionary. It means a top-fermented beer that undergoes a natural secondary fermentation in the cask and which is served without applied gas pressure. Most pubs in this guide serve real ale by a simple suction pump, a beer engine, that draws beer from the cask in the cellar when the handpump on the bar is pulled. Some pubs still serve the beer straight from the cask while others — often in the Midlands and parts of the North of England — use electric pumps. They do exactly the same job as a handpump and beer engine but can be confused with the founts used for keg beers. In Scotland the traditional method of serving real ale is air pressure: when the tap on the tall fount or more modern dispenser is operated, an electric compressor forces air into the cask and beer up to the bar. Many Scottish bars have handpumps as well. For details of all draught beers and their strengths you should consult the annual *Good Beer Guide*. The 1988 edition costs £5.95 from CAMRA, 34 Alma Road, St Albans, Herts AL1 3BW.

The first edition of this guide was a voyage into uncharted territory. Many people signed on for the journey and discovered a wealth of pubs offering the old-fashioned virtues of good ale, victuals and beds. The aim of this second edition is to point readers in the direction of old friends from edition one and many new ones as well. We hope, too, as you travel the country and enjoy the hostelries on offer that you will agree with CAMRA that Britain's traditional pubs and beer are worthy of protection for future generations to savour and enjoy.

ROGER PROTZ

# JOIN CAMRA!

Since the early 1970s the Campaign for Real Ale has been battling to defend and maintain Britain's unique contribution to the world of beer: cask-conditioned draught milds, bitters and strong ales. A decade after its inception it seemed that CAMRA's work was largely done. There was a bountiful supply of draught beer available, much of it produced by buoyant independent companies. But the endemic problems of the brewing industry have surfaced again in the late 1980s. The grim spiral of mergers, takeovers and concentration has re-emerged and threatens once again to obliterate choice and cause terrible damage to the image and fabric of the public house.. The success of much-marketed and highly profitable ersatz lager has prompted the giant brewing combines to seek more outlets for their fizzy products and to concentrate production of both keg beers and traditional draught ones into large brewing complexes with easy access to motorways.

In the two years since this guide first appeared Courage, one of the best-known names in British brewing, has been bought by the Australian group Elders IXL, which includes Foster's lager in its vast portmanteau of interests. The owner of Elders, John Elliott, has a simple ambition in life: to make the whole world drink Fosters. He now sells his brew in both Courage/John Smith's pubs and throughout the Grand Metropolitan/Watney chain. Elders has also bought a sizeable block of shares in the East Anglian independent Greene King with a view to 'encouraging' the company to switch its lager allegiance from Guinness's Harp to Foster's. An outright bid for Greene King cannot be ruled out.

Another Australian tycoon, Alan Bond, owner of Castlemaine XXXX, is busily buying shares in the vast drinks and leisure group Allied Lyons, with such brewing subsidiaries as Ansells, Tetley and Ind Coope. In the wings, the world's largest brewer, Anheuser-Busch of the US, better known as Budweiser, has registered itself on the European stock exchanges and may have thoughts of joining the British beerage.

Home-grown groups have not been idle in the meantime. Scottish and Newcastle (best known as McEwan and Younger) has added Lancashire, North Yorkshire and the East Midlands to its geographic spread through the acquisition of Matthew Brown, Theakston and the Home Brewery of Nottingham. Greenall Whitley of Warrington now owns Davenport of Birmingham as well as Shipstone of Nottingham. It will close its earlier acquisition, Wem of Shropshire, in 1988.

Watney, reviled by CAMRA in the 1970s as Grotney, has, like the Borgias, learnt nothing and forgotten nothing. It has closed Drybrough of Edinburgh, Wilson of Manchester and merged two non-brewing distributors, Mann and Norwich, into one vast wholesaler for the East of England. A looming question mark now hangs over Truman and Usher. Watney has attempted to hang a fig leaf of respectability over its activities by acquiring one of the legendary names of independent brewing, Ruddle of Rutland. But the main thrust of its real ale activity has been to turn Webster's Yorkshire Bitter into a national brand, to denude it of taste and character, and to set a trend of bland and undistinguished cask beers that other companies, both national and regional, have sadly decided to follow.

Offered a pint of Websters and asked, after you have supped it, if 'you've had a good pint', it would not be unreasonable to paraphrase Groucho Marx by replying: 'Yes, and this wasn't one of them.' Bland beer, lacking the exciting smack of malt and hops, is as much an insult to beer lovers as claret reduced to the level of Ribena would be to wine imbibers.

The list of fallen and disabled proliferates: Greene King closed Rayment of Hertfordshire in 1987, Whitbread will close Wethered of Marlow and Chester of Salford in 1988; Wethered will be yet another cask beer trunked around Britain from Whitbread's Cheltenham plant. The Webster's Yorkshire Bitter phenomenon seems likely to set a sorry trend of lack-lustre national brands that offend nobody and excite nobody by their lack of taste and distinction.

The knock-on effect on pubs is clear to see. The egalitarian notion of the 'public house' open to all is being eroded by the ugly newspeak of 'profit bases' and 'demographic studies' that divide brewery outlets into café bars, brasseries and mock-traditional inns replete with plastic beams and food.

These threats to our beer and pubs — and an important element of our national heritage — can be thwarted only by a vigorous campaigning body that can lobby parliament, brewers and the European institutions. CAMRA has achieved much in its short life: many of the pubs in this guide and the beers they serve would not exist but for the campaign's activities. But, as this short piece has emphasised, the past victories were merely minor skirmishes: the great battles lie ahead.

If you value British beer and pubs then CAMRA would welcome you in its ranks. For £9 a year you will receive a monthly newspaper, *What's Brewing*, that will keep you in touch with the latest developments in the world of beer, plus generous discounts on such publications as the *Good Beer Guide* and *Beer, Bed and Breadfast*. You will be able to attend local CAMRA branches, the national annual meeting, and trips to brewing centres in Britain and Europe.

Don't delay ... your local brew and favourite local could be destroyed if you do. Send a cheque for £9 today (payable to CAMRA Ltd) to the Membership Department (B&B), CAMRA, 34 Alma Road, St Albans, Herts AL1 3BW.

Good drinking ... and good pubbing.

# REPORT FORM

County _____

Town or village _____

Name of pub/hotel _____

Address _____

Location (A or B road) _____

Tel no _____ Name of licensee _____

Description of pub (including bars, food, guest rooms and any special facilities) _____

_____

_____

_____

Draught beers (including method of dispense) _____

_____

_____

## Accommodation:

No of single rooms _____ doubles/twins _____ family rooms _____

Cost of B & B per person per day _____ cost for double/twin if price based on room _____ cost for family room _____

No of rooms with en suite baths or showers _____

Can children stay ☐ yes ☐ no Children's reductions _____

Cost of any special 'breaks', eg off-season, weekend, mid-week _____

Name and address of person recommending _____

_____

_____

**Send to**
**Roger Protz, CAMRA, 34 Alma Road St Albans, Herts AL1 3BW**

# ENGLAND

WHEELWRIGHTS ARMS, MONKTON COMBE — *see opposite*

# KEYNSHAM

Crown Inn
3 Bristol Road, ½ mile off A4

Licensee: Geoff Ellis
Tel: 0272 862150

An unspoilt pub with a large collection of photographs of old Keynsham and other local memorabilia. Darts and cribbage are played in the bar and Mrs Ellis, the landlady, has been class 3 ladies European champion five times and world champion once in the sport of land yachting. The Crown, 4 miles from Bristol and 7 from Bath, has graced every edition of the *Good Beer Guide* due to the quality of its ale. Good home-made pub grub is served lunchtime and evening.

Beer: Courage BA, Best Bitter and Directors on handpumps

Accommodation: 2 singles, 3 doubles, 1 family room. B&B £14 per person.
Week £77. Children welcome.

# MONKTON COMBE

Wheelrights Arms
½ miles off A36, 3 miles S of Bath

Proprietors: Ric & Monica Gillespie
Tel: 022 122 2287

A fine old inn built in the middle of the 18th century and first licensed in 1871. The Wheelrights was once owned by a viscount and was in competition with the local monastery, which brewed its own ale. It stands in the lovely Midford Valley and is quiet and remote yet is just three miles from the stately pleasures of Bath. The accommodation is in a converted barn and stables. Each room has a shower, colour TV and tea and coffee making facilities. You can try your hand at darts and cribbage with the locals and in winter you can warm yourself by a roaring log fire. There are bar snacks, lunches and evening grills (no snacks Friday and Saturday evenings).

Beer: Adnams Bitter, Butcombe Bitter, Wadworth 6X, Whitbread West Country Pale Ale plus guest beers served by handpumps and straight from the cask.

Accommodation: 8 doubles/twins. B&B from £19 per person. Winter Break (Oct-March) any two days or more from £26 per day per person, includes B&B plus evening meal. Children over 14 welcome, no reductions. Credit cards: Access, Visa (for stays of 3 days or more. Not accepted for meals or Winter Breaks).

# RADSTOCK

Waldgrave Arms Hotel
Market Place on A367

Licensee: Graham Smith
Tel: 0761 32206

A comfortable family-run pub in countryside that was once the heart of the former Somerset coalfields where all the mines were closed some 30 years ago. The hotel is a handy base for visiting Bath, the stunning cathedral mini-city of Wells, Wookey Hole and Longleat. The Waldgrave has a pleasant lounge where meals and snacks are served every day except Sunday evening. The bar is a haven for indoor sports lovers, with two darts boards and three pool tables. There is also a skittles alley with its own bar and a residents' TV lounge.

Beer: Courage Best Bitter on handpump.

Accommodation: 4 singles, 3 doubles, 1 family room, B&B £10 single, £18 double or twin per person. Children welcome, charged half price.

# TORMARTON

## Compass Inn
B4465 off A46 (junction 18 M4)

Proprietors: Mr & Mrs P Moynard
Tel: 045 421 242/577

The ivy-clad Compass is a carefully modernised 18th century coaching inn, so named because a former landlord decorated the building with chandlery from Bristol's shipyards. The four Cotswold stone bars maintain the sea-going flavour with beams and a pair of ship's lanterns in the Long Bar. The inn has a separate restaurant with à la carte menu, specialising in local game and produce. There is also a hot and cold buffet every lunchtime and evening. There are lawns, gardens and a charming orangery. Many of the guest rooms have private baths and all have TVs and tea and coffee making facilities. In the heart of the Cotswolds, the Compass is close to Tetbury and its annual Woolsack race, Badminton House with its horse trials, the ancient hilltop town of Malmesbury, and the old Roman town of Cirencester.

Beer: Archers Village Bitter, Bass, Wadworth 6X on handpumps.

Accommodation: 19 rooms. B&B £31.50 single, £42.50 double, extra charge for private bath or shower. Winter Break (Oct-March) 2 days £59.95 per person, 3 days £89.95, further days £27.50. Dogs welcome, charged £1 per night.

# WINSCOMBE

## Woodborough
Sandford Road on A371

Licensee: G W Ashdowne
Tel: 0934 84 2167

The Woodborough is a mock-Tudor pub that was rebuilt in the 1930s following a fire. With live entertainment every weekend in the large skittles alley, the pub is the hub of the village and the surrounding area. The warm and welcoming lounge has snacks and bar meals and there is also an à la carte menu. It is a good base for the Cheddar Gorge, Weston Super Mare and Sandford Ski Centre.

Beer: Courage Best Bitter on handpump.

Accommodation: 1 single, 3 doubles, £12.50 single, £12 double per person. No children.

# SALFORD

## Red Lion Country Hotel
Wavendon Road: unclassified road 2 miles NW of M1 junction 13; off A421 & A507

Licensee: John Dicks
Tel: 0908 583117

A 16th-century inn in extensive grounds in a rural village that is only 10 minutes from Milton Keynes. There are exposed beams and cottage décor, bric-à-brac and a roaring log fire in winter. For couples keen on nuptials as well as real ale there is a honeymoon suite. The hotel is a good base for Woburn Sands, Apsley Heath, Milton Keynes shopping centre and Silverstone motor racing circuit. The Red Lion

---

offers bar snacks with a separate restaurant for lunch and dinner.

Beer: Charles Wells Eagle Bitter and Bombardier on handpumps.

Accommodation: 11 rooms, 6 with private baths: 3 singles, 6 doubles, 2 twin. B&B £24 single, double/twin £37, honeymoon suite £40. Children welcome, rates negotiable. Ground-floor facilities for the disabled.

## STEVINGTON

Red Lion
1 Park Road, 1½ miles N of A428

Licensees: Len & Margaret Davis
Tel: 02302 4138

A friendly, half-beamed local in an attractive village next to a medieval stone cross. The lounge bar serves snacks, lunches and evening meals plus traditional Sunday lunch for which you must book. The cheerful public bar has darts, dominoes and crib and there is a garden with a children's play area and a bird aviary. Stevington has John Bunyan connections and a restored 18th-century windmill and holy well. Bromham, 2 miles away, has a water mill and museum on the river Ouse.

Beer: Greene King IPA and Abbot Ale on handpumps.

Accommodation: 2 double rooms. B&B £12 single, £20 double plus VAT. Children welcome, terms negotiable.

## WOBURN

Magpie
Bedford Street on A418, close to M1

Licensees: Pat & Mac McLaren
Tel: 052 525 219

A 400-year-old pub with a warm welcome, handy for Woburn Safari Park and golf course. The comfortable lounge has bar snacks while the separate restaurant has an à la carte menu. The spacious bedrooms have tea and coffee making facilities and colour TVs. The Magpie is famed for its vast breakfasts — duck eggs are always available — and a resident ghost called Algy.

Beer: Ruddles Best Bitter and County, Websters Yorkshire Bitter on handpumps.

Accommodation: 5 double rooms, 3 with showers, 1 family room. B&B £16 single, £20 with shower, double £25, £30 with shower. Children welcome, terms depend on age.

# BERKSHIRE

## KNOWL HILL

Seven Stars
Bath Road on A4 between Maidenhead & Reading, 5 miles from Maidenhead, 2½ miles from junctions 8/9 of M4

Licensees: Robin & Lyn Jones
Tel: 062 882 2967

A 17th-century coaching inn with a Georgian frontage and comfortable panelled rooms with log fires in winter. The large gardens have tree houses and swings for children and the pub has a children's room. The splendid home-cooked grub is served until 9pm every day. The pub has a

skittles alley and there are limited
facilities for the disabled. Knowl Hill
is a good base for Henley-on-
Thames, home of Brakspear's
traditional brewery, Windsor,
Marlow — no longer the home of
Wethered's traditional brewery —
and the Shire Horse Centre.

Beer: Brakspear Mild, Bitter, Special
and Old on handpumps.

Accommodation: 3 double rooms.
B&B £15-£25. Children welcome.

# REMENHAM

Two Brewers
Wargrave Road, junction of A321
& A423

Licensees: Ann & Russell Blumire
Tel: 0491 574375

A warm welcome is guaranteed in
this cosy panelled pub with a
roaring log fire in winter. There are
hanging baskets, a children's room
and a pleasant dining area off the
lounge. Excellent food is served
every day. You can enjoy riverside
walks or stroll across the attractive
18th-century bridge with five arches
into Henley, home of Brakspear's
brewery and the annual boating
festivities.

Beer: Brakspear Bitter and Old on
handpumps.

Accommodation: 1 single, 3 doubles,
1 with private bath. B&B £14 single,
£28 double. Children welcome, no
reductions.

# TWYFORD

Golden Cross
Waltham Road near Reading, 50
yards from BR station

Licensee: Ralph Vines
Tel: 0734 340180

A cheerful, traditional two-bar local
built in 1839 in the centre of the
village with a garden and lunchtime
meals. The Golden Cross is
mercifully quiet, with pub games but
no canned music or electronic
games. The guest rooms have TVs
and tea and coffee making facilities.

Beer: Wethered Bitter, Sam
Whitbread Strong Ale and guest
beers on handpumps.

Accommodation: 2 rooms, one
single, one double. B&B £15-£25.
Half and full board terms on
application.

# WARGRAVE

Bull Hotel
High Street on A321

Licensee: Noel Harman
Tel: 0733 522 3120

The Bull is a 16th-century listed
building with exposed beams and
unusually decorated brick walls in
the bars and dining area and two
enormous fireplaces with blazing log
fires in winter. Wargrave is an
attractive Thames-side village 4 miles
from Henley. The pub has a garden
and patio. The guest rooms have
central heating and colour TVs. The
restaurant, known as Mo's Kitchen,
has a good local reputation for the
quality of its meals and features such
dishes as smoked salmon, Portuguese
sardines, poulet basque and fresh
grilled trout.

Beer: Brakspear Bitter and Special on
handpumps.

Accommodation: 2 singles, 3 doubles. B&B £17 single, £30 double. Evening meals available. No children.

# WOOLHAMPTON

Angel Inn
Bath Road on A4 between Reading and Newbury

Licensees: Roger and Lyn Jarvis
Tel: 0734 713307

A delightful ivy-covered pub near the Kennet and Avon canal. Roger Jarvis is a compulsive collector of bric-à-brac and crams the bar with his garnerings, including 70 blow lamps. The beer garden is a lovely setting in good weather, with a bridge over a large pond. Lyn Jarvis specialises in first-class home-cooked food. Bar snacks include such unusual delicacies as upside-down pie (Stilton and bacon) and spiced Mexican beef with bananas and coconut. The restaurant dishes range from rump steaks and fresh local trout to vegetarian meals.

Beer: Flowers Original, Wethered Bitter, SPA and Winter Royal, Sam Whitbread Strong Ale and such guest beers from the Whitbread range as Chesters and Fremlins, all on handpumps.

Accommodation: 3 singles, 4 doubles in annexe, 5 with en suite showers. £18 single, £30 double. Children welcome, no reductions. Credit cards: Access, Amex, Diners, Visa.

# AYLESBURY

Bell
Market Square on A41

Licensee: Anne-Marie Brennan
Tel: 0296 89835/82141

The Bell was built in the 16th century as a private house and was vigorously extended and developed in the 19th century. The history is reflected in the varying sizes of the beautifully appointed guest rooms, all of which have colour TVs, phones and tea and coffee making facilities. There are welcoming log fires in winter in the cocktail and market bars. The hotel is based at the quiet, lower end of the old market square where statues of John Hampden, a leading parliamentary opponent of Charles I, and Benjamin Disraeli stress Aylesbury's historical connections. The Bell is also a good vantage point for visiting St Mary's Church, one of the town's oldest buildings, the Bucks County Museum, and the County Hall designed by Vanbrugh. Further afield is Waddesdon Manor recreated along the lines of a French chateau by Baron de Rothschild, Mentmore Towers and Winslow Hall. Back at the Bell you can enjoy hot and cold snacks lunchtime and evening as well as full meals in the Chaucer restaurant. There are cots, high chairs and baby-listening facilities for parents with young children.

Beer: Wethered Bitter and SPA on handpumps.

Accommodation: 6 singles, 11 doubles/twins, 16 with own bathrooms. Prices are for rooms only; breakfast is extra. Singles £45-£51, doubles/twins £55-£61. Weekend breaks £33-£38 single, £29-£33 doubles/twins per person per night: prices include breakfast and dinner, service and VAT. Children welcome, terms on application. Credit cards: Access, Amex, Diners, Visa.

# CUDDINGTON

Crown
Aylesbury Road, off A418

Licensee: Phil Goodacre
Tel: 0844 292222

A fine old thatched building dating from the 13th century, the Crown has low beams and inglenooks plus such 20th-century attributes as central heating and tea and coffee making facilities in the guest rooms. The excellent pub food is all home made and the bar has a wealth of traditional pub games. Cuddington won the coveted Best Kept Village in Bucks award in 1987 and the trophy is displayed in the Crown. Aylesbury is 6 miles away and nearby attractions include Waddesdon Manor, and Wotton House in Wotton Underwood, which is almost identical to the original Buckingham House before it became Buckingham Palace. To the north, from Quainton Railway Centre, steam trains run to Aylesbury in the summer.

Beer: ABC Best Bitter, Chiltern Beechwood Bitter, Everard Tiger on handpumps.

Accommodation: 1 single, 1 double. B&B £15 per person. Evening meals available.

# HAMBLEDEN

Stag & Huntsman
Near Henley-on-Thames, 1 mile N of A4155 at Mill End

Licensee: David Vidgen
Tel: 0491 571227

A large brick and flint 17th-century Chilterns pub in a picturesque National Trust village. There are three comfortable bars, including a public bar where locals play darts and crib. The large garden has swings for children. The innovative food, served lunchtime and evening, includes such rare Chilterns dishes as Mexican-style nachos with hot chilli sauce and peppers. The village is close to the Thames and the fine towns of Henley and Marlow.

Beer: Brakspear Bitter and Special Bitter, Eldridge Pope Royal Oak, Wadworth 6X on handpumps.

Accommodation: 1 single, 2 doubles, 1 with en suite facilities. B&B £15-£25 single, £25-£35 double. Credit cards: Access, Visa.

# HIGH WYCOMBE

Bell
Frogmore, close to junction with A40

Licensee: Mr H W J Lacey
Tel: 0494 21317

A 17th-century pub that has retained its charm and character. Its proximity to a multi-storey car park may detract a little from that character but it does make parking easy for visitors. The Bell serves food lunchtime and evening, including full meals in a restaurant area. It is close to High Wycombe town centre and West Wycombe caves are a short drive away.

Beer: Fuller Chiswick Bitter, London Pride and ESB on handpumps.

Accommodation: 2 singles, 3 doubles. B&B £16.50 per person. No reductions, no children.

## LONGWICK

Red Lion
Thame Road, B4129 near Princes
Risborough

Licensees: Anthony & June Goss
Tel: 084 44 4980

The Red Lion is some 200 years old,
a listed building that is thought once
to have been a chapel. It serves as a
centre for the village but a warm
and informal welcome is extended to
visitors. Bar meals — soup,
ploughman's, pâté, burgers, scampi
— are available as well as grills in the
restaurant. The pub is a splendid
base for walkers in the Chiltern hills
and Blenheim Palace and the Hell
Fire Caves at West Wycombe are
close by.

Beer: ABC Best Bitter, Hook
Norton Best Bitter on handpumps.

Accommodation: 4 singles, 4
doubles, all with en suite facilities.
B&B £28 single, £39 double.
Children over 12 welcome, no
reduction. Credit cards: Access, Visa

## RADNAGE

Three Horseshoes
Bennett End, 3 miles from junction
5 on M40

Licensees: Tim & Rene Ashby
Tel: 024 026 3273

An 18th-century country inn in the
secluded Hughenden Valley, nestling
down narrow lanes. The Three
Horseshoes has old beams and open
fires and a fine garden with splendid
views over the rolling Chilterns.
Woodstock, Windsor and Oxford
are close by. The pub offers
lunchtime snacks, a full evening
menu and a traditional roast lunch
on Sundays. The guest rooms all
have colour TVs and tea and coffee

making facilities, and one room has
a king-size waterbed.

Beer: Brakspear Bitter, Flowers
Original, Wethered SPA on
handpumps.

Accommodation: 3 doubles. B&B
£30 single, £40 double. Children
welcome.

## WESTON TURVILLE

Chandos Arms
1 Main Street, B4043, 1 mile from
A413, 2 miles from A41

Licensee: Keith Charlesworth
Tel: 0296 61 3532

A 200-year-old pub with log fires in
winter and a great range of
traditional games, including
dominoes, darts, crib, bar billiards
and Aunt Sally. The large garden has
20 picnic tables and a children's
corner. Mr Charlesworth's German
wife serves dishes based on recipes
from her homeland: snacks and main
meals Tuesday to Sunday, including
a children's menu. Morris Men
perform in the summer, there are
golf and fishing facilities close by as
well as the Prime Minister's
residence at Chequers.

Beer: Benskins Best Bitter, Burton
Ale and Friary Meux Best Bitter on
handpumps.

Accommodation: 2 singles, 2
doubles. B&B £15 per person,
weekend £30, week £60. Children
welcome, no reductions.

## BUCKINGHAMSHIRE

# WEST WYCOMBE

George & Dragon
On A40

Licensee: Philip Todd
Tel: 0494 23602

The George & Dragon, in a delightful National Trust village, is some 500 years old and was renovated and restored in 1720. An archway leads to an attractive cobbled courtyard and a garden and play area. The inn retains some half-timbers and has ancient pigeon lofts: pigeons used to carry messages when bad weather delayed coaches. Two bedrooms have four-poster beds. West Wycombe Motor Museum has a changing collection of vehicles and memorabilia, and nearby West Wycombe Park, Church Mausoleum and Hell Fire Caves are all open to the public.

Beer: Courage Best Bitter and Directors on handpump.

Accommodation: 2 singles, 4 doubles, 3 twins, all with en suite facilities. B&B from £33 single, £43 double or twin. Weekends from £60 double for 2 nights. Children's room; children sharing a guest room are charged £6 per night.

## CAMBRIDGESHIRE

# BYTHORN

White Hart
On A604

Licensee: R G Thornton
Tel: 080 14 226

The White Hart, in common with many pubs in East Anglia, is a former Watney pub that is now free of the tie. It stands in a pleasant village on the Cambridgeshire-Northants border and has been

## CAMBRIDGESHIR

extensively modernised without losing its essential character as a village local. Hood skittles and darts are played and excellent home-cooked food is available in the restaurant, which is a partitioned section of the lounge bar.

Beer: Marston Pedigree, Charles Wells Eagle Bitter and guest beers, all on handpumps.

Accommodation: 1 single, 2 doubles. B&B + evening meal £15 single, £25 double, Weekend Break £12.50 single, £20 double per person per day.

# CAMBRIDGE

Merton Arms
25 Northampton Street

Licensee: Joseph Nunes
Tel: 0223 359236

The plain, 1930s tiled exterior belies the attractive interior of this former coaching inn which stands on land once owned by Merton College in the rival centre of scholarship in Oxford. It now belongs to St John's College and is leased to Greene King: the lease expires at the end of 1988 and it is doubly advisable to phone the pub before setting off as a question mark hangs over its future. The quiet, wood-panelled lounge at the back is cosy, in sharp contrast to the front bar with its unusual cane furniture where pub life gets pretty lively in term time. There is good value home-cooked food with special dishes every day, a courtyard beer garden and ample parking facilities. Let us hope that the college and the brewery can maintain this splendid local which is managed with great enthusiasm by Jon and Steff Garland.

Beer: Greene King IPA and Abbot Ale on handpumps.

Accommodation: 3 doubles, 1 twin.
B&B £15.50 single, £22 double.
Evening meals available by prior
arrangement.

## Spreadeagle
67 Lensfield Road

Licensee: Paul Smith
Tel: 0223 359571

Proof that inside every boring
boozer there is a smashing pub
struggling to get out. Paul and Pat
Smith took over the Spreadeagle in
1986 and concentrated on stripping
away the unnecessary trappings that
had accumulated over the years. The
result is a traditional pub, unfussy
but comfortable, with a superb
collection of old Cambridge pub
photos adding a touch of bibulous
nostalgia. The food is remarkable
value for money, all home cooked
with main dishes not more than £2.
The Spreadeagle is within easy
walking distance of the town centre
and all the guest rooms are centrally
heated and have tea and coffee
making facilities.

Beer: Castle Eden Ale, Flowers
Original and IPA, Wethered Bitter
and Winter Royal on handpumps.

Accommodation: 1 single, 1 double,
2 family rooms. B&B £15 per
person.

# EARITH

Old Riverview Inn
High Street, A1123 near
Huntingdon

Licensee: P Ceeney
Tel: 0487 841405

The inn is an old, beamed riverside
free house on the Ouse, with
gardens leading down to the river
where the pub has a landing stage
for river traffic. It has an à la carte
restaurant that specialises in game
and traditional English food. The
historic town of St Ives, with its
Oliver Cromwell connections, is just
five minutes away and Cambridge is
15 minutes' drive.

Beer: Adnams Bitter, Bass, Courage
Directors, Everard Tiger, Marston
Pedigree, Samuel Smith Old Brewery
Bitter on handpumps.

Accommodation: 3 singles, 3
doubles, 3 with en suite bathrooms.
B&B £16 per person. Chidren
welcome, half price.

# GODMANCHESTER

Black Bull
Post Street, A604

Licensee: Neil Woodrow
Tel: 0480 53310

The Black Bull is rich in history and
dates back some 380 years. The
warm welcome, good food and ale
are underscored by the blazing log
fires in cold weather. There is a
separate function room that holds
150 people. There is a full restaurant
menu while bar food, served every
day lunchtime and evening, includes
pizzas, cannelloni, fresh trout,
steaks, salads and sandwiches.

Beer: Flowers Original, Wethered
Bitter and Winter Royal on
handpumps.

Accommodation: 3 singles, 6 doubles, 1 family room. B&B £16 single, £30 double. Children welcome.

# GREAT EVERSDEN

Hoops
High Street, 1 mile off A603

Licensee: Alan S Hawkins
Tel: 0223 262185

Splendid old village local down a country road yet close to Cambridge. Parts of the building date back to the late 17th century and you can tuck into the excellent home-cooked food under ancient beams. The Hoops is a good base for visiting Grantchester and Wimpole Hall.

Beer: Charles Wells Eagle Bitter on handpump and Bombardier straight from the cask.

Accommodation: 2 doubles (can be used as singles). B&B £10-£12.50. Half and full board terms available. Children 12 and over welcome.

# HEYDON

King William IV
2 miles off A505, near A10

Licensee: John New
Tel: 0763 838 773/331

Jozsi Hanakamp, the exuberant Viennese restaurateur who gave up the Old Vienna in London to run this carefully extended pub-cum-restaurant on the Herts-Cambridge border near Royston, is a horse-and-carriage fanatic too, with many cups, prizes and rosettes to his name. If you stay for the weekend he will be happy to take you driving. The pub, with 16th-century origins, beams, open fires and walls covered with

horse brasses and tackle, is a fine base for Cambridge, Audley End House, Wimpole Hall and Duxford air museum. In the restaurant you can tuck into gargantuan portions of Viennese food, including goulash, Wiener schnitzel, apfelstrudel, and mushrooms in lager batter, a dish that proves that British 'lager' does have a place — in the kitchen. There is a superb Sunday roast lunch and excellent bar meals are also available.

Beer: Adnams Bitter, Greene King IPA, Rayments BBA on handpumps. 'King William' bitter is a house beer brewed by Banks & Taylor.

Accommodation: 3 doubles, 1 family room, 1 room with four-poster bed. Prices per room: single £18, double £25, four-poster £30. Breakfast £2 per person. No children. Special breaks, including horse-riding weekends, on application.

# KIRTLING

Queens Head
Newmarket Road, off A143 (address is Newmarket, Suffolk, but is just over the border in Cambs)

Licensee: Ann Bailey
Tel: 0638 730253

This fine old 16th-century inn, with its distinctive part flint, part whitewashed façade, was built in 1558 when Good Queen Bess stayed at Kirtling Towers for a short period. The inn was built to accommodate the overflow of guests and government officials who came with the monarch on the Elizabethan gravy train. Today the pub is famed locally for its splendid bar meals that include home-made pies and flans, sorbets, meringues and chocolate rum truffle. Mrs Bailey keeps her ale in excellent nick as befits the chairwoman of the local licensed victuallers' association. The inn is a good base for Newmarket, Ely, Clare and Anglesey Abbey.

Beer: Tolly Cobbold Mild, Bitter, Original and Old Strong (winter) on handpumps.

Accommodation: 1 single, 2 doubles. B&B £12.50-£14 single, £25 double. Evening meals available.

# MOLESWORTH

Cross Keys
100 yards off A604

Licensee: Frances Bettsworth
Tel: 08014 283

The Cross Keys is a handsome inn in a quiet village midway between Huntingdon and Kettering. 'It is a *pub* not a restaurant or a hotel,' says Frances Bettsworth. The wide range of home-cooked food — soup, sausage and chips, shepherds pie, smoked haddock, prawn curry, salads, sandwiches — is served informally in the bar and there is a traditional Sunday roast lunch for £3.75, £3 for children. The modern guest rooms have tea and coffee making facilities and central heating and most have their own bathrooms. The welcome is warm and genuine and visitors are encourage to try their hand at darts and skittles with the locals. Molesworth is just 3 miles from Kimbolton Castle.

Beer: Adnams Bitter straight from the cask.

Accommodation: 1 single, 7 doubles, 1 family room. B&B £12.25 per person. Full board available. Children welcome.

# ST NEOTS

Old Falcon
Market Square, A45, off A1

Licensee: T Tyler
Tel: 0480 72749

The market square dates back to 1135 when the monks of the former priory were granted a market charter. The Old Falcon's origins are as a 16th-century coaching inn and today it has a thriving lounge bar and a separate restaurant with an extensive menu. There are several other fine buildings around the square, including the former Cross Keys, another coaching inn that has been transformed into a shopping mews, and Paines Brewery, taken over by Tolly Cobbold of Ipswich and closed in 1987.

Beer: Adnams Bitter, Elgood Bitter, Younger Scotch Bitter on handpumps.

Accommodation: 6 singles, 1 double. B&B from £25 per person. Credit cards: Amex, Visa.

# WHITTLESFORD

Red Lion
Station Road, A505

Licensee: Agapios
Gregorios-Pippas
Tel: 0223 832047/832115

A superb inn founded as a priory in the 13th century by the Order of Carmelites, the old atmosphere is retained by hand-carved beams and traditional furnishings. It is claimed that James I stayed at the inn when he was taken ill on a journey from Newmarket in 1619. There are outdoor seats on a pleasant terrace in summer and coal fires inside in winter. There is a separate restaurant and the cooking, as the landlord's name suggests, has a strong flavour of Greece. The Red Lion is just a few minutes from Duxford air museum.

Beer: Charrington IPA, Courage Best Bitter, Greene King IPA and Abbot Ale on handpumps.

Accommodation: 7 singles, 6 doubles, 5 family rooms. B&B £29.50 single, £39.50 double, £48 family rooms. Children welcome, terms negotiable. Lunch and dinner available.

# CHESHIRE

# CHESTER

Coach & Horses
Northgate Street

Licensee: Ian Turner
Tel: 0244 25533

A city-centre pub close to the cathedral and opposite the medieval abbey gateway, the Coach & Horses is one of Chester's former 18th-century coaching inns and was

rebuilt in the late 19th century. It has a timber framed exterior and inside has been opened out to provide a large comfortable lounge. There is a good menu with a daily special and home-made dishes.

Beer: Greenall Whitley Mild and Local Bitter on handpumps.

Accommodation: 2 singles, 2 twins, 2 family rooms. B&B £11-£11.50 per person. Children under 12 half price.

Pied Bull
Northgate Street

Licensee J Hopkins
Tel: 0244 25829

Another old coaching inn in the heart of the historic city on the former London to Holyhead route. There is a plaque on an exterior pillar indicating the number of miles to such coaching destinations as London, Worcester, Ludlow, Bristol and Bath. The façade is Georgian, the interior much older, opens into one room but with many smaller sections. The striking fireplace has the painted coats of arms of city companies. The hot pub lunches are a feature of this welcoming old inn.

Beer: Davenports Bitter, Greenall Whitley Mild and Local Bitter on handpumps.

Accommodation: 2 singles, 5 doubles, 1 family room. B&B from £12. Children welcome but can stay only in the family room.

# FARNDON

**Greyhound Hotel**
High Street, on B5130, off A534

Licensees: Christopher & Wendy Gray
Tel: 0829 270244

The Greyhound is close to the River Dee; cross the river and you are in Wales. Farndon is a picturesque village, popular with fishermen. Local salmon is a speciality of the pub where Chris and Wendy Gray run a popular and welcoming local with a pottery attached. There are traditional games in the bar and a family garden where children can play with the donkeys, Henry and Guinness, and three goats. Farndon is a good base for Chester, Beeston and Cholmondley castles, Oulton Park, Stretton Water Mill and Snowdonia. The meals include regular vegetarian dishes. The guest rooms have colour TVs and tea and coffee making facilities.

Beer: Greenall Whitley Mild, Local Bitter and Original Bitter on handpumps.

Accommodation: 2 singles, 1 double, 1 family room. B&B £16 single, £23 double, £26 twin plus VAT. There are also self-catering cottages: terms on application. Children welcome, terms negotiable.

# HIGH LANE

Bull's Head Hotel
28 Buxton Road near Stockport, on A6

Licensee: Norman W Bradley
Tel: 0663 62070

The Bull's Head dates from 1763 and has an imposing frontage with the name depicted on a large central cornice. High Lane is on the Cheshire ring of canals and is five

minutes from the National Trust's Lyme Park and a short drive to the heart of the Peak District. The pub has a snug, tap room and lounge with open fires. Meals are available lunchtime and evening.

Beer: Boddingtons Mild and Bitter on handpumps.

Accommodation: 3 doubles, 1 family room. B&B £15 per person including VAT. Children welcome, terms depend on age.

# MALPAS

Red Lion Hotel
Old Hall Street, on B5069 off A41 Whitchurch to Chester road

Licensee: Mrs S Lever
Tel: 0948 860368

The Red Lion is an hospitable and historic brick and timber frame building, one of the oldest hostelries in south Cheshire, with wood-panelled walls and several rambling rooms. It was host to James I in 1624 when Malpas was a major stopping place for traffic between London, Wales and Liverpool. A relic of the king's visit remains in the bar — a chair known as the King's Chair. Customers must pay a penny to sit in it or stand drinks for everybody in the bar. In the heyday of coaches, the famous London to Liverpool coach, known as the Albion, used to stop here. Guest rooms are furnished to a high standard. Each room is individually named and the exposed timbers point up the antiquity of the inn. There is a solarium and a sauna for visitors.

Beer: Bass, Marston Burton Bitter on handpumps.

Accommodation: 2 singles, 2 doubles, all en suite, one suitable as family room. B&B £13.95 per person. Half and full board available.

# CLEVELAND

## HARTBURN

Stockton Arms Hotel
Darlington Raod, ½ mile off A66

Licensee: Ronald Gough
Tel: 0642 580104

A friendly, welcoming pub on the outskirts of Stockton, with open fires, and brasswork on the walls. There are excellent, good value bar snacks and separate dining facilities, including Sunday roast lunch, plus summer barbecues in the garden. The guest rooms have colour TVs. Hartburn is 20 minutes from the coast and the Cleveland Hills while Yarm and Darlington are close by.

Beer: Bass on handpump.

Accommodation: 3 singles, 1 double. B&B £15 single, £19.50 double. Mon-Thurs £52.50. Children sharing half price.

## MIDDLESBROUGH

Eston Hotel
1 mile off A1085

Licensee: W Penketh
Tel: 0642 453256

An early-1960s pub of unusual design, with three attic peaks at the front and large bay windows. There are three bars — lounge, cocktail and public — with darts and pool in the public. Places of interest to visit include the National Trust Ormesby Hall, the Captain Cook Museum in Stewarts Park and the North Yorkshire Moors. To reach the pub, turn right at Eston Baths traffic lights, then first left.

Beer: Samuel Smith Old Brewery Bitter on handpump.

Accommodation: 3 singles, 3 doubles. B&B from £10 single, £18.50 double. Evening meals available. Children welcome, no reductions.

## STOCKTON-ON-TEES

Parkwood Hotel
Darlington road, ½ mile off A66 on old Darlington to Stockton road

Licensees: Bob & Evelyn Smith
Tel: 0642 580800

The Parkwood is a friendly and inviting pub converted from the former mansion of the local ship-owning Ropner family. The Parkwood has a large garden popular with families. The bar features a large range of liqueurs and whiskies and a renowned variety of sandwiches. There is a separate dining room for lunch and dinner. The pub is next to Ropner Park and a mile from Stockton town centre.

Beer: Ward Sheffield Best Bitter on handpumps.

Accommodation: 6 singles, 5 doubles. B&B £21 single, £30 double. Weekend £18 per person, £25 double per day. Children welcome, no reductions.

# ALTARNUN

Rising Sun
Off A30 1 mile N of village, on 5 Lanes to Camelford

Licensee: Les Humphreys
Tel: 0566 332

A popular 15th-century inn built with granite from Bodmin Moor. The Rising Sun has been carefully and lovingly extended since the first edition of the guide and now has four additional guest rooms. The large bar, often packed with local farmers, has fire places at both ends. There are pub games and children's rooms and the locality offers pony trekking and sea and reservoir fishing opportunities. You can visit the Altar of St Nonna church with 79 richly carved bench ends. St Clether Church, with its holy well, is two miles to the north-east. You can tramp over the raw beauty of Bodmin Moor and the famous tourist pub, the Jamaica Inn, made famous by Daphne du Maurier's novel, is just a few miles away along the A30. The Rising Sun serves hot and cold food every day with roast lunch on Sundays. Don't miss the home-made pasties. There is a special children's menu.

Beer: Butcombe Bitter, Cotleigh Bitter, Flowers IPA and Original, Marston Pedigree and regular guest beers, all on handpumps.

Accommodation: 1 single, 1 twin, 2 doubles, 2 family rooms. B&B £9.50 per person. Reductions for long weekends or weeks. Children welcome, rates by arrangement.

# BUDE

Brendon Arms
Inner Harbour

Licensee: Desmond Gregory
Tel: 0288 2713/4542

A charming old country pub overlooking the harbour. A warm welcome is guaranteed — the 'warmest in the West' claims landlord Desmond Gregory. The pub is a few minutes from a spacious beach and is within easy distance of Bude's boating canal, which has some of the finest coarse fishing in the South-west. Sea-fishing trips can be arranged. The pub serves breakfast and dinner in the restaurant, plus pub lunches. Fresh seafood, including local crab and lobster, are regular specialities.

Beer: Bass, St Austell Tinners Bitter on handpumps.

Accommodation: 3 twins, 3 doubles, 1 with private bathroom. B&B from £11 per person. Bargain breaks available on application. Children's room. Children's terms by agreement.

ENGINE INN, CRIPPLESEASE — see p 35

# CALSTOCK

Boot Inn
Tamar Valley, near Albaston, off
A390 & A388

Licensees: Liz & Bob Slack
Tel: 0822 832331

A 17th-century inn in a small
Cornish village on the banks of the
Tamar. There is a lively bar popular
with locals and anglers, with good
bar meals. A separate restaurant has
full à la carte meals, with a carvery
on Tuesday and Friday evenings and
Sunday lunchtimes. The guest rooms
all have en suite showers or baths
plus tea and coffee facilities. The inn
is a good centre for touring the
Tamar Valley, St Anne's Chapel and
Gunnislake.

Beer: Flowers IPA and Original on
handpumps.

Accommodation: 3 doubles, 1 family
room. B&B from £11.50 per person.
Full board available. 7 days'
accommodation for the price of 6.
Children welcome, reductions by
arrangement.

# CAMBORNE

Old Shire Inn
Pendarves Road, B3303

Licensee: Chris Smith
Tel: 0209 71269
A tastefully converted lodge in
beautiful countryside outside
Camborne. The inn stands in large
grounds with its own car park. The
guest rooms are spacious, well
furnished and have colour TVs and
tea and coffee making facilities. The
pub is pleasingly quiet, without
electronic distractions. There are log
fires and excellent meals lunchtime
and evening. You can try your hand
at boules in the garden. There are

facilities for the disabled and
camping can be arranged close by.

Beer: Tetley Bitter, 'Old Shire' is
Plympton Pride by another name.
Both beers are on handpump.

Accommodation: 1 single, 5 doubles,
2 family rooms, all with en suite
bath or shower. B&B £15-£25.
Children welcome, terms by
arrangement. Credit cards: Amex,
Visa.

# CARNKIE

Wheal Bassett Inn
Globe Square, off B3297 Redruth-
Helston road.

Licensees: Ian & Norma Airey
Tel: 0209 216621

A cheery Cornish pub in the heart
of the village with open fires in
winter, male voice choir singing in
the bar and the base of local Morris
Men. The pub is named after a
nearby derelict tin mine and there
are many relics of the defunct
industry in the vicinity. There are
striking views of Carn Brea from the
pub, which is an ideal base for
Redruth, Camborne and west
Cornwall. The guest rooms have
been renovated recently and have tea
and coffee making facilities.

Beer: Butcombe Bitter, Plympton
Pride, Tetley Bitter on handpumps.

Accommodation: 3 double rooms,
£10-£15 per person, children
welcome.

# CRIPPLESEASE

Engine Inn
Nancledra, on B3311 St Ives-
Penzance road

Licensee: Les Rowe
Tel: 0736 740204

A true Cornish pub, a magnificent granite building in the heart of the moorland, that once served as the counting house for the local tin mine. Locals tend to burst into song and visitors enjoy meat roasted on the pub fire. There are stunning views of the Atlantic coast to St Ives and beyond. The guest rooms have private showers, TVs and tea and coffee making facilities. The Engine Inn is the ideal base for walking holidays and free camping is available.

Beer: JD Dry Hop Bitter, Cornish Original, Wessex Stud and GBH — the complete range of the revamped Cornish Brewery Co (formerly Devenish) on handpumps.

Accommodation: 3 doubles, 1 family room. B&B from £10.50 per person; rates vary according to season. Dinner available. Children's room. Credit cards: Visa.

# LAUNCESTON

White Hart
The Square off A30

Licensees: Brian & Ann Baker
Tel: 0566 2013

The White Hart, a former coaching inn and playhouse, is now a large hotel on the main trunk road from Devon to Cornwall, based in a fine old town that was once the capital of Cornwall. It has a Norman castle and the 14th-century church of St Mary Magdalene. An 18-hole golf course, trout and salmon fishing, and pony trekking are available.

Beer: Ruddles County, Ushers Founder's Ale on handpumps.

Accommodation: 25 rooms, all with private bathrooms, let as singles or doubles. B&B £19 single, £17 double per person. Children under 5 free if sharing with parents. Many bargain breaks, including golfing holidays. Brochure on request. Facilities for the disabled. Credit cards: Access, Amex, Diners, Visa.

# LISKEARD

Fountain Hotel
The Parade, A390

Licensee: David Joachin
Tel: 0579 42154

A comfortable, welcoming old Cornish pub with wood panels and oak beams, in the centre of a busy market town. The Fountain is popular with town folk and people from the surrounding rural areas. There is splendid home-made grub including generous portions of steak and kidney pie, plus full restaurant facilities.

Beer: Courage Best Bitter and Directors on handpumps.

Accommodation: 1 single, 2 doubles, 2 family rooms. B&B £12.50 single, £11.50 per person in a double. Children welcome, terms by arrangement.

# LOSTWITHIEL

Royal Oak
Duke Street off A390

Licensee: S J Mann
Tel: 0208 872552

A 13th-century inn in another Cornish town that claims once to have been the county capital. The

Royal Oak's interior has been sympathetically renovated in keeping with the pub's age and character. The back bar is popular with younger people while the lounge and dining room are quieter. The pub is a cask beer lover's paradise with at least five ales on tap. The food is equally renowned for its quality and its quantity. The guest rooms have TVs, tea and coffee making facilities and electric fires. Close by you can enjoy strolls along the banks of the River Fowey and visit Lanhydrock House.

Beer: Butcombe Bitter, Eldridge Pope Royal Oak, Flowers IPA and Original, Fuller London Pride and ESB, Ushers Best Bitter plus guest beers, all on handpumps.

Accommodation: 2 singles, 6 doubles, 2 family rooms. B&B £11.50 single, £19.50 double, £24 with private bathroom: these are winter rates — add approximately £2 to each rate from June to September. Full board available. Children's room; reductions for children sharing with parents.

# MABE BURNTHOUSE

New Inn
Church Road, B3291, ½ mile off
A394

Licensee: Mark Kessell
Tel: 0326 73428

The New Inn is a very old inn — a 300-year-old pub on the site of a monk's hospice, part of the heritage of the old Cornish granite-quarrying industry. The walls are featured granite, there are many old fascinating tools in the bars and rare photographs. The lounge bar has a vast log fire while the traditional Cornish card game of euchre is played in the public bar. There is an extensive cold buffet and hot meals,

including Sunday lunch. Mabe Burnthouse is a good centre for visiting Falmouth, Helston, Truro and Frenchman's Creek, and there are trout and coarse fishing facilities.

Beer: JD Dry Hop Bitter and Cornish Original on handpumps.

Accommodation: 2 doubles, one with additional single bed. B&B £10 single, £18 double. Full board available. Chidren's room; half-price for children sharing.

# MEVAGISSEY

Fountain Inn
Cliff Street, 5 miles S of A390

Licensee: W E Moore
Tel: 0726 842320

The Fountain dates from 1550 and it is wonderfully placed to enjoy the tumbling cliffs and streets of this charming and historic old fishing town. The inn is just a few yards from the harbour and trips for mackerel, pollack and even shark fishing can be booked. The Fountain is an unspoilt local with darts in the bar. The bar food is generous and there is also a separate dining room. Car parking is difficult; use the main public car park as you enter the village.

Beer: St Austell Bosun's Bitter, Tinners Bitter and Hicks Special on handpumps.

Accommodation: 2 doubles. B&B £10 per person. Weekend £20, Week £65. Children's room; children under 5 are charged £5 a night.

# MULLION

Old Inn
Churchtown off A3083 & B3296

Licensees: Jack & Penny Gayton
Tel: 0326 240240

A whitewashed and partially
thatched inn with parts dating back
to the 11th century, the Old Inn has
one bar with a lounge area. A
summer-time restaurant serves buffet
lunches and full à la carte dinners;
there are bar snacks all the year
round. The inn is on the Lizard
Peninsula and you can visit the
spectacular cliffs and harbour of
Porth Mellin, Mullion Cove and
Polurrian beach. Surf-riding and
even surf-fishing are available.
Landlord Jack Gayton is a former
diver who found the treasure ships
*Hollandia* and *Association* off the
Scillies. The attractive and
comfortable guest rooms all have tea
and coffee making facilities.

Beer: JD Dry Hop Bitter and
Cornish Original on handpumps.

Accommodation: 5 rooms, 3 with
private bathrooms. B&B £12-£15 per
person. Children are welcome in
summer if over 14. There are 2 self-
catering cottages, one with 1
bedroom, the other with 2; rates on
application. Credit cards: Visa.

# NANCENOY

Trengilly Wartha
Near Constantine, off B3291, 4
miles off A394

Licensee: Huw Jones
Tel: 0326 40332

A lovely old inn with extensive
grounds set in a peaceful valley close
to the Helford river and well placed
for Helston and Falmouth, it offers
two comfortable bars and has an
excellent restaurant that is open

every evening. Locally produced
meat, fish and shellfish dominate the
menu. Landlord Huw Jones is a
Rugby fanatic and will talk about
great games of the past as he serves
pints of immaculately kept beer. The
guest rooms have central heating,
colour TVs and tea and coffee
making facilities and there is a
separate lounge for visitors.

Beer: Bass, Butcombe Bitter,
Courage Directors, Exmoor Ale, St
Austell Tinners Bitter, Tetley Bitter
and guest beers, all straight from the
cask.

Accommodation: 6 doubles, 3 with
en suite facilities. B&B £15-£25. Half
and full board available. Winter
Break £25 per person per day B&B
+ evening meal. Children's room.
Credit cards: Access, Amex, Diners,
Visa.

# PENDOGGETT

Cornish Arms
On B3314 near Port Isaac &
Wadebridge

Licensees: Nigel Pickstone & Alan
Wainwright
Tel: 0208 88 263

A creeper-clad inn with slate floors,
low beams and an open fire, once an
old ale house. The Cornish Arms is
famous for its fine restaurant, open
(save for occasional Bank Holidays)
for 31 years. There is a buffet lunch
Mon-Sat, roast lunch on Sundays
and two sittings for dinner at 7.15

BOOT INN, CALSTOCK — see p 34

and 8.45. The Cornish Arms is close to the spectacular Tintagel coast with its Arthurian legends.

Beer: Bass, 'Pendoggett Special Bitter' (a house brew), Weston cider and guest beers on handpumps and straight from the cask.

Accommodation: 7 doubles, 5 en suite. B&B £25 single, £35 double. Children's room.

# PENZANCE

Fountain Tavern
St Clare Street, off town centre

Licensee: Dave Pryor
Tel: 0736 62673

'Still no juke box — thank God!' says Mr Pryor, underlining the tranquil and traditional atmosphere in this friendly town pub, a fine centre to enjoy the local beaches, coves, Lands End, the cathedral town of Truro, and St Michael's Mount reached by a causeway at low tide from Marazion. The tavern has been carefully and tastefully improved since the last edition of the guide and all the guest rooms now have central heating.

Beer: St Austell Mild (summer), Bosun's Bitter and Hicks Special on handpumps.

Accommodation: 1 double, 1 family room. B&B from £7 per person. Children welcome, terms by arrangement.

# ST AGNES

Driftwood Spars Hotel
Trevaunance Cove, ½ mile off B3277

Licensees: Gordon & Jill Treleaven
Tel: 087 255 2428

Built in 1660, the Driftwood Spars over the years has been a tin-mining store, chandlery, sail-makers' loft and fish cellar. The old beams come from driftwood washed up on the beach from the many ships wrecked off the rugged coast. The hotel has log fires, guest ales, an extensive range of malt whiskies, three bars and live music at weekends. Food ranges from bar snacks, including real pasties, steak and kidney pie and fisherman's pie, to four-course meals in the dining room. Breakfast can be taken as late as noon. There are fine cliff walks to be enjoyed, mine workings, a model village and nearby Truro. Most of the guest rooms have en suite facilities, sea views, TVs and tea and coffee making machines.

Beer: Tetley Bitter and Burton Ale on handpumps plus a wide range of guest beers.

Accommodation: 3 singles, 7 doubles, 1 family room, 5 with en suite facilities. B&B £15 per person, £18 with bath. Children welcome; babies free of charge, reductions up to 50% according to age.

# ST AUSTELL

Queen's Head
Fore Street, town centre

Licensee: Jerry Ogilvie
Tel: 0726 75452

The Queen's Head is 600 years old and has everything you would expect from such an ancient tavern — oak beams, a cellar, a smugglers' tunnel and a ghost. In harsher times, the town square was the scene of public executions, including the burning of witches. St Austell has its own brewery, with the same name as the town which is a good base for visiting such coastal splendours as Mevagissey, Fowey and Looe.

Beer: Courage Best Bitter and Directors, St Austell Tinners Bitter on handpumps.

Accommodation: 2 singles, 2 twins, 4 doubles, extra beds available for children. B&B from £12 per person. Full board available.

## ST JUST

Star Inn
Fore Street, town centre, A3071

Licensee: Rosie Angwin
Tel: 0736 788767

The Star is St Just's oldest hostelry, a former coaching inn, a traditional Cornish building of mellow stone with a spacious bar and cosy snug. There is a large-stepped mounting block outside, used by horse-borne travellers in earlier times. One of the guest rooms is in the converted stables and has its own bathroom, TV and tea and coffee making facilities. St Just is close to Cape Cornwall and a fine base for a walking holiday with Land's End and Sennen close at hand.

Beer: St Austell Tinners Bitter and Hicks Special straight from the cask.

Accommodation: 3 doubles, 1 with private bath. B&B £8.50 per person, £12 per person in stables room.

## ST MAWES

Victory Inn
50 yards up alleyway from quayside on B3078.

Licensee: Alan Heffer
Tel: 0326 270324

The Victory dates from 1792, is a haunt of fishermen and was once the headquarters of Channel pilots who guided ships in and out of Falmouth. The pub is often full of music as local boatmen burst into song. The Victory has one bar and an adjoining room that serves hot and cold meals all year. From St Mawes you can catch the ferry to Falmouth and visit St Mawes Castle.

Beer: JD Dry Hop Bitter, Cornish Original on handpumps.

Accommodation: 5 doubles. B&B £12.50 per person. No children or dogs. Steep climb to pub makes it unsuitable for disabled people.

## TREBARWITH

Mill House Inn
Off B3263 Tintagel-Camelford road

Licensees: David & Jennifer Liddiard-Jenkins
Tel: 084 0770 200

The Mill House is a former corn mill in the dramatic scenery of the Trebarwith Valley. The mill is surrounded by sycamores and a small trout stream, which once provided the power for the mill, runs outside. The main bar has massive beams, a Delabole stone-flagged floor, oak tables and settles. There are food and terrace bars, a pool and boules in the garden. The beach is a few minutes' walk. The separate evening restaurant specialises in local produce. The inn is a superb base for visiting Tintagel, Port Isaac, Boscastle and Wadebridge.

Beer: Flowers IPA, Marston Pedigree on handpumps.

Accommodation: 1 single, 7 doubles, 1 family room, 6 rooms with private baths, 3 with showers. B&B from £16-£19.50 per person. Evening meals available. Off-Season Weekend Breaks: terms on application. Children's room; children over 10 years welcome.

# VERYAN

New Inn
Off A3078

Licensee: John Dando
Tel: 0872 501362

The New Inn is a small, unspoilt, one-bar granite pub in the heart of a picturesque village famous for its roundhouses, with a warm welcome from the landlord and the locals. Veryan is close to some superb beaches at Pendower and Carne and the breathtaking scenery of the Roseland peninsula. Falmouth and Trelissick Gardens can be reached by the King Harry Ferry and Truro and St Austell are just 11 miles away. There is good pub grub in the inn, served lunchtime and evening.

Beer: St Austell Bosun's Bitter and Tinners Bitter straight from the cask.

Accommodation: 1 single, 2 doubles. B&B £9.50 per person.

# ALSTON

Blue Bell Inn
Townfoot, A686 Penrith to Hexham road

Licensee: Geoff Popay
Tel: 0498 81566

The Blue Bell is a 17th-century listed building with many original beams in an area designated as having outstanding natural beauty. There is a friendly welcome from the locals and from the log fires in winter. Alston is a good base for visiting the lakes, Hadrian's Wall, Killhope Wheel in the restored lead-mining centre in Weardale, and the narrow-gauge steam railway that runs to Gilderdale on part of the old Haltwhistle line. The inn offers excellent bar meals with the emphasis on such home-made dishes as hand-raised Cumberland pie, seafood broccoli pie, chicken cacciatori, hot pot and pork oriental. Vegetarian meals are always available. The guest rooms have tea and coffee making facilities.

Beer: Marston Burton Bitter and Pedigree on handpumps.

Accommodation: 1 twin, 2 doubles, 1 family room. B&B from £11.50 per person. Week £75. Children welcome, half price.

# BARNGATES

Drunken Duck
Near Hawkshead off B5286

Licensees: Peter & Stephanie Barton
Tel: 096 66 347

A superb pub set in stunning scenery of mountains and lakes. The unique name derives from a legend that a landlady in the late 19th century found her ducks stretched out in the road. She thought they were dead but in fact they were squiffy from drinking ale from a leaking cask in the cellar. She began to pluck them in preparation for the oven. This roused them from their stupor and they were saved from an à l'orange finish. To keep them warm, the landlady knitted them jerseys until their feathers grew again. (This tale is believed only after three pints of Old Peculier.) The pub is more than 400 years old. It is cosy and cheerful, with beams, open fires, a separate restaurant and residents' lounge. Locally caught salmon and venison feature on the menu and guests have free use of the pub's private trout tarn. The Drunken Duck is a splendid base for visiting Ambleside, Coniston, Hawkshead and Tarn Hows.

Beer: Jennings Bitter, Marston Pedigree, Tetley Bitter, Theakston XB and Old Peculier on handpumps.

Accommodation: 2 twins, 3 doubles, 2 rooms with private baths. B&B £15 per person, £18 with bath. Children welcome, rates depend on age.

# BROUGHTON-IN-FURNESS

Black Cock Inn
Princess Street off A595

Licensee: Mr K Howarth
Tel: 06576 529

A popular 16th-century country inn in a charter town in southern Lakeland, with a fascinating collection of vintage motor bikes in the town square. The Black Cock has comfortable, modern guest rooms with TVs and tea and coffee making facilities. Tuesday is market day, the pub is open all day and local farmers flock into Broughton with their animals.

Beer: Websters Green Label, Yorkshire Bitter and Choice, Wilsons Mild on handpumps.

Accommodation: 3 doubles, 1 family room. B&B £12.50 per person. Weekend £24, Week £70. Children welcome, half price under 12.

Eccle Riggs Manor Hotel
Foxfield Road, SW of village, off A595

Proprietors: Howard & Susan Loxley
Tel: 06576 398

An imposing 19th-century mansion in 35 acres of gardens and woodland, with stunning views of Coniston Old Man and the Duddon estuary. Eccle Riggs was built by Lord Cross, whose varied parliamentary career encompassed Home Secretary, Secretary of State for India, and Lord Privy Seal (one later holder of the third office observed 'I am neither a lord, a privy nor a seal'). Lord Cross used Eccle Rigg as his summer retreat and brought parts of the demolished Ashton Old Hall at Ashton under Lyme to Broughton: the old dungeon towers from Ashton now stand at the entrance to Eccle Riggs. The lounges and restaurant are elegantly furnished and the 13 guest rooms have colour TVs, in-house video, and tea and coffee making facilities. Bar food includes Morecambe Bay shrimps, Cumberland sausage, jacket spuds with a variety of fillings, chilli, and home-made steak and kidney pie. The hotel has a heated swimming pool, sauna and solarium.

Beer: Whitbread Castle Eden Ale on handpump.

Accommodation: 13 rooms, 10 with private bathrooms, 7 doubles, 6 family rooms. B&B £29 single, £48 double. Weekend £56, Week £165. Special rates for honeymoon couples. Children welcome, reduction on room rates and meals. Facilities for the disabled but no lift.

# CARLISLE

Woolpack Inn
Milbourne Street

Licensee: J McDonald
Tel: 0228 32459

A popular L-shaped local on the edge of the city centre, a former State Brewery pub. The Woolpack is half a mile from the railway station and a comfortable stroll to the main shopping centre, the castle and the cathedral. The pub is famous in the city for the quality of its bar meals, available lunchtime and evening. Make a point of chumming up with Scamp, the pub dog, whose favourite tipple, wise canine, is Jennings bitter: it won't touch the keg Tetley's or lager. Scamp does kangaroo impersonations at closing time. A second bar was being built as the guide went to press.

Beer: Jennings Mild, Bitter and Marathon on handpumps.

Accommodation: 1 single, 3 doubles, 1 family room. B&B £9 per person. No lift; not suitable for disabled people unless they can manage the stairs to the guest rooms.

# CARTMEL FELL

Masons Arms
Strawberry Bank off A5047

Licensees: Helen & Nigel Stevenson
Tel: 04488 486

This delightful and welcoming old pub is devoted to good beer and good food. The seriousness with which Nigel Stevenson takes his beer is measured by the fact that the pub has a beer menu as well as a food one. There is a vast range of foreign bottled beers to try as well as the draught ales. The imported beers include both top and bottom fermented styles and Mr Stevenson ensures that they are all served at the correct temperatures. As well as the regular draught ales, he has a guest beer always on tap and in 1987 served more than 120 of them. The pub got its name in the 18th century when Kendal freemasons had to meet in secret. The Masons Arms is set in lovely countryside close to the heart of Lakeland. Excellent pub grub includes home-made curries, houmous and coachman's casserole, washed down with a Belgian Trappiste beer, a Czech Pilsner-Urquell or a straightforward pint of ale.

Beer: McEwan 80 shilling, Thwaites Bitter, Younger No 3 on handpumps, James White cider from the cask, plus guest beers, ciders and perries.

Accommodation: 3 doubles, 1 family room in converted barn next to the pub. B&B £7.50-£15 per person depending on season. Children welcome, no charge if sharing.

# CONISTON

Crown Hotel
A593

Licensees: E & A Tiidus
Tel: 05394 41243

A cheerful old pub nestling between Coniston Old Man and the famous lake where Donald Campbell broke the world speed record. Nearby are disused copper mines and the home of writer and artist John Ruskin and you can take a trip on the lake in the steam-powered gondola owned by the National Trust. The Crown has a beer garden, a log fire in winter and generous hot food is served lunch and evening.

Beer: Hartleys Mild, Bitter and XB on handpumps.

Accommodation: 3 doubles, 3 family rooms. B&B £12.50 per person. Weekend £70 per person full board, £80 per week. Off-season Weekend £55. Children's room; 50% reduction for children sharing.

Ship Inn
Bowmanstead, A593, ¼ mile from village on Torver road

Licensees: Derrick & Linda Freedman
Tel: 0966 41224

A traditional old pub with beams, a stone fireplace and a log blaze in winter close to Coniston Hall camp site and Park Coppice caravan park. The Ship is a popular venue for campers, hikers and sailors. Pub food is served lunchtime and evening and offers soup, grills, burgers, salmon and meat salads, sandwiches and ploughman's, plus daily specials and a children's menu. There are summer barbecues. A separate games room has darts, shove ha'penny and pool.

Beer: Hartleys Bitter on electric pump (handpull being installed).

Accommodation: 1 double, 1 family room. B&B £10 per person, Weekend £20, Week £70. Children welcome; children's room; 40% reduction 2-12 years; free under 2.

# DALTON-IN-FURNESS

Red Lion Inn
Market Street on A590

Licensee: Rob McDougle
Tel: 0229 62180

A family run, 16th-century inn with a magnificent open fire in the large Tudor beamed bar. Bar meals are served lunchtime and evening and all the food is home cooked. The Red Lion has a strong local following and the separate games and function room is in great demand. Both locals and landlord guarantee a warm Cumbrian welcome.

Beer: Tetley Mild and Bitter from the cask.

Accommodation: 2 singles, 2 doubles, 1 with shower. B&B £10.50-£13 per person, depending on room. Children welcome, terms negotiable.

BRITANNIA INN, ELTERWATER — see p 44

# ELTERWATER

Britannia Inn
Near Ambleside off B5343

Licensee: David Fry
Tel: 096 67 382/210

A friendly, homely, 400-year old inn set in the great beauty of the Langdale Valley. The Britannia is a popular centre for keen walkers and specialises in superb three and four course dinners — you must book well in advance as there is a long waiting list. Children are made welcome and can choose from the bar menu if they join their parents in the dining room. There is a residents' lounge.

Beer: Bass Special Bitter, Hartleys XB, Jennings Bitter, Tetley Bitter plus draught cider on handpumps.

Accommodation: 1 single, 8 doubles, 1 family room. B&B £18.75 per person, dinner £10.50 extra. Weekend £37.50, Week £124. Children half price when sharing.

# FAR SAWREY

Sawrey Hotel
B5285 towards Windermere Ferry on Hawkshead road

Licensees: David & Sheila Brayshaw
Tel: 09662 3425/4651

An attractive, whitewashed, early 18th-century inn made up of three separate buildings. The old stables now form the bar, with the guest rooms above. The pub's original name is thought to have been the Angler's Rest and later was called the New Inn. The stables were converted in 1971 and named the Claife Crier bar after the ghost of a monk in Furness Abbey whose mission in medieval times was to save 'fallen' women. He fell, too, in love with one of them, was rejected went mad and died. The hotel has beams in the bar that are thought to have come from wrecks of the Spanish armada off the Cumberland coast. The bar has old stable stalls for seating, harness on the walls and a variety of traditional games. There are full restaurant meals, while bar meals (not Sunday evenings) offer soup, hiker's lunch, Cumberland sausage and local trout.

Beer: Tetley Bitter, Theakston Best Bitter and Old Peculier, Younger No 3 on handpumps.

Accommodation: 3 singles, 13 doubles, 2 family rooms. B&B £13.50 per person, dinner £6 extra. Week £125, Off-season Weekend £37. Children half price. Facilities for the disabled.

# HAWKSHEAD

Red Lion Inn
The Square, off B5285 & 5286

Licensees: Joan & John Smith
Tel: 09666 213

A fine village inn in Wordsworth country; the poet supped in the Red Lion. Another writer — Beatrix Potter — has a museum in her honour next to the pub. It is a splendid base for visiting Coniston and Windermere, Esthwaite Water and Tarn Hows. The inn offers both bar meals and full restaurant dishes, specialising in game in season and traditional Lakeland fare. The guest rooms are all en suite and are centrally heated. There is a beer garden in summer, a bowling green close by and fishing and boating are available.

Beer: Websters Choice, Wilsons Bitter on handpumps.

Accommodation: 1 single, 8 doubles,

1 family room. B&B £17.50 per person. Weekend £46 including dinner, Week £160 with dinner. Off-season Weekend £28, £42 with dinner. Children welcome; children's room; one-third reduction in rates. No dogs. Credit cards: Access, Visa.

# LANGDALE

Old Dungeon Ghyll Hotel
B5343 at end of Langdale Valley

Licensees: Neil & Jane Walmsley
Tel: 096 67 272

A famous rock climbers' inn in a breathtaking setting at the heart of the Great Langdale Valley. It is a simple and homely pub with great thick walls to keep out the winter blasts, sing-songs in the bar and generous home-cooked meals, including hot soup, curries and Cumberland sausage ... and a choice of snuff.

Beer: Marston Pedigree, Theakston XB in summer, Best Bitter and Old Peculier, Yates Bitter, Younger No 3, Bulmer medium cider and a regular guest beer, all on handpumps.

Accommodation: 2 singles, 3 doubles, 2 family rooms, 4 rooms with bath or shower. B&B £15 per person, £17 with shower, evening meal £10 extra. Mid-Week Special (minimum of 2 nights) £14, £16 with shower. Week from £100. Reduced rates for children.

# NEAR SAWREY

Tower Bank Arms
B5285 Hawkshead road near Windermere Ferry

Licensee: Philip J Broadley
Tel: 096 66 334

The Tower Bank, owned by the National Trust, is a charming cottage pub next to Beatrix Potter's house. It has a kitchen range, stone-flagged floors, high-back settles and a grandfather clock. There are bar snacks — Cumberland sausage, local trout, home-cooked ham — and full meals in a separate dining room. You can enjoy good ale and food in the beer garden in summer. The guest rooms have colour TVs, central heating and tea and coffee making facilities.

Beer: Matthew Brown Mild, John Peel Bitter, Theakston XB on handpumps.

Accommodation: 3 twins, all with en suite facilities. B&B £15 per person. Children welcome.

# PENRITH

Museum Inn
17-18 Castlegate, between Clock Tower and the Castle

Licensees: Ted & Hazel Alway
Tel: 0768 63576

A warm welcome and an informal, relaxed atmosphere are guaranteed at this 200-year-old inn. There are no 'electronic devices' but visitors can enjoy darts, dominoes and the locals' repartee. The inn is a meeting place for many local groups, from the jazz club to the mountaineers, and CAMRA member Ted Alway keeps his ale in splendid condition. The accommodation is excellent value and the traditional breakfasts are legendary. The inn is close to the railway station, the castle and the steam museum.

Beer: Hartleys XB, Jennings Mild and Bitter on handpumps.

Accommodation: 1 single, 2 family rooms. B&B from £9.50 per person.

# SILECROFT

Miners Arms
½ mile off A595, near Millom

Licensee: R A Sawdon
Tel: 0657 2325

The reason is lost in the mists of time, but on Easter Sunday every visitor to the Miners Arms is given a free glass of mulled ale. This welcoming old pub has a golf course nearby, sea fishing, fine beaches and a mining museum. There are bar snacks and meals lunchtime and evening, with such tasty specialities as home-made steak pie, curries and gammon steaks. The guest rooms are centrally heated.

Beer: Younger Scotch Bitter and No 3 on handpumps.

Accommodation: 2 doubles, 2 twins. B&B £10 per person. No children under 14. No pets.

# TALKIN

Hare & Hounds Inn
Talkin Village near Brampton, 1 mile off B6413, 2½ miles off A69

Licensees: Joan & Les Stewart
Tel: 06977 3456/3457

The Stewarts have friends from many countries, united in the belief that this is the friendliest inn in Britain, offering the very best food and accommodation. Close to the serenity of the lovely Talkin Tarn,

the Hare & Hounds has beams, stone fireplaces, lots of etched glass and superb meals lunchtimes and evenings. (*Closed weekday lunchtimes except mid-July to August, Easter and Christmas*) Meals include Talkin Tattie Specials (baked spuds with choice of fillings), home-made soup, rainbow trout, frittarde espagnole, local fillet, deep-fried scampi. Special children's menu.

Beer: Hartleys XB, Theakston XB, Best Bitter and Old Peculier on handpumps.

Accommodation: 1 single, 1 double, 1 family room, 2 with private bath. B&B £14 single, £25 double. Week £7 reduction. Children's room; children half price if sharing. Facilities for the disabled.

# ULVERSTON

Armadale Hotel
Aradd Foot, Greenodd, off A590, 2 miles north of Ulverston

Licensee: Stephanie Gibson
Tel: 022 986 257

A convivial village welcome is guaranteed in this 19th-century hotel, once a doctor's house, that now serves the communities of Aradd Foot and Greenodd on the outskirts of the town. An ideal base for touring the southern lakes, it overlooks the grand sweep of Morecambe Bay. Bar meals, lunch and evening (not Mondays) include home-made steak pie, roast duckling, lasagne, curries, grilled trout, Cumberland sausage and vegetarian dishes. The guest rooms have tea and coffee making facilities; cots for children are available.

Beer: Matthew Brown Bitter, Theakston Best Bitter on handpumps.

Accommodation: 10 doubles, 1

family room, 2 with private bath.
B&B £12.50 single, £22 double, £5
extra for private bath. Family room
(sleeps 4) £35; 4 nights £105.
Children's room; children half price
sharing; no charge for babies.

# ULVERSTON

Kings Head Hotel
Queen Street

Licensees: Jack & Margaret
Lowther
Tel: 022 952 892

A cosy, old oak-beamed, low-
ceilinged pub in the centre of
Ulverston, with two blazing fires in
winter and crown green bowling at
the back — woods are available for
hire. Drinks and food can be
enjoyed on the terrace in warm
weather. Children are welcome. The
pub is open all day on Thursday
market day.

Beer: Theakston Best Bitter plus
guest beers on handpumps.

Accommodation: 2 doubles, 1 family
room. B&B £10 per person.
Children under 12 half price when
sharing with parents.

# BAMFORD

Derwent Hotel
Main Road, A6013, 2 miles off
A57 at Ladybower

Licensees: Angela & David Ryan
Tel: 0433 51395

A superbly situated hotel in the
heart of the Peak District, with Jane
Eyre connections and close to the
spectacular Ladybower reservoirs.
The hotel lounges have old sewing

machines, harnesses, copper, brass
and fascinating pictures and prints.
The emphasis is on home-cooked
food and the guest rooms all have
TVs, tea and coffee making facilities
and fine views of the Derbyshire
hills. Boat and tackle can be hired
for fishing in the reservoirs.

Beer: Stones Best Bitter, Wards
Sheffield Best Bitter on handpumps.

Accommodation: 2 singles, 8
doubles, 2 with private bath. B&B
from £14 per person. Children
welcome, terms negotiable.

# BIRCH VALE

Sycamore Inn
Sycamore Road, B6015, off A6 at
New Mills

Licensees: Christine & Malcolm
Nash
Tel: 0663 42715

A cheerful family pub on the banks
of the River Sett near Stockport,
standing in large grounds that
include a beer garden, children's play
area and barbecue area. There are
patio seats at the front, too, and the
two bars, three eating areas and
guest rooms are beautifully
appointed, the latter enjoying colour
TVs, en suite bathrooms and tea and
coffee making facilities. Food is
served every day lunchtime and
evenings and ranges from lasagne to
Mexican-style grills, fish and
vegetarian dishes and a children's
menu. The inn is well placed for
visiting Kinder Scout, the blue John
Mines and Chatsworth House.

Beer: Marston Burton Bitter and
Pedigree on handpumps.

Accommodation: 5 doubles. B&B
£24 single, £39.50 double. Children
welcome. Credit cards: Access, Visa.

# BUXTON

Grove Hotel
Grove Parade

Proprietor: Peter Marshall
Tel: 0298 3804

This commanding, 18th-century listed building is in the centre of the famous spa town, close to the Opera House, The Crescent and Pavilion Gardens. The Grove offers great comfort, bar meals lunch and evening and the perfect base for such nearby delights as Chatsworth House, Bakewell, Dovedale and the Goyt and Manifold valleys. The guest rooms have TVs and tea and coffee making facilities.

Beer: Robinsons Best Bitter on electric pump.

Accommodation: 20 rooms including 12 doubles and 2 family rooms, 5 rooms with en suite facilities. B&B £18 single, £28 with private bath, double £30, £36 with bath. Children welcome. Credit cards: Access, Amex, Diners, Visa.

Lee Wood Hotel
Manchester Road, A5004 from Whaley Bridge

Licensee: John Millican
Tel: 0298 3002/70421

A privately owned Georgian hotel that faces south in half an acre of delightful garden. There is a lift to all floors and each guest room has colour TV and full central heating. It has a games room and conference facilities, and both French and English cuisine are available in the restaurant.

Beer: McEwan 80 shilling on handpump.

Accommodation: 18 singles, 12 doubles, 8 twins, 3 family rooms, all rooms with private bath. B&B £39-£42 single, £24-£28 double per person, £32-£36 half board per day. Children welcome. Short break terms on application.

# CASTLETON

Castle Hotel
Main Road, Hope Valley, A625

Licensee: José Luis Rodriguez
Tel: 0433 20578

A 17th-century coaching inn in a lovely village of narrow, twisting streets and limestone cottages at the foot of the ruins of Peveril Castle, immortalised by Sir Walter Scott in *The Peveril of the Peak*. The hotel is 10 minutes from the Peak Cavern and is close to the Blue John Mine, Speedwell Cavern and Treak Cliff Cavern. The Castle's lounge and public bars offer a wide range of bar meals and the separate restaurant serves lunch and dinner. Two of the comfortable guest rooms have four-poster beds and all rooms have colour TVs and tea, coffee and hot chocolate making facilities.

Beer: Stones Best Bitter on electric pump.

Accommodation: 5 singles, 5 doubles, 2 family rooms. B&B £35 single, £45 double, four-poster double £49, honeymoon suite from £55. Children welcome, from £8 per night. Bargain Breaks April-Sept, Sunday to Friday: from £27 per person per night.

# HAYFIELD

Royal Hotel
Market Square, off A624 in centre
of village, near junction with
A6015

Licensee: Bob Hadfield
Tel: 0663 42721

The stone-built hotel dominates the
square of this picturesque village
bounded by the River Sett. Built in
1755 as a vicarage, the Royal has
retained some of its old atmosphere.
It has well-appointed rooms and a
restaurant serving à la carte meals.
Home-cooked bar meals are also
available. Hayfield stands on the
highest part of the Peak and is the
natural gateway to Kinder Scout,
where a mass trespass in 1932 struck
a major blow for ramblers' rights.

Beer: Websters Yorkshire Bitter and
Websters Choice, Wilsons Original
Mild and Bitter on handpumps.

Accommodation: 1 single, 1 double,
3 twins. B&B £15 per person.
Children charged £7.50 under 12,
babies free; children's room. Special
rates for 3 nights or more.

# HURDLOW

Bull I'Th' Thorn
A515, Ashbourn-Buxton Road

Licensees: Judith & Bob Haywood
Tel: 029 883 348

A famous hostelry on the old
Roman road between Chester and
Buxton, it has acted as a coaching
inn and resting place for travellers
for more than 500 years. There was
a farmhouse on the site nearly 700
years ago and in 1472 it became an
inn called the Bull. The name
changed to Hurdlow House in the
17th century and documents of the
time refer to it as Hurdlow Thorn.
The present name is a combination

of its two main associations. At the
height of the horse-drawn coaching
period it was a major stopping place
for coaches on the Derby to
Manchester route. All this
fascinating history is caught in the
rich atmosphere of Tudor panelling,
period carvings and stone-flagged
floors. Bar meals — soup,
ploughman's, fish and chips, steaks,
salads, sandwiches, children's meals
plus Sunday roast — are served
lunchtime and evening. As well as
the accommodation in the inn, there
is also a self-catering flat.

Beer: Robinsons Best Bitter on
handpump.

Accommodation: 2 singles, 1 double,
1 family room, 1 room with private
bath. B&B £9 per person. Children's
room; children's terms on
application. Self-catering holiday flat
£95 a week.

# ILKESTON

Durham Ox
Durham Street

Licensee: Frank Barton
Tel: 0602 324570

An old-fashioned (in the best sense)
backstreet pub where beer, grub,
accommodation and companionship
are all marvellous value. The pub is
a real community centre, hosting
cricket, football and quiz teams as
well as offering such games as darts,
skittles and pool. Durham Street is a
back road and you will reach this
splendid boozer, the oldest pub in
the town, from either Station Road
or Bath Street. The pub fare is
simple and nourishing: sausage, egg,
chips and beans, fish, chips and peas
and chicken, chips and peas, all at
£1.20.

Beer: Wards Mild, Sheffield Best
Bitter on hand and electric pumps.

Accommodation: 1 single, 2 doubles. B&B £7.50 per person. Weekend £22.50. Half board available. No children.

# TIDESWELL

George Hotel
Commercial Road, ¼ mile off A619 Chesterfield-Stockport road

Licensee: Dale Norris
Tel: 0298 871382

A much photographed, handsome 18th-century coaching inn in a medieval market town and next to the soaring Cathedral of the Peak. The friendly atmosphere of the George is emphasised by a log fire in winter and a cheerful informality that happily allows guests to choose to eat in either the separate dining room or by the fire in the lounge. The menu, lunch and evening, includes daily specials chalked on a board, soup, old ale and mushroom pâté, poacher's pie, lasagne, beefburgers, and a wide variety of fillings for wholemeal rolls. Within a 10-mile radius of the hotel you can visit Chatsworth, Castleton, the Derwent Valley, Buxton, Bakewell and Hathersage, the legendary — in every sense — burial place of Little John. The guest rooms in the George have colour TVs.

Beer: Hardys & Hansons Kimberley Best Mild and Best Bitter on handpumps.

Accommodation: 1 single, 3 doubles, I family room. B&B £14 per person. £13 per day for a stay of 2-3 days. Half board available. Children's room; 20% reduction.

# WHALEY BRIDGE

Jodrell Arms Hotel
39 Market Street on A6, next to railway station

Licensees: Mr & Mrs J D Bond & Mr & Mrs L Jenkins
Tel: 066 33 2164

A fine old pub in the centre of the village close to the canal basin terminus. It was built in the late 17th century and is a Grade II listed building with a Tuscan porch and Elizabethan gables. There is a welcoming fire on winter days, good-value bar snacks and a separate restaurant for lunch and dinner. All the guest rooms have colour TVs and tea and coffee making facilities. Whaley Bridge is at the entrance to the lovely Goyt Valley which offers sailing on the reservoir and canal cruises. Mr J D Bond is former Lancashire country cricket captain Jackie Bond, who held one of the most remarkable catches ever seen in a Lord's one-day final when Lancashire won the Gillette Cup.

Beer: Wilsons Original Mild and Bitter on handpumps.

Accommodation: 2 singles, 9 doubles/twins, 2 with private showers. B&B £18 single, £30 double. Children welcome, terms negotiable. Credit cards: Access, Visa.

DERWENT HOTEL, BAMFORD — see

# WHITEHOUGH

## Old Hall
Chinley, ¼ mile off B6062

Proprietors: Michael & Ann
Capper
Tel: 0663 50529

The Old Hall is in a quiet hamlet
with panoramic views of the Peak
District. The hall dates back to the
13th century and for 15 generations
it was the home of the Kirke family.
Sir David Kirke's sister Mary was
maid of honour to Queen Catherine
of Braganza. George Kirke was
groom to the royal bedchamber of
Charles I and was present when the
monarch lost his head on the block.
Colonel Percy Kirke put down the
Monmouth Rebellion with terrible
severity after the battle of
Sedgemoor in 1685. The hall retains
splendid beamed ceilings, mullioned
windows and a minstrel gallery in
the Rafters Restaurant, where there
is a three-course menu for residents
at £6 per person. Comprehensive bar
food is also available.
Accommodation in both the hall
and a house in the grounds includes
private baths or showers, colour
TVs, central heating and tea and
coffee making facilities.

Beer: Bass, Marston Pedigree and
Stones Best Bitter on handpumps.

Accommodation: 4 doubles in the
hotel, 5 singles in separate house, 2
rooms available as family rooms.
B&B £20 single, £30 double. Half
and full board available. Rates for
special breaks on application.
Children welcome; reductions up to
100% according to age. Credit cards:
Access, Amex, Diners, Visa.

# BLACKAWTON

## Normandy Arms
2 miles off B3207, near Totnes

Licensees: Jos & Mark Gibson
Tel: 080 421 316

A 15th-century village pub with a
warm and cosy atmosphere in an
unspoilt village close to Totnes,
Kingsbridge and the beaches of the
South Hams. There are facilities for
sailing, boating, windsurfing and sea
and trout fishing. The Normandy
Arms has a small, comfortable bar, a
separate restaurant and a children's
room upstairs with toys, games and
books. Bar snacks offer home-made
soup, local smoked mackerel,
omelettes, ploughman's and
sandwiches while the restaurant
(open lunch and dinner) has a
sensibly short menu. This includes
such house specials as chicken
Normandy cooked with local cider
and Calvados and sauté of game
Normandy. There is a beer garden
for warmer days and the brews
include ales from the local
Blackawton brewery, one of the first
of the new crop of small
independent brewers to set up in the
late 1970s.

Beer: Blackawton Bitter, 44 (summer
only) and Headstrong (winter),
Burton Ale and local cider on
handpumps.

Accommodation: 3 doubles, 1 twin,
1 bunk-bedded room, 2 rooms with
private bath. B&B £13-£15.50 per
person. Children's terms by
arrangement.

## BRANSCOMBE

Three Horseshoes
On A3052, Exeter to Lyme Regis
road, inland from Branscombe

Licensees: Geoff & Roberta Hunt
Tel: 029 780 251

A traditional inn with beams, brasses
and a log fire, a fine base for visiting
Ottery St Mary and the coastal
towns of Sidmouth, Beer and Seaton.
The accommodation comprises 8
rooms in the inn and 4 with en suite
facilities in an annexe. It is a
splendid family inn, with a dining
room that welcomes children, a
games room and an outdoor
adventure playground. Food ranges
from bar snacks to full meals and
there is a children's menu. Skittles,
darts and pool are played.

Beer: Bass, Burton Ale and
Plympton Pride, Wadworth 6X on
handpumps.

Accommodation: 2 singles, 2 twins,
7 doubles, 1 family room, 5 with en
suite facilities. B&B from £10.50 per
person. Weekend from £23, Week
from £66.15. Off-season rates on
request. Children half price. Credit
cards: Access, Amex, Diners, Visa.

## BUTTERLEIGH

Butterleigh Inn
Near Cullompton, 3 miles from M5

Licensees: Mike & Penny Wolter
Tel: 08845 407

A small, 16th century, mid-Devon
pub in a tiny hamlet between
Tiverton and Cullompton, close to
Bickleigh Castle and set in delightful
countryside. Food ranges from a
cheese sandwich to grilled quail in
port sauce. The modern guest rooms
have tea and coffee making facilities.

Beer: Cotleigh Kingfisher, Tawny
and Old Buzzard, plus guest beers
(including Boddingtons) on
handpumps.

Accommodation: 3 doubles. B&B
£14.50 single, £10.50 per person
sharing. Children over 14 years
welcome. Half and full board
available.

## COLEFORD

New Inn
2½ miles from A377, near
Crediton

Licensees: R G & V A Knowles
Tel: 036 34 242

The New Inn is a very old inn, built
in the 13th century. Many New Inns
were so-called because they were
built by monasteries to provide ale
and victuals for travellers. The New
Inn in Coleford has a thatched roof
and cob and granite walls. It was
formerly a monks' retreat and was
later a staging post for coaches. The
bars have oak beams, stone walls and
large log fires with a profusion of
gleaming brass and copper and old
prints. A small stream runs by the
inn and the village has many other
old and attractive houses. Lunch
snacks include soup, ploughman's,
seafood platter, hamburgers and a

daily vegetarian dish. There is a separate evening restaurant. Fishing and golf are available nearby.

Beer: Flowers Original and IPA on handpumps.

Accommodation: 1 single, 3 doubles, 1 room with en suite facilities. B&B £20 single, double £12-£14 per person. Children welcome; under 10 years charged £8 when sharing with parents.

# CULLOMPTON

Manor House Hotel
Fore Street off M5

Licensees: Ron & Eileen Peters
Tel: 0884 32281

A manor house built in 1603, this listed building in the heart of the wool town has original panelling and Adam ceilings. It was one of the few buildings to survive the great fire of Cullompton in 1735. The Peters have spent time and money in carefully restoring this fine building, encompassing an adjoining house formerly owned by a doctor. There are many reminders of the old woollen industry, such as an ancient wool winder, in corners of the hotel. It is a genuine village local that welcomes visitors. There is a separate restaurant offering high standards of cooking and the guest rooms have colour TVs. Keep an eye open for the resident ghost, a friendly chap in knee breeches and carrying a stave.

Beer: Flowers Original and IPA on handpumps.

Accommodation: 2 singles, 8 doubles. All the doubles have private baths and several also count as family rooms. B&B £14 per person, £2 supplement if single person in double room. Half and full board terms available. Children welcome, terms by arrangement.

# DODDISCOMBSLEIGH

Nobody Inn
2½ miles from A38 at Haldon Hill (signposted Dunchideock)

Proprietor: N F Borst-Smith
Tel: 0647 52394

A famous old 16th-century inn six miles from Exeter and close to Dartmoor and the coast, its name, according to local legend, stems from an unknown buyer of the inn who locked the doors and refused hospitality to travellers seeking bed and refreshment. They went wearily on their way, reporting that 'nobody was in the inn'. You are assured of a welcome today, backed by fine food, ale, 170 whiskies and 500 wines, ports and brandies. The restaurant is open Tuesday to Saturday evenings and offers dishes made from local produce; local trout cooked in pastry is a speciality. Guest rooms have tea and coffee making facilities; breakfast is served in the rooms.

Beer: Bass, Eldridge Pope Royal Oak, Flowers Original, Marston Owd Rodger on handpumps.

Accommodation: 1 single, 6 doubles, 5 with en suite facilities. B&B £11-£19. £2 reduction per person for stays of 4 days or more. No children. Accommodation is also available at Town Barton house in the village, 150 yards from the inn, which acts as the reception and where meals, including breakfast, are taken.

## ERMINGTON

Crooked Spire Inn
B3211, 2 miles off A38 near
Ivybridge

Licensee: J L Shield
Tel: 0548 830202

A cosy and welcoming village inn
with such traditional games as darts
and euchre in the bar and excellent
pub food. Bar snacks include sausage
and chips, pasties, pizzas,
ploughman's, sandwiches and
toasties while the separate restaurant
has local trout, grills, salads, lasagne,
chilli and curries.

Beer: Flowers Original and IPA on
handpumps.

Accommodation: 3 doubles. B&B
£15 per person. Half and full board
available. Children welcome, no
reductions. Credit cards: Access,
Visa.

## FREMINGTON

Fox & Hounds
A39 on Barnstaple to Bideford
road

Licensee: Brian Hannam
Tel: 0271 73094/42317

A small village inn and genuine local
where darts, skittles and shove-
ha'penny are played with
enthusiasm. It is a good base in
north Devon for Exmoor and
Dartmoor and the beaches of
Lynton, Lynmouth, Woolacombe
and the Taw estuary. There are
facilities for riding and fishing. Pub
food includes soup, trout,
ploughman's, salads and a children's
menu with bangers and chips and
fish fingers. There is a sitting room
for guests with colour TV.

Beer: Ruddles Best Bitter and Ushers
Best Bitter on handpumps.

Accommodation: 3 doubles, 2 family
rooms. B&B £12 per person.
Weekend £22, Week £65, Off-Season
Weekend £18. Children's room; 30%
reductions. Cot available. Pets
welcome.

## FROGMORE

Globe Inn
Centre of village, 3 miles from
A379 and 3 miles from Kingsbridge

Licensees: Richard & Maureen
Hardman
Tel: 054 853 351

Circumnavigation is, reasonably
enough, the theme of the Globe.
The interior walls are papered with
navigational charts and hung with a
collection of oil paintings showing
famous circumnavigators. The inn
has stone-flagged floors. Darts and
bar billiards are played by locals in
the public bar. It is a good family
pub with an adventure field, terraced
garden and family room. The guest
rooms have colour TVs and tea
making equipment. Pub food
includes soup, steak and kidney pie,
local plaice with chips, ploughman's,
sandwiches and daily specials. There
is Sunday lunch, too, and children
have their own menu. Frogmore is
within easy reach of Dartmouth,
Plymouth and Torquay. Mr and Mrs
Hardman are happy to advise on
local rambles.

DARTMOOR INN — *see opposite*

Beer: Flowers Original and IPA on handpumps. Other cask beers from the Whitbread stable are often available. The pub has six pumps and other regular guest beers include Badger Best, Boddingtons, Blackawton, Exmoor Ale, Marston Pedigree and Plympton Pride.

Accommodation: 4 doubles, 1 family room. B&B £14 per person; additional charge of £1.50 when one person occupies a room. Week £84. 10% reduction in winter for stay of two nights or more. 40% reduction for children. Credit cards: Access, Amex, Diners, Visa.

# LYDFORD

### Castle Inn
Next to Lydford Castle, 1 mile off A386 Okehampton to Tavistock road

Licensees: David & Susan Grey
Tel: 082 282 242

A small, snug inn with beams, log fires and low ceilings in a lovely Devon village that was once an important Saxon borough with its own mint. The inn's Foresters' Bar has seven original Lydford pennies made in the mint during the reign (circa AD 1000) of Ethelred the Unready. The bar also has old lamps hanging from the beams, a collection of old plates and a great Norman fireplace. The Tinners' Bar has a unique collection of antique stallion posters. There is a buffet lunch every day as well as bar snacks lunchtime and evening. A separate à la carte restaurant is open every evening. All the guest rooms have colour TVs, central heating and tea and coffee making facilities.

Beer: Bass, Courage Best Bitter, Ruddles County (summer only), Ushers Best Bitter on handpumps.

Accommodation: 1 single, 7 doubles, 3 with en suite facilities (other rooms have wash basins). B&B £20 single, double £12.50 per person, Weekend £42.75 for 2 nights including dinner. Midweek £61 for 3 nights with dinner. 7 nights B&B £79, £146.50 with dinner. Private bathrooms £2 per person extra. Children's room; children charged £5 per night sharing. Credit cards: Access, Visa.

### Dartmoor Inn
On A386

Licensee: Chris Padget
Tel: 082 282 221

A cheery, 16th-century pack-horse inn on an old route from north to south Devon, an excellent base for walking and riding holidays, with the moors close at hand. There are two welcoming bars where darts and dominoes are played. Bar meals and full meals are available and the guest rooms all have colour TVs, central heating and tea and coffee making facilities. Mr Padget has more than 40 single malt whiskies on offer. Beer: Bass, Flowers Original on handpumps.

Accommodation: 1 single, 5 doubles, 1 family room, 4 with en suite facilities. B&B from £11.50 per person. Off-Season Weekend up to 25% reduction. Children welcome, 60% reduction. Credit cards: Access, Amex, Diners, Visa.

## LYDFORD GORGE

Manor Inn
1 mile W of Lydford off A386

Licensee: Bill Squire
Tel: 082 282 208

The Manor Inn is at the entrance to the lovely Lydford Gorge with its spectacular 90-foot cascade. Guests can enjoy free admission to the gorge, which is owned by the National Trust, and to other NT properties in the vicinity. There are also opportunities in the area for horse riding and pony trekking. The Manor Inn is renowned for the comfort of its well-appointed guest rooms and the quality of the food prepared by Mr Squire's son, Richard, who trained as a chef in British and Swiss hotels. There is an evening à la carte restaurant and lunchtime bar meals include sandwiches, toasties, ploughman's, pasties, baked spuds with choice of fillings, fish and chips, vegeburgers and omelettes. The inn has a traditional Devon skittles alley.

Beer: St Austell Tinners Bitter and Hicks Special on handpump and straight from the cask.

Accommodation: 2 singles, 4 doubles, 4 rooms with en suite facilities. B&B £14.50-£16.50 per person. 3 nights charged at £13.50 per person per day, 7 nights £12.50 per day. Children over 10 years welcome. Credit cards: Access, Amex, Diners, Visa.

## NORTH BOVEY

Ring of Bells
Off A382, 1½ miles from Moretonhampstead

Licensees: George & Cora Batcock
Tel: 0647 40375

A 13th-century inn in a stunning village of whitewalled, thatched and slated cottages. The Ring of Bells has great oak beams and in the dining room there is an old oven next to the vast inglenook, where the village baker used to bake his bread. The small bar has another large inglenook and a brass-faced grandfather clock built into the three-foot-thick wall. The guest rooms all have en suite facilities and a four-poster bed is available. There is also a residents' lounge. Buffet lunch — sandwiches, salads — and evening table d'hôte meals specialising in local produce and game are served.

Beer: Adnams Bitter, Eldridge Pope Royal Oak, Exmoor Ale, Hall & Woodhouse Tanglefoot, Wadworth 6X straight from the cask.

Accommodation: 1 single, 4 doubles, 1 family room, 4 rooms with en suite facilities. B&B £16.60. Full board available. Off-Season Weekend £60. Two-thirds reductions for children.

# NORTH TAWTON

White Hart
Fore Street, ½ mile off A3072
Crediton to Okehampton road

Proprietors: Meik & Derek Stratton
Tel: 083 782 473

The White Hart is a 17th-century coaching inn in a pleasant market town on the banks of the Taw. The pub has a resident ghost. Less fragile locals play darts and pool inside and cricket and football outdoors. Derek Stratton runs activity holidays that include fishing and clay pigeon shooting, with tuition if required. There are bar snacks and full meals lunch and evening; Meik Stratton specialises in Asian cooking. The guest rooms have TVs and tea and coffee making facilities.

Beer: Wadworth 6X and Old Timer on handpump and straight from the cask, with regular guest beers.

Accommodation: 1 single, 2 doubles. B&B £9.50 per person. Weekend half board £27, Week £90. Children welcome. Riding, fishing and shooting special holidays: terms on application.

# PAIGNTON

Parkers Arms
Totnes Road (A385)

Licensee D W Bennatto
Tel: 0803 551011

There is a friendly welcome in this popular small hotel in Devon's most boisterous seaside resort. The lounge is comfortable and in the public bars darts and skittles are played. Bar snacks include a hot special, salads, ploughman's, scampi, steaks, quiche, plaice, sandwiches and sweets. Bar meals are served lunchtime and evening. The pub is a good base for visiting Berry Pomeroy Castle, Paignton Zoo and Aircraft Museum, the River Dart and local beaches.

Beer: Plympton Best and Plympton Pride on handpumps.

Accommodation: 1 single, 4 doubles. B&B from £12 per person. Week £70. Children's room; children 14 years and over are welcome.

FOX & HOUNDS, FREMINGTON — *see p 54*

# RINGMORE

Journey's End Inn
3 miles from A379, near
Kingsbridge

Licensees: Robert & Tessa Dunkley
Tel: 0548 810205

The Journey's End dates from the
13th century and boasts many tales
of smuggling activity. It has a
delightful backdrop of hills and sea
and the village is decked out with
many thatched cottages. This is the
heart of the South Hams area, with
sandy beaches and moorland and
easy access to Salcombe and
Plymouth. The inn has good bar
meals and a wide choice of cask
beers.

Beer: Butcombe Bitter, Exmoor Ale,
Plympton Best and Pride, plus guest
beers, on handpumps and from the
cask.

Accommodation: 1 single, 3 doubles,
2 with en suite facilities. B&B £16.50
per person. Off-Season Weekend
£20.50 per person including evening
meal. Children's room; children
welcome to stay, no reductions.

# SIDFORD

Blue Ball Inn
On A3052 near Sidmouth

Licensee: Roger Newton
Tel: 039 55 4062

A cob and flint inn dating from
1385 with a thatched roof, large
inglenook fireplaces in both bars and
low-beamed ceilings. The public bar
has a stone-flagged floor and there
are carpets and comfortable
furnishings in the lounge. Food
ranges from chunky sandwiches and
a ploughman's that will satisfy the
most ravenous appetite, to salads and
hot dishes, which include such
specials as grilled pork steak with

barbecue sauce and game pie. There
are summer barbecues in the
attractive garden. Honiton, Farway
Countryside Park, Salcombe Donkey
Sanctuary and Sidmouth, the stately
Regency seaside town, are all close
by. Guest rooms have tea and coffee
making facilities and there is a
residents' TV lounge.

Beer: JD Dry Hop Bitter and
Wessex Stud on handpumps,
Bulmers sweet and dry ciders from
the cask and pump.

Accommodation: 3 doubles. B&B
£12 per person, single room
supplement £4. Children welcome
but no reductions. No dogs.

# TOPSHAM

Lighter Inn
The Quay, off A377

Licensee: D T Horton
Tel: 039 287 5439

This striking old pub has a
commanding position on the banks
of the River Exe in the fine old
town of Topsham with its listed
16th-century buildings of great
architectural interest. The inn offers
both bar snacks and full restaurant
meals while the guest rooms all have
central heating, TVs and tea and
coffee making facilities.

Beer: Hall & Woodhouse Tanglefoot
on handpump.

Accommodation: 1 single, 3 doubles,
1 family room. B&B £15 per person.
Week £95. Children welcome; half
price when sharing.

# TORQUAY

Clarence Hotel
Newton Road, near BR station

Licensee: Alan Hancock
Tel: 0803 24417

A friendly hotel on the edge of
Torquay town centre; a hail-and-ride
bus service will drop you at the
Clarence, named after the Duke of
Clarence, the future William IV, the
sailor king, who was popular in
Devon if nowhere else. The hotel
has a cheerful bar with darts, bar
billiards and pool and an elegant
Victorian lounge. There are bar
snacks and full evening meals, plus a
large garden with children's swings.

Beer: Bass on handpump.

Accommodation: 8 rooms, 4 with
private showers. B&B £11 per
person with shower, £10 without. £1
reductions in winter. Children
charged at two-thirds of adult rates.

# BRIDPORT

Tiger Inn
Barrack Street, off A35

Licensees: Geoff & Gill Kenyon
Tel: 0308 27543

A modernised and redecorated free
house in an historic Dorset town,
home of Palmer's ales, the only
thatched brewery in Britain.
Bridport's port at West Bay is just
1½ miles to the south. From there
you can take the coast path over the
dramatic cliffs as far as Lyme Regis.
The Tiger offers a warm welcome,
with full meals and bar snacks, and
you can join the locals in skittles
and pool.

Beer: Marston Pedigree, Wadworth
6X on handpumps, Taunton dry
cider from the cask.

Accommodation: 1 single, 2 doubles,
B&B £10 per person. Children's
reductions on application.

# BROADSTONE

Broadstone Hotel
Station Approach, off A349

Licensees: Wilf & Diane Dawkins
Tel: 0202 694220

A cheery, traditional local with an
emphasis on entertainment. There
are live music evenings and a new,
separate skittles alley. The beer
garden has a patio and a barbecue.
Broadstone is handily placed for
Wimborne, Bournemouth and Poole.
The hotel offers hot and cold bar
food and the guest rooms all have en
suite facilities, TVs, central heating,
and tea and coffee making
equipment.

Beer: Flowers Original and Strong
Country Bitter on handpumps.

Accommodation: 5 doubles, 1 family
room. B&B £15 per person. Reduced
rates for 3 days or more. Bargain
Breaks: details on request. Credit
cards: Access, Amex, Diners, Visa.

SCOTT ARMS, KINGSTON — see p 60

# KINGSTON

Scott Arms
On B3069, near Corfe Castle

Licensees: Philip & Marcelle
Stansfield
Tel: 0929 480 270

There are breathtaking views of the
chilling ruins of Corfe Castle, Poole
Harbour and the rolling Purbeck
hills from this fine, ivy-clad pub 400
feet above sea level. There are two
comfortable bars with log fires in
winter — one bar is a family room.
Excellent pub fare includes home-
made soups, ploughman's, pasties,
quiche, chilli, lasagne, vegetarian
meals and Dorset apple cake. The
guest rooms have central heating and
tea and coffee making facilities.
Kingston is a fine base for Corfe,
Poole, Lulworth, Tolpuddle,
Swanage, Chesil Beach and the
Abbotsbury swannery and tropical
gardens.

Beer: Cornish Wessex Stud on
handpump.

Accommodation: 6 doubles, 1 family
room. B&B £12 per person in
winter, £14 in summer. Children
welcome, half price.

# MILTON ABBAS

Hambro Arms
3 miles off A354, near Milton
Abbey

Licensee: K A Baines
Tel: 0258 880233

A delightful, 18th-century thatched
inn in a picturesque village. Milton
Abbas was the first purpose-built
village in England and all the
cottages are in the same thatched
style. The Hambro Arms has two
charming guest rooms, one with a
four-poster bed, both with en suite
facilities. There is splendid pub food,

plus a separate restaurant and a
Sunday carvery.

Beer: JD Dry Hop Bitter and
Cornish Wessex Stud on
handpumps.

Accommodation: 2 doubles, B&B
from £15 per person. Children
welcome, terms by arrangement.

# POOLE

Inn in the Park
26 Pinewood Road, Branksome
Park

Licensees: Paula & Alan Potter
Tel: 0202 761318

A comfortable inn converted from a
handsome Victorian house, with log
fires in a bar decorated with postage
stamps and old cigarette cards. In
pleasant weather, you can enjoy
drink and food on a patio. There is
an extensive hot and cold menu
lunchtime and evening. All the guest
rooms have colour TVs and tea and
coffee making facilities. The inn is a
good base for visiting Bournemouth
and Poole.

Beer: Ringwood Bitter, Wadworth
IPA and 6X on handpumps.

Accommodation: 5 doubles, 1 family
room, 4 rooms with private bath.
B&B £12.50-£19.50 per person.
Children half price when sharing.

# POWERSTOCK

**Three Horseshoes**
Off A35 east of Bridport.
OS 516962

Licensees: Pat & Diana Ferguson
Tel: 030 885 328/229

A remote, Victorian stone-built pub, well worth the effort of finding. Take the Askerswell exit from the A35, keep left round Eggardon Hill and pick up the Powerstock road. The village has a Norman church and cows wander down the main street. There are fine views and country walks, trout and sea fishing facilities. The pub has been extended since the last edition of the guide: a separate restaurant built with local stone, with pine-clad walls, has been added and two of the guest rooms now have en suite facilities. There are good bar snacks and the restaurant specialises in local sea food such as Lyme Bay plaice, crab, lobster and skate, as well steaks and venison and a Sunday roast.

Beer: Palmer BB, IPA and Tally Ho on handpumps and Taunton traditional cider from the cask.

Accommodation: 1 single, 2 doubles, 1 family room. B&B £15 single, £28 double, family room £32 (1 double bed and 2 singles). Bargain Breaks: 3 days half-board £114 (Nov-March).

# SHAFTESBURY

**Royal Chase Hotel**
Royal Chase roundabout
off A30/A350

Licensee: George Hunt
Tel: 0747 3355

A small, beautifully appointed 3-star hotel in the old Saxon hill town in the heart of Wessex, with its tumbling cobbled streets, thatched cottages and breath-catching views over Dorset. The hotel was a monastery until 1922 and it still enjoys a wonderful serenity and seclusion. There is a genuine locals' bar with an open fire and a fine old-fashioned cash register. It also has an indoor swimming pool. The Country Kitchen restaurant offers fine food based on local produce. It is a good base for visiting the Fox Talbot Museum of Photography, Montacute House Tropical Bird Garden, Wookey Hole, Thomas Hardy's cottage and Stonehenge.

Beer: Eldridge Pope Royal Oak (usually in winter), Ushers Best Bitter, Wadworth 6X plus regular guest beers, all on handpumps.

Accommodation: 3 singles, 18 doubles, 10 family rooms, all with private bath or shower. B&B from £27.50 per person. Weekend (B&B plus evening meal) £58-£86. Real ale breaks from £58. Children's room; children free if sharing.

# SHILLINGSTONE

**Seymer Arms**
On A357 Blandford road

Licensee: Tony Stone
Tel: 0258 860488

A pleasant, one-bar roadside pub set in gorgeous countryside and close to the famous Bulbarrow Hill beauty spot. It is a genuine local with darts and crib played in the bar, which has a wood-burning stove that heats all the rooms. Good pub grub is served lunchtime and evening and there are caravan facilities nearby.

Beer: Hall & Woodhouse Badger Best Bitter and Tanglefoot, Hook Norton Best Bitter on handpumps.

Accommodation: 2 doubles. B&B £10-£15 per person. Half-board terms available.

# STURMINSTER NEWTON

White Hart
Market Cross, A357

Licensee: D G Rice
Tel: 0258 72590

A splendid, early 18th-century thatched coaching inn in the heart of the Blackmore Vale and Hardy country. Coarse fishing is available in the picturesque River Stour nearby. The lovely old pub is free from noisy music, it has a pleasant garden, fires in winter and such traditional games as skittles, crib, shove ha'penny and darts. Pub food is served lunchtime and evening. Camping facilities are available.

Beer: Hall & Woodhouse Badger Best Bitter on handpump.

Accommodation: 3 doubles, 1 family room. B&B £10-£15 per person.

# WAREHAM

Red Lion Hotel
Town. Cross, off A351

Licensees: Jim & Claire Doole
Tel: 092 95 2843

The Dooles offer a warm welcome in this recently modernised one-bar hotel, set in the heart of a delightful old market town. Parts of the hotel are more than 200 years old and the Lion bar, with its comfortable settles, has a welcoming fire in winter. It now has 20 guest rooms, a restaurant seating 50 and a large area for families. As well as full restaurant meals, there are good bar snacks, including jacket potatoes with choice of fillings, burgers, steak and kidney pie, lasagne, and fish and chips. There is a boisterous skittles alley and live music is played on Tuesday evenings. You can visit the

town walls, St Martin's Church and Corfe Castle.

Beer: Flowers Original and Wethereds Bitter on handpumps.

Accommodation: 8 singles, 4 doubles, 3 twins, 5 family rooms, 6 rooms with en suite facilities, all with colour TVs and tea and coffee making equipment. B&B £12.50 per person. Weekend £37.50, Week £87.50. Children half price.

# WEST LULWORTH

Castle Inn
On B3070

Proprietors: Patricia & Graham Halliday
Tel: 092941 311

A picturesque, thatched cottage pub near Lulworth cove, the Castle is some 450 years old. It takes its present name from the castle at East Lulworth designed by Inigo Jones and destroyed by fire in 1929. The inn, first known as the Jolly Sailor, has two bars, rolling gardens, outdoor seats at the front, bar meals and full restaurant facilities where you can enjoy local sea food as well as poultry and game. The guest rooms have central heating, colour TVs and tea and coffee making facilities.

Beer: JD Dry Hop Bitter and Cornish Wessex Stud on handpumps.

Accommodation: 1 single, 7 doubles, 2 family rooms, 8 rooms with private bath. B&B £15.50 single, £21 double. Weekend £12.50 per person per day. Week £62.50. Children welcome, rates negotiable. Facilities for the disabled. Credit cards: Access, Amex, Visa.

# WIMBORNE

Albion Hotel
19 High Street, town square A31

Licensees: Ray & Marion Edmonds
Tel: 0202 882492

The Albion is the oldest licensed premises in Wimborne, the last surviving part of an ancient coaching inn with an original inglenook fireplace. This is very much a locals' pub, with a warm, friendly atmosphere, where dominoes, crib and darts are played. Marion Edmonds specialises in traditional food such as beef cobbler and Minster pie, jacket potatoes and ploughman's. There is a large garden with a swing and climbing frame. The pub is a fine base for Wimborne Hall and Kingston Lacy House (NT).

Beer: Hall & Woodhouse Badger Best Bitter on handpump.

Accommodation: 2 doubles, 1 with bath, shower and colour TV. B&B £8.50-£12.50 per person.

# DARLINGTON

Coachman Hotel
Victoria Road, town centre, near main BR station

Licensee: Bob Salmon
Tel: 0325 286116

The hotel is the former North Eastern Hotel dating from the early 1880s and the great railway boom. There is a bustling Ostler Bar and quieter, comfortable Victoria Lounge. Guest rooms have colour TVs, tea and coffee making facilities and private showers.

Beer: Whitbread Castle Eden Ale on handpump.

Accommodation: 10 singles, 4 doubles, 8 twins, 3 family rooms. B&B £25 per person. Reductions for weekends.

# MIDDLETON ONE ROW

Devonport Hotel
18 The Front, off A67 near Darlington

Licensee: Richard Whincup
Tel: 0325 332255

An elegant, early 18th-century hotel overlooking a scenic stretch of the River Tees and close to Teesside Airport. There is a large carpeted lounge and a smaller bar where pub games are played. Bar snacks and meals are served lunchtime and evening. Most of the rooms have en suite facilities and all have colour TV and tea and coffee making equipment.

Beer: McEwan 80 shilling, Younger Scotch Bitter and No 3 on handpumps.

Accommodation: 3 singles, 8 doubles (1 double can be used as family room), 8 rooms with en suite facilities. B&B £20 single, £26.50 with bathroom. Weekend (any 2 nights) £15.50 per person per night, £20 with bath. Children welcome, terms by arrangement. Credit cards: Access, Amex, Diners, Visa.

## NEASHAM

Newbus Arms Hotel
Hurworth Road, off A1 and A67

Licensee: John Wilmott
Tel: 0325 721071

A fine, old country-house hotel approached along an avenue of trees, it is a 17th-century listed building with 19th-century embellishments. It has an ornate Victorian bar and first-class restaurant. The management can arrange fishing rights on the Tees.

Beer: Theakston Best Bitter, Younger IPA on handpumps.

Accommodation: 3 singles, 12 doubles, 4 family rooms. B&B from £35 per person. Facilities for the disabled.

---

ESSEX

## BURNHAM-ON-CROUCH

Olde White Harte Hotel
The Quay, B1010, off A12

Licensee: G John Lewis
Tel: 0621 782106

This fine old waterside inn is a good pull-up for yachtsmen on the River Crouch and is equally popular with landlubbers. The front bar has comfortable seats, oak tables and parquet floors. There are several other rooms, some with bare brick walls covered with emotive seascapes. Excellent bar snacks include lasagne, fish pie and lamb chops while the restaurant — open for lunch and dinner — offers Dover sole, lobster, steaks and salads plus a children's menu. There are riding, fishing and golf facilities available.

Beer: Adnams Bitter, Tolly Cobbold Bitter on handpumps.

Accommodation: 2 singles, 3 doubles/twins, 3 rooms with private bath. B&B from £17 single, £30 double, £5 extra for room with bath.

## COLCHESTER

Rose & Crown Hotel
East Gates, off A12 & A133

Manager: J De Andrade
Tel: 0206 866677/867676

The Rose & Crown bills itself as the oldest inn in England's oldest recorded town. It is an imposing building with an impressive half-timbered edifice and a sumptuous interior with low beams, wooden pillars, log fires and beautifully appointed guest rooms, including some with four-poster beds. Built in the 15th century, the hotel stands at the corner of the old Ipswich and Harwich roads and was once a leading coaching inn. Food is available every day of the year: the restaurant offers fresh turbot, Dover sole, lobster, steaks, roast duckling and pheasant and venison in season. There are bar meals in the Prison Bar — the present building incorporates the site of an old jail.

Beer: Tolly Cobbold Original, XXXX and Old Strong (winter) on handpumps.

Accommodation: 15 singles, 13 doubles, 2 family rooms, 21 rooms with en suite facilities, all rooms with colour TVs. B&B £25 single, £35 with bath/shower, double/twin £36, £45.50 with bath/shower, £49.50 with four-poster bed. Weekend Break: £32.50 B&B per person sharing a double room. Additional accommodation at same rates in adjoining cottages. Children welcome, terms negotiable. Credit cards: Access, Amex, Diners, Visa.

# DEDHAM

Marlborough Head
Off A12

Licensee: Brian Wills
Tel: 0206 323250

An impressive medieval inn in the heart of Constable country with, inevitably, a Constable Bar that has alcove seating, beams and timbers, and a comfortable lounge. There is also a garden with seats for fine-weather eating and drinking. The vast range of food at reasonable prices includes soup, jacket potatoes with choice of fillings, ploughman's, pâté, steak and kidney pie and a daily vegetarian dish.

Beer: Ind Coope Bitter on handpump.

Accommodation: 2 singles, 2 doubles, most with en suite facilities. B&B £20 single, £35 double with continental breakfast, cooked breakfast extra.

# EARLS COLNE

Drum Inn
21 High Street, A604,
7 miles off A12

Licensee: L E Grieves
Tel: 07875 2368

A handsome, 200-year-old inn on the Cambridge-Colchester road, with a log fire in the bar, copper and brass decorations and a collection of chamber pots and other china ornaments. There is excellent home-cooked pub grub and the Drum is a good base for railway buffs visiting the Colne Valley Steam Railway.

Beer: Greene King IPA and Abbot Ale, Mauldons Bitter and Special on handpumps.

Accommodation: 2 doubles, 1 family room. B&B £13 per person. Children welcome, terms by arrangement.

# ELMDON

Kings Head
Heydon Lane, near Saffron Walden, just off B1039, 4 miles from M11 at Duxford

Licensees: Bernard & Rona Farrell
Tel: 0763 838358

A delightful, 350-year-old Essex inn with tables on the lawn, a beer garden and clay shooting. It has two bars, a separate dining room and accommodation in a modern adjoining building. The Kings Head has a wide range of pub games, including darts, pool and a quiz league. Food is served seven days a week with both bar snacks and full restaurant meals. The pub is a good base for visiting Duxford Air Museum, Linton Zoo, Audley End and Saffron Walden.

Beer: Benskins Best Bitter, Ind Coope Bitter and Tetley Bitter on handpumps.

Accommodation: 1 twin, 1 double, both en suite. B&B from £10 to £15 per person. Weekends from £25, Week from £85. Half and full board available. Children's room; children welcome to stay.

ROSE & CROWN HOTEL, COLCHESTER —
*see opposite*

# FINCHINGFIELD

Red Lion Inn
Church Hill, on B1057

Licensee: R J Mizon
Tel: 0371 810400

A picturesque, 500-year-old inn in one of England's most celebrated and prettiest villages. There are old beams a-plenty, cheerful log fires in winter and live music every weekend. There is an extensive menu seven days a week with a roast lunch on Sundays.

Beer: Ridley Bitter on handpump, Adnams Extra straight from the cask.

Accommodation: 4 doubles, 2 family rooms. B&B £12 per person. Half and full board available. Children's room; children half price, depending on age.

# TILLINGHAM

Cap & Feathers
South Street, off B1021,
A130 and A12

Licensees: Olly & Carol Graham
Tel: 062 187 212

A superb, weather-boarded listed building in a remote part of Essex, close to the coast, Dengie Marshes and St Peter's on the Wall, England's oldest church. The pub is the first tied house owned by the tiny Crouch Vale brewery and the Grahams' aim is to keep it as a firmly traditional pub with blazing fires, pub games and 'no flashing lights'. It has a resident ghost authorised by Willie Rushton. Excellent pub food is always available and families are welcome. Local CAMRA Pub of the Year in 1987.

Beer: Crouch Vale Woodham Bitter, Best Bitter, South Anglian Special. Willie Warmer and Tillingham Christmas Porter on handpumps (the last two beers are seasonal)

Accommodation: 3 singles, 3 doubles, 1 family room. B&B £12 single, £18 double. Children welcome.

# GLOUCESTERSHI

# BROCKWEIR

Brockweir Country Inn
30 yards over Brockweir Bridge off A466, 6 miles from Severn Bridge (M4)

Licensee: George Jones
Tel: 029 18 548

A 17th-century inn in the Lower Wye Valley, a few yards from the river and close to Tintern Abbey, the Forest of Dean and Chepstow and its race course. It stands on Offa's Dyke and fishing, riding and walking can be enjoyed. The inn has oak beams, an open fire, two bars and a dining room with excellent food. Outside there is a covered courtyard, a walled beer garden and beyond there are beautiful forests and pastures. Brockweir is a fascinating village with a rather shady past. It was a port in the 19th century, feeding the Severn, had all the usual port-side associations and was chosen by Lord Nelson as the place to court Lady Hamilton.

Beer: Boddingtons Bitter, Flowers Original, Hook Norton Best Bitter plus guest beers and Bulmers traditional cider, all on handpumps.

Accommodation: 3 doubles, 1 family room. B&B from £12 per person. Half board available. Children welcome; children's room.

# CHELTENHAM

High Roost
Cleeve Hill, A46 between
Cheltenham and Winchcombe

Licensee: John English
Tel: 0242 67 2010

The High Roost gets its name from its commanding position overlooking the Cotswolds and the Severn Valley towards Wales. It is a welcoming, family-run free house close to a golf course, Sudeley Castle and the ancient town of Winchcombe. There is always a choice of 20 meals or more on the lunchtime menu, plus home-made pies and baps with a variety of fillings.

Beer: Hook Norton Best Bitter and Old Hookey plus a house beer, High Roost Special Bitter, all on handpumps.

Accommodation: 2 singles, 2 doubles, 1 room with en suite facilities. B&B £11 per person. Weekend £20, Week £60, Off-Season Weekend £11. No children.

# GREAT BARRINGTON

Fox
Off A40 between Little and Great Barrington

Licensees: Pat & Bill Mayer
Tel: 045 14 385

A low-ceilinged inn with stone walls, rustic seats, and welcoming fires in winter. There is a skittles alley and you may sit outside by the River Windrush in summer. Locally quarried stone was once taken down the river to build St Paul's Cathedral. Bar food includes 'home-brewed' soup, salads, sandwiches and pies.

Beer: Donnington XXX, BB and SBA on handpumps.

Accommodation: 5 rooms. B&B £14 single, £26 double.

# GREAT RISSINGTON

Lamb Inn
6 miles off A40 near Bourton

Licensee: Richard Cleverly
Tel: 0451 20388/20724

A Cotswold stone inn, with parts dating back to the 17th century, but offering such modern accoutrements as an indoor swimming pool and central heating, the Lamb has fine views over the surrounding countryside from its delightful garden. The two small bars are comfortably carpeted, with wheel-back chairs, round tables and wall decorations of old cigarette tins. Bar food, lunch and evening, includes home-made soups, prawns with garlic and mushrooms, ploughman's, jacket potatoes with cheese, salads, omelettes and curries. There is a separate restaurant. Mr Cleverly says there is a resident ghost 'but he does not use the four-poster bedroom' — clearly an inducement to book the most expensive room! The inn offers a residents' lounge with colour TV and there are several golf courses nearby.

Beer: Fuller London Pride, Wadworth 6X on handpumps plus a regular guest beer.

Accommodation: 8 doubles, inc 1 four-poster room. 5 rooms with en suite facilities. B&B £19.50 per person, double room £28, £34 with private bath. Four-poster room, en suite, £39. Credit cards: Access, Visa.

# LECHLADE

Red Lion Hotel
High Street, A417

Licensee: Keith Dudley
Tel: 0367 52373

A cheery, oak-beamed atmosphere in an old Cotswold pub busily regenerated by the Dudley family since 1985. It is just 100 yards from the river and offers fine food and comfort. The separate restaurant has an extensive menu. There is yet another pub ghost: this one is claimed to pop out of the wardrobe in the family room to say goodnight: Arkell's ale does have that effect on some people.

Beer: Arkell Bitter and BBB straight from the cask.

Accommodation: 1 double, 1 family room. B&B £26 double, £36 family room. Children welcome, no reductions.

# LOWER SWELL

Golden Ball Inn
Off A429, 1 mile from
Stow-on-the-Wold

Licensees: Stephen & Vanessa Aldridge
Tel: 0451 30247

The Golden Ball, in keeping with its beer supplier, Donnington, the most picturesque of all Britain's country breweries, is a delightful old building of mellow Cotswold stone, dating back to the 17th century. There is a log fire in winter, a profusion of pub games — darts, shove ha'penny, dominoes and cribbage — and a garden with a stream where Aunt Sally is played and where there are occasional summer barbecues. Bar snacks (not Sunday evening) include home-made soups and pies, filled jacket potatoes, salads and

sandwiches, with steaks and fish dishes in the evening. There is a small restaurant, the Hideaway, open in the evenings. You can visit Broadway, Stratford, Warwick or walk 20 minutes to Donnington's brewery.

Beer: Donnington XXX, BB and SBA on handpumps.

Accommodation: 2 singles, 2 doubles. B&B £12.50 single, £25 double. Half and full board available. Children over 5 welcome. No dogs.

# NAUNTON

Black Horse Inn
1 mile from B4068 Andoversford to Stow road, near Guiting Power

Licensees: Adrian & Jennie Bowen-Jones
Tel: 04515 378

A 17th-century inn in a lovely old Cotswold village by the River Windrush and close to the unnervingly named hamlets of Upper and Lower Slaughter. The Black Horse is a superb base for walking through the Cotswolds and visiting such famed beauty spots as Bourton-on-the Water. Excellent pub food is served lunchtime and evening and includes home-made soups, salads, daily specials listed on a blackboard, curry, lasagne, scampi and ploughman's.

Beer: Donnington BB and SBA on handpumps.

Accommodation: 2 doubles. £12.50 per person excluding breakfast. No children.

# NYMPSFIELD

Rose & Crown Inn
1½ miles from B4066

Licensees: Bob & Linda Woodman
Tel: 0453 860240

A 300-year-old, stone-built coaching inn in an unspoilt village close to the Cotswold Way and with easy access to the M4 and M5. The Woodmans run the Rose & Crown as 'a real pub — we don't worry too much about muddy boots.' Food ranges from simple bar snacks to full meals and special buffets. You can enjoy delicious home-made soups, ploughman's, pizzas, sandwiches, pasties, faggots, trout, and steak and kidney pie, and there is a special children's menu.

Beer: Arkell BBB, Flowers Original and Whitbread West Country Pale ale on handpumps.

Accommodation: 1 double, 2 family rooms. B&B £10 per person. 7 days for price of 6. Children welcome, reductions 40% minimum. Credit cards: Access, Visa.

# SHEEPSCOMBE

Butchers Arms
Off B4070; 1½ miles off A46

Licensee: Alan Meredith
Tel: 0452 812113

Of all the Cotswolds pubs, the Butchers Arms has arguably the finest view out over a lovely valley of woods, fields and a few nestling houses. The pub certainly has the most unusual pub sign around — a carving of a butcher drinking next to a bound pig. The pub has one cheerful room with bay windows, rustic benches and a collection of bottled beers from around the world. It is the HQ of the local cricket club and there is a pleasant,

steep garden with seats. Bar food includes soup, toasties and ploughman's.

Beer: Flowers Original and Whitbread West Country Pale Ale plus guest beer on handpumps, Bulmer traditional cider on electric pump.

Accommodation: 1 double. B&B £11 per person (£13 for single occupant). No children.

# TEWKESBURY

Berkeley Arms
Church Street, A38

Licensee: R J Jones
Tel: 0684 293034

A 15th-century inn with a fine timbered exterior and original interior beams, in this famous and historic abbey town. The pub has darts and cribbage but, says Mr Jones, 'no place for a pool table': Bacchus be praised. There are lounge and public bars and excellent pub grub.

Beer: Wadworth Devizes Bitter, 6X, Farmer's Glory and Old Timer on handpumps.

Accommodation: 1 single, 1 double, 1 family room. B&B £9 per person. Evening meals available. Children welcome, up to half price, according to age.

HORSE & GROOM INN, UPPER ODDINGTON –
*see p 70*

# UPPER ODDINGTON

**Horse & Groom Inn**
Off A436 near Moreton-in-Marsh

Licensees: Cyril & June Howarth
and Nicholas & Sally Evans
Tel: 0451 30584

A superb 16th-century inn of
Cotswold stone, with original beams
and timbers in the bars and some of
the guest rooms. The delightful
village of Upper Oddington has an
ancient church, St Nicholas', dating
back to the 12th century. The inn
has a splendid beer garden with a
stream, fishponds, an aviary and a
children's area with swings and a
climbing frame. Inside, the bars have
wood panelling and masses of brass
on the beams and fireplaces. Local
produce abounds in the dining
room. The guest rooms all have en
suite facilities and tea and coffee
makers. French, German and
Spanish as well as Gloucestershire
are spoken.

Beer: Hall & Woodhouse Badger
Best Bitter, Wadworth 6X on
handpumps.

Accommodation: 6 doubles. B&B
£16-£18 per person. Winter Weekend
Breaks: £42-£45 per person for 2
nights. Midweek Special: £20-£21 per
person per night, £5 supplement for
single occupancy. Children welcome,
terms on application. Guide dogs
only.

# WATERLEY BOTTOM

**New Inn**
Near North Nibley, Dursley. Off
A38, B4058, B4060 and A4134

Licensee: Ruby Sainty
Tel: 0453 3659 (add 54 prefix
after summer 1988)

Ruby Sainty is the kind of character
that makes finding this remote old
pub in a lovely wooded valley worth
the effort. 'There are two golf
courses two miles from the pub,
where you can work off excess ale,'
she says. As for the accommodation:
'Although I only let two bedrooms I
have in the past put up a cricket
team and a party of six lads who
bring their own sleeping bags —
they're only here for the beer!'
Don't let that put you off — the inn
has every modern comfort, with
central heating, colour TVs and tea
and coffee making facilities in the
guest rooms. Darts, dominoes,
draughts, chess and crib are played
in the bar. If you tear yourself away,
Berkeley Castle is just four miles
distant. The pub has a fine range of
pub food, including home-made
soups, pâté, ploughman's, salads,
steak and kidney pie, toasted
sandwiches and brown baps with a
choice of fillings.

Beer: Cotleigh Tawny and a house
brew, Waterley Bottom, Greene
King Abbot Ale, Smiles Best Bitter
and Exhibition, Theakston Old
Peculier, guest beers and Inch cider,
all on antique beer engines.

Accommodation: 1 twin, 1 double
with children's beds if required.
B&B from £10.50 per person. Half
price for children under 12.

# WOTTON-UNDER-EDGE

## Falcon
Church Street, B4058 between Stroud and Bristol; 5 miles from M5

Licensees: William Suffell & Tony Stephenson
Tel: 0453 842138

A 17th-century coaching inn at the bottom of the High Street, with splendid views from the stone portico of the sweeping escarpment that gave the town its name. The inn is run by Bill and Irene Suffell and their daughter and son-in-law Cathy and Tony Stephenson. The emphasis is on a good welcome, good pub accommodation and victuals. The food ranges from bar snacks to daily specials and full meals. A short walk brings visitors to a group of charming alms houses with their own tiny chapel.

Beer: Courage Best Bitter, Directors, John Smiths Bitter on handpumps.

Accommodation: 1 double, 1 family room. B&B £10.50 per person. Children welcome, 2 for the price of 1 when sharing with parents.

# ANDOVER

## Railway Tavern
71 Weyhill Road, off A303

Licensee: Bob Cummings
Tel: 0264 62474

A large, welcoming roadside pub, rebuilt in 1930, with a lounge and public bar. Darts and cribbage are played but there is no pool table, much to Mr Cumming's satisfaction. Pub food is available lunchtime and evening. There are open coal fires in winter and there are animals in the large gardens for children to enjoy. In summer, the pub is decked out with hanging baskets and barbecues are held in the garden.

Beer: Flowers Original and Strong Country Bitter and regular guest beers from the Whitbread stable, on handpumps.

Accommodation: 2 twins. B&B £14.50 per person.

# CHERITON

## Flower Pots
Off A272, on B3046

Licensee: Patricia Bartlett
Tel: 096 279 318

An unspoilt village pub in an award-winning village near Tichbourne, Alresford and the Watercress Steam Railway. The pub has two bars with striped wallpaper, hunting scenes and old copper distilling equipment. Mrs Bartlett offers a homely welcome and excellent bar snacks such as ploughman's and toasted sandwiches. There are seats at the front of the pub and, inside, locals join in darts, crib, dominoes and shove ha'penny. The beer is tapped from casks on a stillage behind the bar. The guest rooms are small and cosy, with a separate bathroom.

Beer: Flowers Original and Strong Country Bitter from the cask.

Accommodation: 1 single, 2 twin rooms. B&B from £11 per person.

# DAMERHAM

Compasses Inn
East End, 3 miles W of
Fordingbridge on B3078

Licensees: H & J C Reilly
Tel: 072 53 231

A fine old inn in a pleasant rural
setting, with a jolly landlord. At the
rear is an antique brewery. There are
two bars, a separate dining room
with food lunchtime and evening,
and live jazz every Friday evening. It
is a good family pub with a large
garden and in winter there are three
blazing fires.

Beer: Tetley Bitter, Wadworth 6X
and Coates traditional cider on
handpumps.

Accommodation: 2 doubles, 2 family
rooms. B&B £10-£15 per person.
Children welcome, terms on
application. Full board available.

# EAST STRATTON

Plough Inn
Just off A33 near Micheldever,
between Basingstoke and
Winchester

Licensees: Richard & Trudy Duke
& Gill Moran
Tel: 0962 89 241

A former 17th-century farmhouse,
the Plough is set amid pretty
thatched cottages in a tiny hamlet
surrounded by farmland. The pub
has its own green with swings, a
seesaw and an ancient tractor. The
public bar has darts and a quiet
jukebox. The lounge is cosy and
there are seats in a courtyard. The
thriving skittles alley also has a bar
and there is a children's room in the
old bakehouse off the courtyard.
Food is available lunchtime and
evening and ranges from snacks,
including home-made soups, to
three-course meals. Children's

portions are available. The guest
rooms have tea and coffee making
facilities and are large enough to
accommodate two adults and two
children.

Beer: Courage Best Bitter and
Directors, Gales BBB and HSB on
handpumps.

Accommodation: 3 twins. B&B £15
per person. Children under 10 £8.50.

# FACCOMBE

Jack Russell
Near Hurstbourne, off A343

Licensee: Paul Foster
Tel: 026487 315

A remote but comfortable, recently
renovated inn, overlooking the
village pond, on a private estate
midway between Andover and
Newbury. The pub is quiet and free
from electronic devices. There are
fires in winter, a garden for summer
drinking and eating, and good pub
food is served lunchtime and
evening: don't miss Jill Foster's
beefstew with dumplings. It is a
splendid base for the Wayfarers'
Walk, which begins three miles
north at Inkpen Beacon, site of the
Combe gibbet. The Bourne Valley,
with its painted railway viaduct, is
close at hand, and Newbury and
Andover are both a short drive
away. The guest rooms in the Jack
Russell have TVs and tea and coffee
making facilities.

Beer: Palmer BB and regular guest
beers, all on handpumps.

Accommodation: 3 doubles, 1 family
room, 1 room with en suite
facilities. B&B £15 per person. Half
and full board available. Credit
cards: Access, Visa.

# GRATELEY

Plough Inn
On main road through village, 1½
miles S of A303, near Andover

Licensees: Chris & Joy Marchant
Tel: 0264 88221

A splendid old country inn run by
an enthusiastic couple. Darts, crib,
pool and ring the bull are played in
the bar and a restaurant leads off the
comfortable lounge. Pub food,
ranging from snacks to full meals, is
served every day, including Sundays.
Both Grateley and nearby Quarley
have 13th century churches, while
the flying museum at Nether Wallop
and the Hawk Conservancy at
Weyhill are just short journeys. The
guest rooms in the Plough have tea
and coffee making facilities.

Beer: Gibbs Mew Wiltshire
Traditional Bitter, Salisbury Best
Bitter and Bishop's Tipple (in
winter) on handpumps.

Accommodation: 1 double, 2 twins.
B&B £13 per person. Half and full
board available. Credit cards: Access,
Visa.

# HAVANT

Bear Hotel
East Street, off A27

Licensees: M A Hothersall & S E
Kennedy
Tel: 0705 486501

A lovely old coaching inn, with a
large public bar, that combines the
comfort of an AA three-star hotel
with the genuine cheer of a country-
town pub. The restaurant has à la
carte and set meals, with quick
lunches such as a platter of
mackerel, pâté, prawns and avocado,
lasagne, seafood rissotto, and
tagliatelle. There is a Sunday lunch
and a separate children's menu. The
guest rooms all have en suite
showers and baths, colour TVs and
tea and coffee making facilities.
Havant is a good base for the New
Forest, Portsmouth and Chichester.

Beer: Flowers Original on
handpump.

Accommodation: 14 singles, 9 twins,
19 doubles. B&B £45 single, £55
double. Weekend from £36 per
person, Week from £164. Children
welcome, terms by arrangement.
Credit cards: Access, Amex, Diners,
Visa.

# HORNDEAN

Ship & Bell
6 London Road, take Horndean
exit from A3

Licensee: S R Williams
Tel: 0705 592107

The Ship & Bell is the original site
of Gale's sturdily independent
brewery. It is the brewery tap now
and is owned by Horndean Hotels, a
subsidiary of the brewery. The pub
is 18th century and is reputed to
have a lady ghost in a blue dress
who is seen from time to time
descending the back stairs. The pub
has an excellent range of reasonably
priced food in the bars, pub games
and live folk or jazz on Wednesday
nights.

Beer: Gales XXX, BBB, HSB and 5X
(in winter) on handpumps.

Accommodation: 3 singles, 3 twins,
3 rooms with bath or shower. B&B
£16 single, twin with shower £30,
with bath £35.

# HURSTBOURNE PRIORS

Hurstbourne
On B3400 between Whitchurch
and Andover, off M3

Licensee: Dave & Joy Houghton
Tel: 0256 89 2000

A century-old inn, recently
renovated with open-plan rooms and
cosy niches in the bar where darts,
bar billiards, shove ha'penny,
dominoes and crib are played. The
nearby River Test offers trout
fishing and walks along its banks.
The inn's food ranges from a light
snack to a full meal in the
restaurant, seven days a week. The
guest rooms have central heating and
tea and coffee making facilities.

Beer: Flowers Original and
Wethered Bitter, Wadworth 6X on
handpumps.

Accommodation: 2 twin rooms, 1
family room. B&B £17 single, £24
double. Children welcome, terms by
arrangement.

# LYMINGTON

King's Arms
St Thomas' Street, just off A337

Licensee: Paul Elford
Tel: 0590 72594

The King's Arms is a 15th-century
coaching inn in an historic old
town, mentioned in the Domesday
Book, which has a cobbled street
leading down to the quay. It is a
thriving sailing town today and both
the town and the pub are popular
with yachting people. There is a
jolly, welcoming atmosphere in the
pub where Mrs Elford provides good
value bar food seven days a week.
The guest rooms have TVs and tea
and coffee making facilities.

Lymington is close to the New
Forest and has rail links via
Brockenhurst to Southampton and
the Isle of Wight.

Beer: Flowers Original and Strong
Country Bitter straight from the
cask.

Accommodation: 1 double, 1 family
room with 3 beds. B&B from
£10-£15.

# MINSTEAD

Trusty Servant
1 mile off A337 between Cadnam
and Lyndhurst

Licensee: David Mills
Tel: 0703 812137

This delightful, small and friendly
two-bar pub lives up to its name.
The welcome, the food and the
accommodation are so good that
guests — 'friends' is Mrs Mills's term
— come back year after year. She
preferred not to give details of prices
for B&B (£18 per person in the last
edition) because she likes people to
phone and discuss what they want.
The pub overlooks the village green
and its name is depicted on the end
of the building. It is in the heart of
the New Forest close to Furzey
Gardens and the part-Saxon
Minstead Church, the last resting
place of Conan Doyle. There is an
excellent range of hot and cold
snacks. Friday night is music night,
when Mr Mills is known to burst
into song.

Beer: Flowers Original and
Wethered Bitter on handpumps.

Accommodation: 3 doubles. Phone
for details of prices. No children.

# PETERSFIELD

## Old Drum
16 Chapel Street, off A3

Licensee: Brian Barnes
Tel: 0730 64159

A friendly old pub with a relaxing atmosphere just north of the market square in a bustling and prosperous town. There is no piped music in the Old Drum so visitors can engage in the ancient art of pub conversation free from electronic ear-bashing. There are pub games and excellent bar food at lunchtimes. The large back garden, once a bowling green but now laid with lawns and fishponds, is the current holder of the Friary Meux Best Garden award. The guest rooms have colour TVs.

Beer: Burton Ale, Friary Meux Best Bitter and Tetley Bitter on handpumps.

Accommodation: 3 doubles. B&B £10-£15.

# PORTSMOUTH

## George
84 Queen Street, Portsea

Licensees: John Goodall & Denis Mort
Tel: 0705 821040

The George is Pompey's oldest surviving tavern dating back to the 18th century. It is now a free house but was once owned by Jewell & Sons, whose name is still enshrined in the entrance. The long, sumptuous and highly polished single bar is reminiscent of a navy wardroom. It is packed with naval artefacts and paintings, many of them featuring Nelson. There are sailors' caps, lights suspended from the ceiling in an old ship's wheel, beams from old Portsmouth boats and a well that once stood in a courtyard when the present bar was two separate buildings. The pub is just two minutes' walk from the sea and the historic splendours of HMS Warrior, HMS Victory and the Mary Rose. The pub offers tasty food, including a daily hot special, and Messrs Goodall and Mort plan to open a separate restaurant next to the pub, due to open in 1988. There are piano sessions on Saturday evenings. The guest rooms have tea and coffee making facilities.

Beer: Flowers Original and Pompey Royal, Gale HSB, Greene King Abbot Ale, Hermitage Warrior Ale (house brew), Fuller ESB on handpumps.

Accommodation: 5 doubles, all en suite. B&B £30 per room. Half and full board available.

## Sally Port
High Street, Old Portsmouth

Licensee: C A Galloway
Tel: 0705 821860

The Sally Port is ideally placed in historic old Portsmouth, close to the Round Tower, the Cathedral of Thomas of Canterbury and the gate in the old fortified sea wall known as the sally port, from which naval officers 'sallied forth' to the ships. The original tavern dates back to the 17th century and was rebuilt in the 1970s from a bomb-damaged site. The present imposing, four-storey hotel includes many of the original beams and more 'modern' ones from the early 19th century. The bars and guest rooms have beams and sloping floors and the hub of this fine Georgian building is a magnificent cantiliver staircase. Most of the delightful guest rooms have en suite facilities and all have colour TVs and tea and coffee making equipment. There is excellent bar food and an à la carte restaurant.

Beer: Bass, Courage Directors, Gale HSB, Marston Pedigree on handpumps.

Accommodation: 14 rooms including 3 singles. B&B £18 single, £35 double. Credit cards: Access, Visa.

### Surrey Arms
1-3 Surrey Street

Licensee: Liam McKee
Tel: 0705 827120

The Surrey Arms, in Portsmouth's city centre and close to the railway station, was originally a free house and was bought by the former Brickwoods Brewery in 1924. The bar on the right-hand side of the pub was once the bar from the brewery itself, while the fireplace came from another defunct brewery, Mrs Langton on the Isle of Wight. To add to the nostalgia and breweriana, two doors leading into the bar were rescued from the George & Dragon at Cosham. The Surrey Arms, rich in pub and brewing history, is sumptuously done out with wood panels and etched glass mirrors. Families are welcome at lunchtime in a separate lounge. The guest rooms have tea and coffee making facilities.

Beer: Flowers Original and Strong Country Bitter, Wadworth 6X on handpumps.

Accommodation: 7 singles, 3 doubles. Single £15, double £25. Double used as family room: £29.50 for 2 adults, 1 child; £35 for 2 children, £40 for 3 children. Small deposit required.

# SOUTHAMPTON

### Royal Albert
Albert Road South

Licensee: Ron Ousby
Tel: 0703 229697

A solid, unpretentious town pub dating back to the 1930s and extensively modernised a few years ago. There is one large room with a horseshoe bar where pool and darts are played. The Royal Albert is in a side street in the shadow of Itchen toll bridge and close to the Ocean Village complex and the Aviation Museum. The pub has lunchtime food, and facilities for families.

Beer: Gale BBB, HSB and 5X (winter) on handpumps.

Accommodation: 7 singles, 2 twins, 1 double. B&B £13.50 per person.

# TADLEY

### Treacle Mine
Silchester Road, 450 yards NE of A340

Licensees: Neil Annal & Maggie Pilkington
Tel: 073 56 4857

In the early days of aviation, when a pilot was forced to land in a field in Tadley, he commented that the soft, sticky soil was like treacle. Hence the name of this homely pub with games in the public bar, occasional live music and a weekday happy hour between 5.30 to 6.30. The excellent pub food is served lunchtime and evening (no evening food at weekends) and includes a vast range of open sandwiches — ham and fried egg, ham and Stilton, tuna and egg — jacket spuds with choice of fillings, ploughman's, chilli, curry and bacon butties. Disappointingly, there is no treacle pud. The pub is a good base for visiting Silchester ruins.

Beer: Adnams Bitter, Hall & Woodhouse Badger Best Bitter, Flowers Original and Wethered SPA, Wadworth 6X on handpumps plus regular guest beers.

Accommodation: 2 singles, 2 twins, 3 doubles. B&B £20 single, double £26. No children.

# TITCHFIELD

Queen's Head Hotel
High Street, ¼ mile off A27

Licensee: K A Blackmore
Tel: 0329 42154

There is a wealth of oak beams, open fires and history in this 17th-century inn in the centre of a small, historic village. The hotel is named after Catherine of Braganza, the second wife of Charles II, who built Titchfield Abbey. Bar food is available lunchtime and evening and offers soup, ploughman's, jacket potatoes, burgers, plain and toasted sandwiches, steak and kidney pie, salads and fish and chips. There is a separate à la carte restaurant. The hotel is handy for Portsmouth, Southampton and the cross-channel ferries.

Beer: Strong Country Bitter on handpump.

Accommodation: 3 singles, 4 doubles, 1 family room. B&B £18.50 single, £28 double. Children welcome, no reduction.

# WINCHESTER

Rising Sun
14 Bridge Street, B3404

Licensee: Steve Sankey
Tel: 0962 62564

A superb, timber-framed Tudor town inn just a minute's walk from King Alfred's statue in this stunning old city. Once the capital of England, its architecture is so ancient and remarkable that even Barclays Bank and Dixon's look like listed buildings. The Rising Sun is one pub where you may hesitate before asking to see the cellar; it was once a prison. The pub has open fires, welcomes families and serves excellent food lunchtime and evening.

Beer: Courage Best Bitter, Directors and John Smith's Bitter on handpumps.

Accommodation: 1 double, 2 twins. B&B £9 per person.

# HEREFORD & WORCESTER

# BROADWAY

Crown & Trumpet
Church Street, off A44

Licensees: Andrew & Stella Scott
Tel: 0386 853202

A fine 16th-century inn behind the village green in the famous and lovely village of Broadway. The Crown & Trumpet has oak beams, log fires and first-class food lunchtime and evening, with soups, steak and kidney pie, lamb and aubergine pie, beef and Guinness pie, vegetable gratin, ploughman's, steaks and salads. There is a roast lunch on Sundays. The inn is an excellent base for visiting Warwick, Stratford, Worcester, Tewkesbury and the

Malvern hills. The guest rooms have colour TVs and tea and coffee making facilities.

Beer: Flowers Original and IPA, guest beers and Bulmer traditional cider, all on handpumps.

Accommodation: 2 doubles, 1 family room. B&B £13.50 per person. Weekend £16.50 with evening meals, Week £115 with evening meals. Off-season Weekend £15.50 per person for 2 nights with evening meals. Children's room; children's terms on application.

# BROMYARD

Crown & Sceptre
Sherford Street, A44

Licensees: Liz & John Parry
Tel: 0885 822441

The Parrys have spent two years energetically improving and updating this charming old pub in the centre of a small market town. The cottage atmosphere has been carefully retained and the improved accommodation includes colour TVs, and tea and coffee making facilities. The pub is famed for its hearty breakfasts and there is also a good selection of bar meals, including beef and venison pie and game pies, while the separate restaurant offers steaks and gammons. Bromyard is a good base for visiting both Hereford and Worcester.

Beer: Flowers Original and IPA with regular guest beers (including Woods from the Craven Arms in Shropshire) on handpumps.

Accommodation: 1 twin/double. B&B £9 per person. 1 single, twin or double with en suite shower £14.50 per person. Children welcome, reductions according to age.

# CAREY

Cottage of Content
Off A49 1½ miles NE of
Hoarwithy. OS SO 565310

Licensee: Michael Wainford
Tel: 043 270 242

A beautiful country pub in a remote area of gorgeous scenery. The timber-framed building was originally three labourers' cottages built in 1485. One of the conditions of tenancy was that one labourer should keep an ale and cider parlour in one room and the cottage has been licensed ever since. The bars have wooden benches and high-back settles, and darts, dominoes and cribbage are played in the public bar. Two other rooms are set aside for eating and a converted bar is also used when the pub is busy. Splendid food, lunch and evening, includes vegetable hot-pot, beef in beer, crab mornay and rabbit casserole, with soup, sandwiches and ploughman's. The restaurant is closed Sunday evenings. In summer there are tables at the front of the pub and on a back terrace.

Beer: Hook Norton Best Bitter and Old Hookey, Marston Burton Bitter, Pedigree and Owd Rodger (winter) on handpumps plus local draught ciders.

Accommodation: 2 doubles, 1 twin, all with en suite facilities. B&B £22.50 single, £30 double. Children welcome; terms on application; children sleeping in additional room with bunk beds charged for meals only. Credit cards: Visa.

# EVESHAM

### Norton Grange Hotel
A435, Norton hamlet outside
Evesham

Licensee: M Smith
Tel: 0386 870215

Lots of old world charm in this
spacious building, which has a large
lounge bar and a separate room for
weekend country music. The small
restaurant has a good range of meals
in an intimate atmosphere. Bar
snacks include sandwiches, salads,
steak and kidney pie, fish and chips,
seafood platter and grilled trout.
There is a large play area for
children. Stratford and Worcester are
nearby.

Beer: Marston Burton Bitter and
Pedigree on handpumps.

Accommodation: 4 singles, 3
doubles, 1 family room, 1 room
with en suite facilities. B&B £12.50
per person. Week £85. Children
welcome, no reductions. Credit
cards: Access, Visa.

# FOWNHOPE

### Green Man
B4224

Licensees: Arthur & Margaret
Williams
Tel: 0432 77 243

The Green Man dates from 1485 and
in coaching days it was on the main
Hereford to Gloucester road. Petty
sessions were held at the inn in the
18th and 19th centuries. Relics of
those times include the iron bars to
which prisoners were chained, the
cell, the visiting judge's bedroom
and a notice dated 1820 showing the
scale of costs of prisoners'
subsistence. One former landlord
was Tom Spring, bare-knuckle prize
fighter and Champion of All

England. This fine timbered and
brick building has two bars, log fires
in winter, good hot and cold bar
food, a separate restaurant and
Sunday roasts.

Beer: Hook Norton Best Bitter and
Sam Smith's Old Brewery Bitter on
handpumps, with Westons
farmhouse cider from the cask.

Accommodation: 1 single, 11
doubles, 3 family rooms, all with
private bath. B&B £25 single, double
£31.50-£34. Winter Breaks £44 per
day for 2 people with evening meal
allowance of £15. £5 reduction for
third night. Reduced rates for
children. Dogs welcome. £2 per
night. Self-catering cottage also
available.

# HEREFORD

### Castle Pool Hotel
Castle Street

Licensees: John & Lisa Richardson
Tel: 0432 56321

An imposing city centre hotel that
has in its grounds the pool that is
the remains of the moat of Hereford
Castle. The castle, once 'high and
strong and full of great towers', has
sadly all but disappeared. The hotel
was built in 1850 and was once the
residence of the Bishop of Hereford.
The handsomely appointed hotel has
guest rooms with en suite facilities,
colour TVs and tea and coffee
makers. There are good bar snacks
while the separate restaurant offers
an unusual range of dishes, including
mackerel funchal, gravlax, celeriac
niçoise, duck Agincourt, chicken
rififi and vegetarian dishes. In
summer there are barbecues on the
lawn overlooking the moat.

Beer: Hook Norton Best Bitter,
Wadworth 6X and guest beers on
handpumps.

Accommodation: 8 singles, 7
doubles, 8 twins and 3 family rooms.
B&B £33 single, £46 double.
Children's terms by arrangement.
Dogs welcome. Credit cards: Access,
Amex, Diners, Visa.

# KINGSLAND

Angel Inn
B4360, 4 miles W of Leominster
off A44 Kington Road

Licensees: Nigel & Jayne Godwin
Tel: 056881 355

A fine roadside inn of 16th-century
origins that has plenty of remaining
beams in the cosy bar with its open
log fire. The smaller beamed
restaurant opens seven days a week
and specialises in local game and
fish. The extensive bar meals (lunch
and evening, including Sundays)
offer soups, whitebait, several
ploughman's, salads, pizzas,
omelettes, and various fish dishes.
There is a menu for children too.

Beer: Banks Bitter on electric pump,
guest beers on handpumps.

Accommodation: 3 twins/doubles.
B&B £12 single, £22 twin/double, 3
nights £30 per person. No children.

# KNIGHTWICK

Talbot Hotel
B4197, just off A44 7 miles W of
Worcester

Licensee: Derek Hiles
Tel: 0886 21235

A superb 14th-century inn in a
lovely setting by the bridge over the
Teme. The spacious lounge has
comfortable seats, including settles in
the bow windows, coaching prints
and Jorrocks paintings on the walls,
and a great wood-burning stove in
the fireplace. Thoughtful food (with
the same menu for the bar and the
small restaurant) includes pasta
pescatore, soup, baked avocado,
mushroom gougère, lamb noisettes,
rabbit in red wine, guinea fowl in
oyster sauce, whole lemon sole, cod
fillet and coriander, vegetarian dishes
and excellent schoolday puddings
such as treacle tart, damson crumble
and chocolate fudge cake. You can
walk that off in the Malvern Hills
and visit Edward Elgar's birthplace.

Beer: Bass, Banks Bitter, Flowers
Original and IPA on handpumps.

Accommodation: 3 singles, 7 doubles
(including 1 family room), 7 rooms
with private baths. B&B £15-£17.50
single, £25-£34 double. Well-behaved
children and dogs welcome.

# PEMBRIDGE

New Inn
Market Square, on A44 between
Leominster and Kington

Licensee: Jane Melvin
Tel: 054 47 427

An ancient and impressive building
that dominates the centre of
Pembridge, the inn was built in 1311
and was known to travellers in
coaching times as the 'Inn with No
Name'. Six miles away at

Mortimer's Cross is the site of a decisive battle in the Wars of the Roses in 1461; it is thought that the treaty was signed in the court room of the inn. There is also a prison warders' room and wool market in the forecourt. The bar food is first-class and there is a separate restaurant.

Beer: Flowers Original and IPA, Bulmer traditional cider on handpumps and guest beers.

Accommodation: 2 singles, 3 doubles, 2 family rooms, 1 room with private shower. B&B £11-£12.50 per person. Children welcome, terms by arrangement.

## WHITNEY-ON-WYE

Rhydspence Inn
A438 Brecon to Hereford road

Licensees: Peter & Pamela Glover
Tel: 049 73 262

A justly famous, 16th-century timber-framed inn on a hill overlooking the Wye valley and the Black Mountains. It is either the first or the last inn in England, depending on whether you are coming to or from Wales. The border is a stream running through the pub's garden. The inn has been lovingly and carefully restored. Centuries ago it offered ale, food and accommodation to Welsh drovers on their way to English markets and it was mentioned several times in Kilvert's *Diary*. There is a large stone fireplace in the central bar, seats built into the timbered walls and a profusion of beams. Food is served in the bar and in a pleasant dining room. The menu includes soup, lemon sole, seafood thermidor, spit-roasted duckling, steak and kidney pie, curries, vegetarian platter and ploughman's. Dominoes, crib and

quoits are played. Cwmnau Farmhouse, owned by the National Trust, a 17th-century working Here-fordshire farmhouse (open 2-6 pm weekends and some Bank Holidays) is three miles to the north.

Beer: Robinson Best Bitter on handpump, Dunkertons cider from the cask and occasional guest beers.

Accommodation: 1 single, 1 twin, 3 doubles all with en suite facilities. B&B £18 per person. Winter Weekend £50 per person for 2 nights.

## WOOLHOPE

Butchers Arms
Off B4224, signposted from Fownhope. OS 618358

Licensees: Mary Bailey & Bill Griffiths
Tel: 043 277 281

The Butchers Arms, found down a country lane, is a delightful 14th-century half-timbered inn with low beams in the bars and a terrace with flowers overlooking a rockery and a small stream. In winter there are cheerful log fires. Bar food (lunch and evening) offers home-made soups, Woolhope Pie (rabbit and bacon cooked in local cider), steak, kidney and mushroom pie, mushroom biriani, salads, and ploughman's. A separate restaurant is open Wednesday to Saturday evenings. Guest rooms have TVs and tea and coffee-making facilities. Woolhope got its name from Wulviva's Hope or valley. In the 11th century, Wulviva, the sister of the better-known Lady Godiva, gave the manor of Woolhope to Hereford Cathedral.

Beer: Hook Norton Best Bitter and Old Hookey, Marston Pedigree on handpumps.

Accommodation: 2 doubles, 1 twin. B&B £15.50 per person; £19.50 for one person occupying a room. Children 14 and over welcome; terms by arrangement. No dogs. Winter Breaks: any 2 days £39.50 per person for double room.

## HERTFORDSHIRE

# AYOT ST LAWRENCE

Brocket Arms
Shaw's Corner, near Welwyn, off A1

Licensee: Toby Wingfield-Digby
Tel: 0438 820250

The Brocket Arms is a handsome 14th-century building with a walled garden, formerly part of the Brocket Hall estate. The hamlet of Ayot St Lawrence nestles down narrow lanes and is yet only a few minutes from the A1. There are timbered cottages, the ruins of a 12th-century church and its restored 18th-century Palladian successor. George Bernard Shaw lived down the road and his house, now owned by the National Trust, is open to the public in the summer. It is not known whether the writer drank in the pub, though his temperance has been exaggerated. Tackled on the subject, he declared: 'I am a *beer* teetotaller.' The pub gets very busy at weekends with visitors arriving on horse as well as car, foot and cycle. During the week, though, it has the atmosphere of a quiet country pub with its two small bars and a vast inglenook in the back room. Bar food, with a buffet in summer, includes soup, ploughman's, game pie, jacket potatoes, smoked mackerel and pâté. There is a roast lunch on Sundays. A separate à la carte restaurant is open Tuesday to Saturday evenings and for lunch every day.

Beer: Adnams Bitter, Greene King IPA and Abbot Ale, Fuller London Pride, Wadworth 6X on handpumps.

Accommodation: 3 double rooms. B&B £30 single. Children over 12 welcome, no charge if sharing with parents.

## ODSEY

Jester Inn
Ashwell Station, near Baldock, 300 yards from A505

Licensee: Jo Badham
Tel: 046 274 2011

A 300-year-old pub with oak beams and blazing log fires in winter, just off the Baldock-Royston road and two minutes from the Cambridge to London railway. The pub is steeped in horse-racing memorabilia and has a mass of horsey decorations and prints. The large beer garden has three aviaries with 200 birds and there is also a goat named Lucy. The inn offers both bar snacks and full meals in a separate restaurant, with a traditional roast on Sundays. All the guest rooms have en suite facilities and TVs, and — a nice touch — a small library for residents. The four-poster bedroom is reputedly haunted by a ghost named Walter.

Beer: Adnams Bitter, Ruddles County, Webster's Yorkshire Bitter on handpumps.

Accommodation: 4 singles, 8 doubles. B&B £30 single, £42 double, £45 four-poster. Off-season Weekend £25 single, £35 double. Children welcome, 25 per cent reductions. Credit cards: Access, Visa.

# ROYSTON

Jockey
31-33 Baldock Street

Licensee: C A Booth
Tel: 0763 43377

The Jockey is a cheerful town pub
with red tiles on the roof and over
the two bow windows at the front.
Inside, the theme is aviation rather
than equestrian. Duxford and Old
Warden air museums are close by
and the pub has many old aircraft
prints and memorabilia. The Jockey
has a large garden ideal for summer
barbecues. Bar food is served
lunchtime and evenings (not
Sundays). There is a daily special and
such regular favourites as beef
Wellington, coq au vin, beef
Stroganoff, venison and rabbit pie,
cod steaks in cider or chicken in
brandy and cream, plus ploughman's
and omelettes. Curries, seafood
lasagne and macaroni cheese appear
in the evenings. Royston has a
challenging golf course and wall
paintings can be viewed in Royston
cave.

Beer: Castle Eden Ale, Flowers IPA,
Sam Whitbread Bitter, Wethered
Bitter and Winter Royal (in season)
on handpumps with occasional guest
beers.

Accommodation: 2 singles, 2 twins.
B&B £13.50.

# ST ALBANS

Black Lion Hotel
198 Fishpool Street

Licensee: M A P Culleton
Tel: 0727 51786

A large and imposing inn that marks
the end of Fishpool Street. It is just
a few yards from an old working
water mill and the great stretch of
Verulam Park with its large lake and
the looming abbey. The Black Lion
has been bought by Bass, giving the
national giant its first foothold in
the city. From the large car park at
the rear, you enter through a small
door that leads to the low-ceilinged
spacious bar that offers ample
seating. There is a separate restaurant
serving rack of lamb, duck, trout,
lemon sole, steaks and daily
vegetarian dishes, such as pasta
parmigiana and lentil croquettes.

Beer: Bass, Charrington IPA, Fuller
ESB (winter) on handpumps.

Accommodation: 2 singles, 6
doubles, 5 rooms with en suite
facilities. B&B £40 single, £50
double. £5 reduction per head for
Friday, Saturday and Sunday. (4
additional rooms will be available
during 1988.)

Lower Red Lion
36 Fishpool Street

Licensee: J S Turner
Tel: 0727 55669

A 17th-century pub in the heart of
St Albans conservation area. You
will find it in a winding street of
fine houses and artisans' cottages
that leads to Verulam Park and the
Black Lion. There is a cheery

WHITE HART HOTEL — *see p 84*

welcome in the pub with its three blazing fires (two of them real) in winter. Both bars have comfortable red seating and brick and half-timbered walls. The pub's name distinguishes it from the now defunct Great Red Lion by the historic Clock Tower. The Lower Red prides itself on the lack of juke box, background music, fruit machines and video games.

Beer: Adnams Bitter, Fuller London Pride and ESB, Greene King IPA and Abbot Ale on handpumps.

Accommodation: 1 single, 6 doubles, 1 family room. B&B £25 single, £35 double, £40-£45 family room.

## White Hart Hotel
Holywell Hill

Licensee: P R Lloyd
Tel: 0727 53624/40237

A late 15th-century inn, first known as the Harts Horn and built for pilgrims to the abbey. The White Hart, which was first stop on the road north from London, later became a major coaching inn. It is immediately opposite the great abbey and cathedral with its Norman tower and breathtaking shrine to Alban, the first Christian martyr. The inn has two comfortable bars, a separate restaurant and a residents' lounge with a minstrels' gallery on the first floor, reached by a barley-twist staircase. Bar meals are served every day lunchtime and evening and include home-made soup, mushrooms baked in cider, calamari, home-made steak and kidney pudding, lasagne, curry and scampi. With the other St Albans' entries, the White Hart is a good base for visiting the abbey; French Row, where French troops were garrisoned in 1217 during the

struggle with King John; the street market on Wednesdays and Saturdays and the Clock Tower.

Beer: Benskins Best Bitter and Burton Ale on handpumps.

Accommodation: 1 single, 10 doubles, 8 rooms with en suite facilities, all with colour TVs and tea and coffee making facilities. B&B £42 single, £50 double. Friday/Saturday nights £28 single per day, £38 double. Children welcome, £10 per night sharing with parents. Credit cards: Access, Amex, Visa.

# BARTON UPON HUMBER

## George Hotel
George Street, Market Place, A1077

Licensee: Diane Cowen
Tel: 0652 32433

The George is a small, old hotel with a busy public bar, a quiet lounge, a pool room and a function room. Bar meals are available lunchtime and evening and there is also a separate dining room. Barton was once an important port and shipbuilding centre and has two ancient churches, including a restored Saxon one. The Humber Bridge has magnificent views and access to Hull and East Yorkshire. North of the town, strung along the banks of the Humber, there are a number of meres of great interest to naturalists and offering facilities for anglers and weekend sailors.

Beer: Stones Best Bitter on electric and handpumps.

Accommodation: 1 single, 5 doubles, 2 rooms with en suite facilities (will become 5 rooms during 1988). B&B £15 per person. Half board available. Credit cards: Access.

# BRIGG

Angel Hotel
Market Place, A15/A18

Licensee: Charles Shrosbee
Tel: 0652 53118

The Angel is one of Brigg's best-known buildings, a comfortable old inn with a cheerful public bar, a large lounge, a separate dining room and a pleasant, vine-covered courtyard. Renowned bar meals are served lunchtime and evening. Brigg is a small market town on the banks of the river Ancholme, which provides facilities for anglers and boating people. The town was granted a royal charter in 1205 to establish a market. The market still operates on Thursdays and the pubs celebrate by staying open until 4pm.

Beer: Bass on handpump.

Accommodation: 3 singles, 4 doubles, 5 twins. B&B £15-£25 per person. Credit cards: Access, Visa.

Woolpack Hotel
Market Place, on A15 & A18

Licensees: Barrie & Wendy Creaser
Tel: 0652 55649

A cheerful old pub in the town centre with a large lounge and log fire in winter. Darts and pool are played by keen locals. Bar lunches are served Monday to Saturday and the pub is open until 4pm on market day. There is a traditional roast lunch on Sundays.

Beer: Tetley Mild and Bitter on electric and handpumps.

Accommodation: 1 single, 3 doubles. B&B £11.50 per person. Half and full board available. Children welcome.

# CLEETHORPES

Crows Nest Hotel
Balmoral Road, off Humberston Road, A1031

Licensee: Stewart Slater
Tel: 0472 698867

A substantial, friendly estate pub in a quiet residential area with a large car park and separate residents' entrance. There is a public bar and a comfortable lounge. The welcome is warm and the pub is deservedly popular with locals. Bar food is available both lunchtime and evening. There is a television lounge for residents with tea and coffee making facilities.

Beer: Sam Smith's Old Brewery Bitter on handpump.

Accommodation: 4 singles, 2 doubles, 1 family room. B&B £15 per person.

# GRIMSBY

County Hotel
Brighowgate, A180

Licensee: David Butler
Tel: 0472 354422/44449/241560

A large and bustling pub with a lounge and restaurant decorated in Victorian style. There is always something going on in the bar — quiz nights, discos, live music and fund-raising events, but there is a secluded area for those who want to rest or read. The restaurant has à la carte and table d'hôte menus, with the emphasis on fish and steaks. Bar meals, available lunchtime and evening, include chilli, filled jacket potatoes and sandwiches. The accommodation has been recently modernised and all rooms have colour TVs and tea and coffee making facilities. The hotel is close to the main railway station.

Beer: Younger Scotch Bitter and No 3 on handpumps.

Accommodation: 3 singles, 6 doubles (including honeymoon suite), 1 family room with cot. B&B from £25 per person. Reduced weekend rates on application. Reductions for children. Facilities for the disabled. Credit cards: Access, Amex, Diners, Visa.

# SCUNTHORPE

Beacon Hotel
Burringham road, B1450, just off A159

Licensee: D Birkby
Tel: 0724 844139

A large 1950s pub with stone window dressings, up-market public bar and plush lounge. There are popular bar meals lunchtime and evening (not Friday or Sunday evenings). The Beacon stands in a quiet residential area away from the town centre. Scunthorpe has lost its famous steelworks but small industrial workshops have sprung up in their place. The town has a good museum while, two miles north, Normandy Hall has furniture and art from the Regency period. Eight miles to the west is Epworth, the home of the Wesley family.

Beer: Bass XXXX Mild and Stones Best Bitter on handpumps.

Accommodation: 4 doubles, 1 with en suite facilities. B&B £11-£15 per person.

# SLEDMERE

Triton Inn
Near Driffield, 4 miles off A166 on B1252

Licensees: John & Carol Regan
Tel: 0377 86644

An 18th-century coaching inn, the Triton lies in the shadow of the famous Sledmere House in a delightful Wolds village. The attractive lounge has blazing fires in winter and high-back settle seats. Darts and dominoes are played in the public bar. Bar food offers soups, ploughman's, crab or prawn salads, burgers and steaks. There is a separate restaurant. The inn is famous for both its vast breakfasts and the warm welcome and attention of the Regans. Watch for the genuine sign outside: 'Licensed to let post horses'.

Beer: Younger Scotch Bitter on handpump.

Accommodation: 2 singles, 5 doubles, 1 family room, 3 with en suite facilities. B&B from £10.50 per person. Week £122.50. Half and full board available. Children half price.

# CARISBROOKE

Shute Inn
Clatterford Shute off Newport-Shorwell road

Licensees: Tony Simmons & Trevor Stewart
Tel: 0983 523393

The Shute is a delightful old inn in a lovely rural setting a mile from Newport. There are fine views from the inn of Carisbrooke Castle, where Charles I was imprisoned, and over the Bowcombe valley. A few yards from the inn a ford crosses Lukeley Brook, a tributary of the River Medina. The Shute's guest rooms all have colour TVs and tea and coffee making facilities. Bar food is served lunchtime and evening and there is a family room.

Beer: Bass, Courage Directors on handpumps, Burt VPA from the cask.

Accommodation: 1 single, 1 twin, 1 double. B&B £9.50 single, £18 twin, £20 double en suite. 10% reduction for 4 nights or more. Credit cards: Access, Visa.

# CHALE

Clarendon Hotel & Wight Mouse Inn
B3399, off A3055

Licensees: John & Jean Bradshaw
Tel: 0983 730431

Two for the price of one in this 17th-century hotel, with an attached inn. At the inn, there is live music most nights of the week — jazz, country and western, and singer/guitarist. The stone-built buildings have wood-panelling from a 19th-century shipwreck. There is a strong family emphasis: the garden has swings, slides and a menagerie for children and there are two children's rooms. Generous bar food, leaning on local produce and home-cooking, includes soups, ploughman's, burgers, salads, crabs, prawns, cockles, sandwiches and sweets. There is a separate restaurant.

Beer: Burt VPA from the cask, Flowers Original and Strong Country Bitter on handpumps.

Accommodation: 14 doubles, 8 family rooms, 8 rooms with private bath. B&B £15-£17 per person. Full board £22-£24. Weekend £44-£48, Week £125-£140. Top prices are for rooms with baths. Off-Season Weekend: 15% reductions. Children half price.

# NETTLESTONE

Roadside Inn
On Ryde-Bembridge road

Licensee: David Fletcher
Tel: 0983 612381

A splendid pub that is a combination of a good locals' local and a visitors' hotel, with a cheerful public bar and a pleasant, comfortable lounge. It is close to the picturesque yachting harbour of Bembridge.

Beer: Flowers Original and Strong Country Bitter on handpumps.

Accommodation: 2 singles, 1 double, 1 family room. B&B £10 per person. Children's room; children welcome to stay, half price.

# NEWPORT

Wheatsheaf Hotel
St Thomas Square

Licensees: David & Sally Rudge
Tel: 0983 523865

The Wheatsheaf is a handsome 17th-century coaching inn in the centre of the old market town. The inn has Cromwellian connections — the leader of the republic held a parliamentary meeting here. The guest rooms have all been thoughtfully modernised and refurbished, with colour TVs, tea and coffee makers and most have en suite facilities. There is a comfortable lounge, with an open fireplace and chairs placed round circular tables; a family room; a separate dining room and a function room overlooking the square. Bar food served every day lunchtime and evening includes home-made soup, seafood pancakes, chilli, curry, trout, lasagne, cheese and mushroom quiche, sandwiches, ploughman's and a children's menu.

Beer: Flowers Original and Strong Country Bitter on handpumps.

Accommodation: 11 rooms. B&B £20 single, £23 with shower, £30 twin/double, £35 with shower.

# SEAVIEW

Seaview Hotel
High Street

Licensees: Nicola & Nicholas Hayward
Tel: 0983 612711

An imposing and elegant three-storey hotel in a pleasant Edwardian seaside setting. The Haywards, who have a young family of their own, welcome other families, and well-behaved dogs, providing cots and children's menus. There are two

bars, a plush cocktail bar with many naval photos, and the Pump Bar with an open fire in winter, popular with locals and yachtsmen. Elegance is everywhere: antique clocks, watercolours and French cuisine in the acclaimed restaurant (closed Sunday evening). Bar food is out of the rut and includes scallops, fresh crab cooked with cheese and spices, and Bembridge lobster.

Beer: Burt VPA on handpump.

Accommodation: 14 rooms, 12 with private bathrooms and including 1 family suite. B&B from £21 single (£23 with dinner), twin £30-£37. Weekend £60 per person including dinner. Children's terms according to age and season. Credit cards: Access, Amex, Visa.

# ASH

Volunteer Inn
43 Guilton, A257 near Canterbury

Licensees: Terry & Pam Smith
Tel: 0304 812506

The Volunteer is an attractive Victorian pub on the Sandwich to Canterbury road, handy for Sandwich golf course, Richborough Castle, Howletts Zoo and the cross-channel ferries — the Smiths provide dawn breakfasts for channel hoppers. The inn has a public bar and a lounge. Bar billiards — a game that must not die — is played as well as darts. Good bar snacks and meals include provision for special diets.

Beer: Adnams Bitter and Old (winter), Harvey Mild and Bitter on handpumps, Pippen cider from the cask and guest bitter.

Accommodation: 1 double, 1 family room. B&B £14 single, £24 double. Children welcome, half price. Bargain winter breaks available.

# BROADSTAIRS

Royal Albion Hotel
Albion Street

Licensee: Roger Family
Tel: 0483 68071

A striking whitewashed building in a commanding position on the cliffs of this fine old seaside resort made famous by Charles Dickens, who finished *Nicholas Nickleby* while staying there. The original Bleak House is nearby. The hotel began life as the Phoenix Inn in 1760 but, by 1816, had changed its name to the Albion. Visits by several members of the royal family added the appendage. The hotel has been run by the Marchesi family for a hundred years and the separate restaurant (open every day for lunch and dinner) carries the family name. Reasonably priced dishes include home-made soups, scallop and bacon salad, poached fillet of turbot, Dover sole, rack of lamb and vegetarian dish of the day. The Broadstow Bar was once a separate house and was where Dickens lived and worked for several years. The immaculate guest rooms all have en suite facilities, colour TVs and tea and coffee makers. The hotel can arrange day trips to France.

Beer: Fremlins Bitter, Shepherd Neame Master Brew Bitter on handpumps.

Accommodation: 3 singles, 13 doubles, 4 family rooms. B&B £25 per person, £35 half board. Weekend £66 half board, Week £230. Children's room; children welcome to stay, half price. Credit cards: Access, Amex, Diners, Visa.

# LAMBERHURST

Chequers Inn
Hastings Road, A21

Licensee: Keith Smith
Tel: 0892 890260

An attractive tile-hung pub in a picturesque village on the London-Hastings road. The Chequers dates back to the 15th century and has an abundance of exposed beams to prove the point. The basic public bar is popular with young people who enjoy darts, bar billiards and pool. The saloon is comfortable and relaxed. First-class meals are available lunchtime and evening. There is also a separate family room and the bedrooms all have colour TVs and tea and coffee makers. Lamberhurst is a good base for visiting Scotney Castle, Bewl Bridge Reservoir and the successful commercial vineyard, which takes its name from the village.

Beer: Flowers Original and Fremlins Bitter on handpumps.

Accommodation: 4 doubles, 1 family room, 4 rooms with private baths. B&B £21.50 single, £31.50 double. Children welcome, charged only for food if sharing with parents.

VOLUNTEER INN, ASH — *see opposite*

# PLUCKLEY

Dering Arms
Station Raod. At Charing (A20)
take B2077 to Pluckley

Licensee: Jim Buss
Tel: 023 384 371

The Dering Arms is a striking 17th-century hunting lodge with a Dutch gabled roof and stone and wood bars. The 30-seat restaurant specialises in fresh fish, local game and home-made specialities: you can choose from home-made soup, Sussex smokies, local trout, seafood special, ploughman's, blacksmith's (ham), gamekeeper's (rabbit and pigeon) and squire's (Stilton) lunches. There are good puds, too: fruit crumble, banana pancake and orange in caramel. The guest rooms all have colour TVs and tea and coffee making facilities. Pluckley is a good base for touring the country and taking in Canterbury; and Leeds and Bodiam castles.

Beer: Dering Ale is a house beer brewed by Goachers of Maidstone, with Adnams Bitter and Extra, Goachers Maidstone Ale, Shepherd Neame Master Brew Bitter, Young Special all on handpumps.

Accommodation: 3 doubles (double and single bed in each room: can be used as single). B&B £12 -£16. Special rates for long stays. Children welcome, no reductions.

# ROCHESTER

Granville Arms
83 Maidstone Road, B2097 off A2

Licensees: Ray & Joyce Gowers
Tel: 0634 45243

A cheerful and friendly old pub built in 1750 in the heart of this historic old Medway town and port with its naval and Dickens connections. The Gowers have developed a strong local loyalty to their well-kept ales and hospitality, backed by live music and traditional singing at weekends. The pub is a good base for visiting the Medway towns. Whitstable and Herne Bay offer traditional seaside pleasures in the summer.

Beer: Benskins Best Bitter and Burton Ale on handpumps.

Accommodation: 1 single, 3 doubles. B&B £10 per person. No children.

# SMARDEN

Bell
B2077, ¾ mile from the village, off A20

Licensee: Ian Turner
Tel: 023 377 283

A fine old Kentish inn in unspoilt countryside near Leeds and Sissinghurst castles. The Bell has three large bars with oak beams, candlelight, inglenooks with welcoming winter fires, flagstone floors and pews and chairs round wooden tables. The front bar, popular with locals, offers bar billiards, darts, shove ha'penny and dominoes. The tile-hung and rose-covered exterior is a delight in summer when you can sit among the trees in the garden. Splendid bar food includes home-made soups, ploughman's, Greek-style shepherd's pie, sandwiches and toasties, steak and kidney pie, pizzas and home-made chocolate crunch cake and apple crumble. Bar meals are served every day. The guest rooms have colour TVs.

Beer: Flowers Original and Fremlins Bitter, Fuller London Pride, Goachers Maidstone Ale, Shepherd Neame Master Brew Bitter, Theakston Best Bitter and Old Peculier on handpumps.

Accommodation: 4 doubles. Bed and continental breakfast £15 single, double £12 per person. Children's room; children welcome, no reductions. Closed Xmas Day. Credit cards: Access, Visa.

# WINGHAM

Anchor Inn
On A257

Licensee: Roger Field
Tel: 0227 720866

A delightful old pub with tall chimneys on a rambling roof, close to the historic pleasures of Canterbury. Mr Field offers a warm welcome and specialises in excellent pub grub. You can tuck into soup, omelettes, home-made shepherd's pie, cold beef, hot potatoes, pickle and salad, ploughman's with Cheddar or Stilton, sandwiches, Anchorburgers, steaks and fish and chips. The Anchor has a pleasant garden in summer, families are welcome and there are camping facilities.

Beer: Flowers Original and Fremlins Bitter on handpumps.

Accommodation: 3 singles, 2 doubles, 1 family room. B&B £10-£15 per person. Weekend £20-£30, Week £70-£105. Children welcome to stay.

# BLACKO (LANCS)

Moorcock Inn
Gisburn Road, on A682, 3 miles from M65

Licensees: Elizabeth & Peter Holt
Tel: 0282 64186

A splendid pub high on the moors with panoramic views of the valleys and Pendleside villages. It is just three miles from Clitheroe Castle and the Forest of Bowland. The bar is cheerful and comfortable, with bow windows, high ceilings, and log fires in winter. The imaginative bar food, served until late in the evening as well as lunchtime, includes both Italian and Austrian dishes such as schweinschnitzel, bratwurst, goulash, lasagne bolognese and canneloni. More traditional fare includes soups, home-made steak and kidney pie, steak burger, grilled trout, omelettes, chilli, savoury pancakes, seafood platter, sandwiches, ploughman's, garlic bread and sweets — fruit tart and home-made cheesecake. Full meals and a roast on Sundays are served in a separate restaurant. There is a landscaped garden at the rear which is popular and busy in summer. The inn has a late supper licence until midnight during the week and 11.30 on Sundays.

Beer: Thwaites Best Mild and Bitter on handpumps.

Accommodation: 1 twin, 1 double, 1 family room, all rooms with showers. B&B £12.50 per person. Half and full board available. Children welcome, half price under 12.

# LANCASHIRE, MANCHESTER & MERSEYSIDE

## BLACKPOOL (LANCS)

**Empress Hotel**
59 Exchange Street, North Shore

Proprietors: Chris & Jean Murray
Tel: 0253 20413

An imposing, three-storey, red brick Victorian hotel with a traditional vault (public bar to Southerners) and plush lounge. There is a full snooker table in the vault — welcome relief from the ubiquitous 'keg' pool table. The Empress, which boasts some of the most comfortable beds found anywhere in Britain, was built by the son of a local brick merchant in 1847, using hand-made bricks. Some of the ceilings were sculpted by Venetian craftsmen. The roll call of stars of stage, screen and politics who have visited the Empress over the years includes Vesta Tilley, G. H. Elliott, Florrie Forde, Elizabeth Welch, Mae West, Johnny (Tarzan) Weismuller, Sir Robin Day and Edward Heath. It remains a genuine local, though, and Blackpudlians put on their best bib and tuckers for a night of dancing there.

Beer: Thwaites Best Mild and Bitter on handpumps.

Accommodation: 7 doubles, 3 twins, 3 family rooms. B&B £12 per person, £17 with evening meal. Blackpool Lights Weekend (3 nights) £36. Winter reductions, mini-breaks. 4 Day Xmas Special £125. Children welcome, reductions if sharing.

**Ramsden Arms Hotel**
204 Talbot Road

Licensees: Christine & Albert Caffrey
Tel: 0253 23215

The Ramsden is an impressive mock-Tudor, country-style pub on the edge of Blackpool town centre. It has a large oak-panelled lounge and a games room popular with darts and snooker players. Three blazing log fires help to brighten the coldest winter day. Bar lunches are served every day and include home-made pies, ham, roast beef, scampi and chilli. There is a residents' TV lounge and the guest rooms, recently refurbished, have central heating, colour TVs and tea and coffee making facilities. The pub is close to the bus and railway stations.

Beer: Burton Ale, Jennings Bitter, Tetley Mild and Bitter on handpumps.

Accommodation: 3 twins. B&B £10 per person. Three-day Break £50 for two. Long stays: every 7th day free. Children under 12 half price.

## BURSCOUGH (LANCS)

**Martin Inn**
Off A570, B5242. OS 414127

Licensee: John Mawdesley
Tel: 0704 892302

A remote, welcoming inn on Martin Mere in the heart of the west Lancashire countryside. A wildfowl trust, leisure lakes and riding schools are nearby. Bar snacks are served lunchtime and evening until 10pm and there are full meals in the popular Cottage Grill restaurant.

The guest rooms all have showers, colour TVs and tea and coffee making equipment.

Beer: John Smiths Bitter on handpump.

Accommodation: 3 singles, 7 doubles. B&B £25 single, £30 double. Reduced rates for children.

# GARSTANG (LANCS)

Royal Oak Hotel
The Square, Market Place, B6430, off A6

Licensee: Mrs L Hewitson
Tel: 099 52 3318

The Royal Oak is a 500-year-old coaching inn and a listed building. It once stood on the main coaching route between London and Edinburgh. Garstang is still a small but thriving market town and the Royal Oak continues to offer excellent ale and victuals to locals and visitors. It provides both hot and cold bar snacks, has two dining rooms and a large car park.

Beer: Robinson Best Mild, Best Bitter and Old Tom on electric and handpumps.

Accommodation: 5 doubles, 2 rooms with private baths. B&B £14 per person. Weekend £42, Week £98. Children and dogs welcome.

# ROCHDALE (GREATER MANCHESTER)

Reed Hotel
Reed Hill, Yorkshire Street

Licensees: Pat & Frank Williams
Tel: 0706 46696

The Reed is a 200-year-old coaching inn with an impressive three-storey façade. Its name, depicted above the entrance, derives from the reed, a weaver's comb used for separating warp threads in the mills of the industrial revolution. The first Co-op shop was opened in Rochdale, just 75 yards from the hotel, and is now a museum. The Williams have extensively improved and refurbished the hotel and offer excellent lunchtime food, including home-made soups, steak pie, curry, fish and chips, vegetarian dish of the day, salads, ploughman's, sandwiches and toasties, and 'Frenchies' — cheese and ham or sausage served on hot French bread with salad.

Beer: Bass Dark Mild and Special Bitter on handpumps.

Accommodation: 2 singles, 4 doubles, 1 family room, 3 en suite. B&B from £16 per person. Weekend from £32, Week from £98. Children's room; children welcome to stay.

## SOUTHPORT (MERSEYSIDE)

Herald Hotel
16 Portland Street

Licensee: D W Bentley
Tel: 0704 34424

A smart and welcoming pub in this stately Victorian seaside town of Parisian-style boulevards and vast beaches. The Herald offers bar snacks lunchtime and evening, with a hot special dish for lunch. All the well-appointed guest rooms have colour TVs and tea and coffee making facilities. The full English breakfast should satisfy even the heartiest of appetites. Mr Bentley, the landlord, is a founder member of the Honorary Order of Bass Drinkers but he serves a rival brew.

Beer: John Smiths Bitter on handpump.

Accommodation: 3 singles, 7 doubles, 3 with private baths. B&B £17 single, £27 double. Week and long-stay terms available. Children welcome, terms by arrangement.

## STOCKPORT (GREATER MANCHESTER)

Tiviot Hotel
8 Tiviot Dale

Licensee: David Walker
Tel: 061 480 4109

A friendly, welcoming town-centre pub offering excellent value for both food and accommodation. It is close to the historic market place and handy for the M63 and Ringway Airport. The guest rooms are quiet and secluded from the bars. Sandwiches will be made up until midnight and breakfasts are served from 6am. The energetic and dying art of table football can be enjoyed. Stockport is a good stepping stone for the Peak District and has an art gallery, the Garrick Theatre and Lyme Park ... and Robinson's brewery.

Beer: Robinson Best Mild, Best Bitter and Old Tom (winter) on electric and handpumps.

Accommodation: 2 singles, 4 doubles, 1 family room. B&B £10-£15 per person. Evening meals available.

## WHITEWELL (LANCS)

Inn at Whitewell
Forest of Bowland, near Clitheroe, 9 miles from A59

Licensee: Richard Bowman
Tel: 022008 222

A superb whitewashed and mullioned inn, set in remote and lovely countryside. Parts of the building date back to the 14th century and it has Georgian and Victorian additions. It belongs to the Duchy of Lancaster and has extensive fishing rights on both banks of the river. Inside there are carved stone fireplaces, oak beams, wood panels and sonorously ticking antique clocks. The Hodder Bar has darts, dominoes and shove ha'penny. There is also an art gallery — not something you find in your average local — with work by artists from all over Britain. The inn is also a wine merchants, which means there are exceptional vintages to enjoy if you prefer the grape to the grain. Home-cooked food includes local salmon and trout, game in season, black pudding and Cumberland sausage. Food is served as bar snacks or in the restaurant. In warm weather you can sit on trestles in the garden and enjoy the splendour of the setting.

Beer: Moorhouse Premier Bitter and Pendle Witches Brew on handpumps.

Accommodation: 12 doubles, 7 family rooms, 6 rooms with en suite facilities, doubles let as singles when necessary. B&B £28 single, double £39, single with bath £32, double with bath £43. 10% reduction for week's stay. Children welcome, 60% reduction in family room.

## ICESTERSHIRE

# BELTON

George Hotel
Market Place, off B5324

Licensees: Hector & Penny Houston
Tel: 0530 222426

A large country inn dating from 1753 noted for its excellent home-cooked food lunchtime and evening. It is next to an old church and has a maypole in the grounds. There are summer barbecues in the spacious garden. Guest rooms, with en suite facilities, also have tea and coffee makers. All the rooms have TVs. The hotel is handy for Donington Park race circuit and is close to the M1 and East Midlands airport.

Beer: Shipstone Mild and Bitter, Wem Best Bitter on handpumps.

Accommodation: 15 doubles, 4 family rooms, 7 rooms en suite. Bed £15-£25, breakfast extra. Children and dogs welcome.

# HINCKLEY

New Plough Hotel
24 Leicester Road, off A5 and M1

Licensee: Michael Duckworth
Tel: 0455 615037

A warm, friendly and welcoming pub, with a real fire and wooden seats in the bar, and a comfortable lounge. The locals play backgammon. The last edition of the guide said the pub was 'a splendid base for visiting Hinckley Castle'. This caused interest in history circles as it was the first known siting of a castle in the town. Apologies to Mr and Mrs Duckworth for having to explain to visitors, including many Americans, that the castle is a figment of the imagination.

Beer: Marston Burton Bitter and Pedigree on handpumps.

Accommodation: 1 single, 2 doubles, 1 twin. B&B £12.50 per person. Children welcome, half price.

# LEICESTER

Empire Hotel
217 Fosse Road North, A5125, off A50, 10 minutes from city centre

Licensee: Roger Huckall
Tel: 0533 21602

Built in the late 19th century as a mansion next to a spa, the Empire has been a pub since the spa dried up in the 1920s. It has live entertainment at least two nights a week and is within easy walking distance of Abbey Park with its ruins of Leicester Abbey and Cardinal Wolsey's burial site.

Beer: Ansells Mild and Bitter on handpumps.

Accommodation: 1 single, 6 doubles. The rooms were due to be refurbished early in 1988: check that accommodation is available. Rate likely to be £15 B&B per person.

# LOUGHBOROUGH

Corporation
1 Wharncliffe Road, off A6

Licensee: Alan Hudson
Tel: 0509 263778

The Corporation is a large and friendly pub on Loughborough's inner ring road, flanked by commercial buildings but facing private houses. It has a garden, welcomes families and serves good lunchtime food. Pool, darts and dominoes are played in an upstairs games room and there is a large aquarium downstairs.

Beer: Bass and M&B Mild (winter) on electric pumps.

Accommodation: 1 single, 2 doubles, 1 family room. B&B £10-£15. Credit cards: Access, Visa.

# OAKHAM

Rutland Angler
Mill Street, off A6

Licensee: Cliff Horton
Tel: 0572 55839

A friendly and welcoming old Rutland pub, once Oakham's maternity hospital. It stages live jazz every Thursday evening in the spacious cellar bar. Based in the historic market town, it is just $1\frac{1}{2}$ miles from the vast man-made Rutland Water with lakeside walks, birdwatching, sailing and fishing facilities.

Beer: Sam Smiths Old Brewery Bitter and Museum Bitter on handpumps.

Accommodation: 4 singles, 3 twins, 1 double, 2 rooms with private baths. B&B £16.50 single, double/twin £27, £30 with bath. Children welcome, terms by arrangement. Discounts for stays of more than 4 nights.

# QUORN

White Horse
2 Leicester Road, on A6

Licensee: Barry Montgomery
Tel: 0509 412338

There has been a pub on the site since the 1650s and there are still a few reminders of the period in the spacious residents' room. The White Horse was the first ale house in the famous hunting village to be granted a wine and spirits licence. As well as the friendly lounge bar, there is also a large pool room with two full-size tables. The pub is in the centre of Quorn and has good car parking facilities.

Beer: Adnams Bitter, Everards Bitter, Tiger and Old Original on handpumps, with occasional guest beers.

Accommodation: 1 family room. B&B £11 single, £20 double. Children welcome, half price. Tea and coffee making facilities and a TV are available.

# WHISSENDINE

White Lion
Main Street, 3 miles from A606

Licensee: Mr Parkinson
Tel: 066 479 233

A cheery, friendly pub with first-class food lunchtime and evening (including vegetarian meals) and a strong emphasis on pub games: as well as darts and pool you can join in the rarer pub pastimes of Shut the Box and Devil Among the Tailors. There is a fine garden, where you can enjoy a drink and a meal in warm weather. The White Lion is well placed for Rutland Water and the lovely Vale of Belvoir.

Beer: Everards Bitter, Tiger and Old Original on handpumps.

Accommodation: 11 rooms, can be arranged as single, double or family. 2 rooms with showers. B&B £16-£30.

TALLY HO, ASWARBY

# ASWARBY

Tally Ho
On A15 near Sleaford

Licensee: C Davies
Tel: 052 95 205

A striking 18th-century inn built of Ancaster stone and topped by a fine slate roof, the Tally Ho is in an isolated area of lovely parkland close to Sleaford. It is renowned for its lively and friendly atmosphere and the bar is the meeting and watering place of the local hunting fraternity. Meals are served lunchtime and evening in the bar or separate restaurant. There are welcoming log fires in the winter and the guest rooms — in the tastefully modernised old stable black — have private baths, TVs and tea and coffee making facilities. It is a good base for visiting Stamford, Boston and Grantham.

Beer: Adnams Bitter, Bateman XB on handpumps and guest beers.

Accommodation: 6 doubles. B&B £18 single, £30 double. Weekend £36 per person for 2 nights with £4 allowance for dinner. Children welcome. Facilities for the disabled: 4 guest rooms on ground floor.

# BOSTON

Carpenters Arms
Union Street, off Wormgate

Licensee R Newberry
Tel: 0205 62307

A lively, bustling pub hidden away in the small streets behind Boston Stump, the largest parish church in England with a tower that dominates the Fens and has acted as a navigation aid for sailors for centuries. The main bar of the Carpenters Arms is a meeting place for young and old and there is

imaginative lunchtime food —
curries, pasta and vegetarian dishes.
Evening food is by arrangement
only. The six large guest rooms have
brass bedsteads and pine furniture.
Prices vary according to whether
you want a full breakfast,
continental or prefer to cook your
own in the kitchen provided for
early leavers. In Boston you can visit
the Stump, the memorial to the
Pilgrim Fathers, the Guildhall and
the market place.

Beer: Bateman Mild, XB and XXXB
on handpumps.

Accommodation: 6 doubles,
including 2 family rooms. B&B up
to £15 per person. Half and full
board available.

## BURGH LE MARSH

White Hart Hotel
19-21 High Street, A158

Licensee: Mrs C Watson
Tel: 0754 810321

A comfortable and welcoming pub
five miles from Skegness, a good
base for touring the Lincolnshire
coast and Tennyson region. The
White Hart has a pleasant lounge
with a fine collection of Crown
Derby china, a lively public bar with
games and juke box, and a separate
restaurant called Harts that serves
distinctive, good-value food. The
charming guest rooms all contain tea
and coffee making equipment.

Beer: Bateman XB and XXXB,
Marston Pedigree on handpumps.

Accommodation: 3 doubles, 2 family
rooms, all with en suite facilities.
B&B £15-£25. Half and full board
available. Credit cards: Amex.

## FREISTON

Castle Inn
Haltoft End, A52

Licensee B Thompson
Tel: 0205 760393

An attractive inn four miles from
Boston, with a comfortable and
spacious bar warmed by open fires
in winter. This is a rip-roaring
family pub with a superb adventure
playgound that includes an aerial
runway and fishing boats. Bar food
is served lunchtime and evening. The
inn is well placed for visiting the
Pilgrim Fathers memorial near
Fishtoft and the Sibsey Traders Mill,
a six-sailed windmill owned by
English Heritage and open to the
public.

Beer: Bateman Mild and XB on
handpumps.

Accommodation: 3 doubles with tea
and coffee makers. B&B £10-£15.
Half board available.

## GREAT LIMBER

New Inn
High Street, A18

Licensee: C Spencer
Tel: 0469 60257

A large and popular pub in the
centre of this North Lincolnshire
village, with a splendid range of
beers, offering a welcome relief from
the expensive hotels in the area. It
has a quiet lounge free from
electronic music or games, real fires
in winter, a welcome for families
and a garden, plus good lunchtime
(not weekends) and evening food
(residents only in the evening). The
pub is owned by the Earl of
Yarborough whose family seat,
Brocklesby Park, is close by. The
hand at bridge or whist containing
no card higher than a nine is called a

Yarborough and is named after one of the earl's ancestors. The wife of the first baron is buried in a magnificent mausoleum within walking distance of the pub. It stands on a barrow with excellent views of the countryside and Humber estuary. The inn is a good base for the Humber industries and Humberside airport.

Beer: Bateman XXXB, Tetley Bitter, Ward Sheffield Best Bitter and regular guest beers on handpumps.

Accommodation: 5 singles, 2 doubles, 1 family room. B&B £10-£15 per person. Half and full board available (no full board at weekends). All rooms have tea and coffee making facilities.

## STAMFORD

Bull & Swan
High Street, St Martins, B1081

Licensee: William Morgado
Tel: 0780 63558

A fine stone-built coaching inn in one of England's most superb and unspoilt old towns. It has a wood-burning stove, low beams hung with copper kettles and comfortable plush seating in the three-level bar. The food has a strong Portuguese bias in both the bar and separate restaurant. Look out for pork braga, smoked bacon kebabs and salmon transmontana. If your tastes are simpler, go for steak and kidney pie, soup, ploughman's, steak and seafood platter.

Beer: Sam Smiths Old Brewery Bitter on handpump.

Accommodation: 6 rooms. B&B £23 single, £30 double.

## TATTERSHALL

Fortescue Arms
Market Place, A153

Tel: 0526 42364

A cheerful village local, close to Tattershall Castle, between Sleaford and Horncastle with a large quiet lounge free from piped music, small bar and separate games room. It offers good pub grub both lunchtimes and evenings. The pub has a pleasant garden and there are camping facilities nearby.

Beer: Bass and Stones Best Bitter on handpumps.

Accommodation: 4 doubles. B&B £15-£25. Full board available. Credit cards: Access, Visa.

## CLAPHAM SW4

Olde Windmill
Windmill Drive, Clapham Common South Side, A24

Licensee: Paul Nazer
Tel: 01 673 4578

The Windmill is just a few yards from an old Roman road that has been carrying traffic for more than 19 centuries. An inn has stood on the site since 1665 and the mill from which it took its name was once the winning post for the Clapham Races. The present building is largely Victorian in origin and the vast main bar has windmill pictures on the walls. Bar food includes ploughman's, chilli, curries and salads. There are terrace seats outside and, in good weather, the crowds of drinkers spill out on to the common. Accommodation is in an adjoining house that was once the home of the founder of Young's brewery. There is a resident ghost known as Croaker.

Beer: Young Bitter, Special Bitter and Winter Warmer on handpumps.

Accommodation: 9 singles, 4 doubles, 1 room with private bath. B&B £27 single, £32 double. No children.

# PECKHAM SE15

Stuart Arms
40 Stuart Road

Licensee: Mick McCann
Tel: 01 639 0563

The Stuart Arms, formerly the Newlands Tavern, is a large, two-bar local in a quiet residential area near Peckham Rye railway station. It has a real fire, darts and pool and lunchtime food. The guest rooms all have colour TVs.

Beer: Websters Yorkshire Bitter on handpump.

Accommodation: 11 rooms. B&B £15 single, £25 double, £40 treble.

# NORFOLK
# ATTLEBOROUGH

Griffin Hotel
Church Street, A11

Licensee: Gary Drabble
Tel: 0953 452149

A handsome 16th-century coaching inn in the town centre, with half timbers and a low-slung roof outside and beams and open fires — one with a stove — inside. The walls and fires are decorated with old shields, brass jugs, china and guns. There are excellent bar snacks, ranging from a

steak to a sandwich. The separate restaurant is open Monday to Saturday evenings and serves a traditional roast lunch on Sundays. The guest rooms are centrally heated and are equipped with TVs. Attleborough is close to Snetterton race circuit and Sunday market, and Kilverstone Wildlife Park.

Beer: Greene King Abbot Ale, Wethered Bitter on handpumps, with a weekly guest beer.

Accommodation: 2 singles, 6 doubles. B&B £16-£18.50. 10% reduction for week's stay. Children welcome to stay, no reductions. No animals.

# CLEY-NEXT-THE-SEA

George & Dragon Hotel
A419

Licensee: Rodney Sewell
Tel: 0263 740652

This historic building was rebuilt in 1879 but dates from the 17th century. It stands in an area of bleak beauty by the salt marshes leading down to the sea. It is ideal bird-watching territory and the George & Dragon has a room dedicated to the Norfolk Naturalist Trust. The pub has many 'G&D' artefacts, including a stained glass window of England's patron saint slaying the mythical beast. Good bar meals are served lunchtime and evening. There is a garden as well as camping facilities. Families are welcome and there is a TV lounge for residents.

Beer: Greene King IPA and Abbot Ale on handpumps, with regular guest beers including Bateman's and Rayment's.

Accommodation: 8 doubles, 1 family room, 2 rooms en suite, including four-poster. B&B £15-£30. Winter

Breaks: details on application.
Facilities for the disabled.

# CROMER

Bath House
The Promenade

Licensees: Bertice & Barbara
Wheston
Tel: 0263 514260

A lovingly restored, elegant Regency
inn on the promenade of this fine
Victorian seaside resort, the county's
most northerly coastal town, famous
for its crab fishing, sea fret and small
lifeboat museum. The guest rooms
of the Bath House are on the first
floor and most have views of the
sea. All the rooms are en suite and
have central heating, colour TVs and
tea and coffee makers. There is a
residents' lounge, a garden and
excellent lunches and evening meals
are served. The inn is just a few
yards from the beach, the pier and
the crab landing area.

Beer: Bateman XXXB, Greene King
IPA and Abbot Ale, Hall and
Woodhouse Tanglefoot on
handpumps.

Accommodation: 1 single, 3 doubles,
3 family rooms. B&B £15-£25. Half
board available. No pets.

# DERSINGHAM

Feathers Hotel
Manor Road, ½ mile off A149

Licensees: Tony & Maxine Martin
Tel: 0485 40207

A 17th-century sandstone inn with
two bars, a cheerful welcome and
royal connections: Edward VII used
to slip out to the Feathers for a
quick one when he was staying at
Sandringham. The Prince of Wales's
feathers are emblazoned over the
fireplace. The emphasis is on
comfort, with well-carpeted lounges,
carved wooden chairs and high-back
settles. There is a patio with
children's swings and slides. The
garden has a sandpit. Excellent bar
food includes Cheddar and Stilton
ploughman's, chicken, scampi,
sandwiches and soup. The separate
restaurant, busy and popular, serves
à la carte and three course meals.
The Feathers is a good resting place
for visiting Sandringham, King's
Lynn, Hunstanton and the North
Norfolk coast.

Beer: Adnams Bitter and Old,
Charrington IPA on handpumps.

Accommodation: 4 twins, 2 doubles.
B&B £18 single, £30 double.

SCOLE INN, SCOLE — *see p 105*

## GREAT BIRCHAM

King's Head Hotel
Lynn Road, B1153 off A148

Licensee: I Verrands
Tel: 048 523 265

The King's Head is a comfortable country inn near Sandringham and the Peddars Way. There is a gracious lawn for warm-weather eating and drinking. Bar meals are available lunchtime and evening and the candlelit restaurant uses local produce for its varied menu. There is a traditional roast at Sunday lunchtimes. The guest rooms all have baths or showers, TVs and tea and coffee making facilities.

Beer: Adnams Bitter, Bass and Charrington IPA on handpumps.

Accommodation: 1 single, 5 doubles. B&B £17.50 per person. Credit cards: Access, Amex, Diners, Visa.

## HOLKHAM

Victoria Hotel
On A149

Licensees: Geoff & Gemma Whitehead
Tel: 0328 710469

An imposing, late-19th century brick and flint hotel on the coast road opposite the long drive that leads down to the great sweep of Holkham beach and wildlife reserve, one of the finest coastal stretches in eastern England. The bar enjoys darts, dominoes, crib and shove ha'penny while the pleasant lounge has bay windows with fine views of the coast. There are tables in the old stableyard in summer. Bar meals include soups, ploughman's, sandwiches, salads, steaks, local fish and shell fish — the Whiteheads concentrate on local, freshly-cooked produce. There is a residents' TV

lounge and the guest rooms have tea and coffee making facilities. Holkham Hall, open to the public, is close by.

Beer: Tolly Cobbold Bitter and Old Strong (winter) on handpump and straight from the cask.

Accommodation: 3 singles, 5 doubles. B&B £17 person Easter to October, £14 in winter. Winter Breaks 2 nights £38 per person with evening meal.

## KING'S LYNN

Bank House
King's Staithe Square

Licensees: Konrad & Susie Szymanski
Tel: 0553 76508

A delightful and elegant Georgian building in the heart of this fine old East Anglian port and market town. The Bank House has risen phoenix-like from a terrible fire in 1985. As a result, the upper floors, with the guest rooms, have been rebuilt but retain much of the original panelling. Downstairs, the bar offers excellent bar snacks — soup, steaks, fish, sandwiches, pizzas — while the beamed restaurant, once the kitchen of the old house, serves lunch Tuesday to Friday, with a traditional roast on Sunday and an evening à la carte menu. The guest rooms, with views of the river and old courtyard, have colour TVs and tea and coffee making equipment.

Beer: Bass and Charrington IPA on handpumps.

Accommodation: 2 singles, 2 doubles, 1 room en suite. B&B £25.50 single, £32.50 double. Weekend £12.50 per person per night. Children welcome, half price. Credit cards: Access, Visa.

# MUNDESLEY

Royal Hotel
30 Paston Road, A1159

Licensee: Michael Fotis
Tel: 0263 720096

A 300-year-old inn with superb views of the sea from Mundesley cliffs, that retains its original beams and timbers. Admiral Lord Nelson stayed at the inn, then known as the New Inn, while he attended Paston school in North Walsham. The change of name followed a visit by royalty in the late 18th century. The Nelson Bar of the hotel has splendid bar meals that feature locally caught fish and shellfish as well as cold meats and salads. The separate Buttery and Beachcomber Restaurant is open for lunch and dinner. The guest rooms all have private baths or showers, colour TVs, radios and tea and coffee making equipment. The hotel is a good base for visiting the many delights of North Norfolk: the shrine to Our Lady of Walsingham, the pleasant seaside resort of Sheringham, its steam railway and the miles of unspoilt coast.

Beer: Adnams Bitter and Old, Charrington IPA, Greene King Abbot Ale on handpumps.

Accommodation: 26 singles/twins, 14 doubles. B&B £19.95 single, £31.50 double. Weekend (2 nights) £50 for 2, Week £160 for 2. Children welcome, 20% reductions. Credit cards: Access, Amex, Diners, Visa.

# NEATISHEAD

Barton Angler Lodge
Irstead Road, off A1151; after Wroxham take road signposted Neatishead and Barton Turf; in Neatishead village follow Irstead road for 1½ miles.

Licensee: John Harrison
Tel: 0692 630740

An elegant hotel on the banks of lovely Barton Broad, 280 acres of Anglian water where Nelson learnt to sail. The hotel can arrange for dinghy and boat hire. The hotel has large, sweeping, flower-filled gardens, guest rooms and suites named after Nelson's battles, two bars — the Mahogany and Tangler with lunchtime bar snacks — and top-class cooking in the Harlows Restaurant. In summer there are barbecues on the patio. Lunches range from soup, salads and ploughman's to filled baps, lasagne and crab.

Beer: Greene King IPA and Abbot Ale on handpumps.

Accommodation: 2 singles, 4 doubles, 4 rooms with en suite facilities. B&B £25 per person. No children. Credit cards: Access, Amex, Diners, Visa.

# NORTH WOOTTON

Red Cat Hotel
Station Road, 1½ miles off A148 & A149

Licensee: P J Irwin
Tel: 0553 87 244

A popular marshland pub near the Wash, close to King's Lynn and the ancient monument at Castle Rising. Mr Irwin is a keen CAMRA man and offers ale in fine nick, good bar snacks and evening meals. It is a good base for visiting the Norfolk-Lincolnshire borders. The comfortable guest rooms have tea and coffee making facilities. The Red Cat has a garden, family room and open fires.

Beer: Red Cat Special Bitter is brewed for the pub by Woodforde, plus Adnams Bitter and Old, Greene King Abbot Ale and occasional guest beers on handpumps and straight from the cask.

Accommodation: 4 singles, 3 doubles, 2 rooms with en suite facilities. B&B £19 per person. Half board available. Weekend £35, Week £70. Children welcome, charged £5 a night.

## NORWICH

Sir Garnet Wolseley
36 Market Place

Licensee: Colin Earthy
Tel: 0603 615892

The Sir Garnet is a white and blue part-Regency pub standing akimbo on the steep rise of Norwich's famous street market with its maze of striped-awning stalls. The pub was once two separate inns and is the only remaining pub in the market place where once no less than 44 operated. The dual character of the pub is caught by the distinctive nature of the two bars. The lower bar, festooned with programmes from Norwich City football club, is a lively haunt of stall holders. Climb the stairs and you enter a tranquil and elegant room with superb views of the market. There are busts of Sir Garnet, an Irish soldier, and General Gordon: it was Wolseley who lead an unsuccessful expedition to find the general. There are good pub lunches including fresh Cromer crab.

Beer: Courage Best Bitter and Directors on handpumps.

Accommodation: 3 doubles. B&B £12.50 per person. *Pub closed Sunday evenings.*

## ORMESBY ST MARGARET

Grange Hotel
Off A149 & B1159

Licensees: Mr & Mrs K R Smith
Tel: 0493 731877

The Grange is a former Georgian country house with two acres of grounds that include a camping site, a pets corner and adventure playground. It is an ideal family pub with a room for children and parents. The recently refurbished bars offer good home-cooked food. The guest rooms have colour TVs and tea and coffee making facilities. The Grange is a good base for visiting Caister Castle and car museum, Thrigby wildlife park, local beaches and golf courses.

Beer: Adnams Bitter, Ruddles Best Bitter and 3 guest beers every week, all on handpumps.

Accommodation: 3 singles, 11 doubles, 3 family rooms, 11 rooms with en suite facilities. B&B £30 single, £33.50 double as single, £40 double and family room. Weekend £60 double/family. Week £200 double/family. Credit cards: Access, Visa.

# SCOLE

Scole Inn
The Street, junction of A1066 and
A410, near Diss

Managers: Bob & Maggie Nylk
Tel: 0379 740481

A famous old East of England 17th
century coaching inn and a Grade I
listed building. Its most famous
claim to fame — its inn sign — no
longer exists. When village carpenter
John Fairchild was commissioned by
a wealthy Norwich wool merchant,
John Peck, to build the inn, he
added a gallows sign that straddled
the road and cost the astonishing
sum for 1655 of £1,057. It included
many mythical and classical figures,
including Neptune rising from the
waves, with pride of place going to a
white hart, the inn's original name.
It was demolished about 250 years
later, but an engraving of it by
Joshua Kirby hangs in the bar. The
notorious highwayman, John
Belcher, used the inn as his
headquarters. The inn today retains
many of its original features, with a
wealth of beams, oak doors and
inglenook fireplaces. There is both
good bar food and a separate
restaurant.

Beer: Adnams Bitter, Greene King
Abbot Ale on handpumps.

Accommodation: 20 doubles,
including 3 family rooms, all with
en suite facilities, 12 rooms in
converted stable block. B&B £33
single, £48 double; 4 poster room
£55. Bargain Breaks £54 per person
sharing double room for any 2
nights. Credit cards: Access, Amex,
Diners, Visa.

# SEA PALLING

Hall Inn
Waxham Road, B1159

Licensee: R J R Self
Tel: 069 261 323

An old building dating back to the
16th century in a remote coastal
setting close to beautiful Hickling
Broad, the most northerly of the
chain of small waterways linked by
the great rivers of Norfolk and
Suffolk. The inn is a wonderful
place to rest and to take long and
refreshing walks along the beaches.
There are open fires, a family and
games room, a small garden and
camping facilities. There is bar food
and a separate dining room.

Beer: Adnams Bitter, Greene King
Abbot Ale on handpumps and guest
beers.

Accommodation: 2 doubles, 2 family
rooms. B&B £10-£15.

# THORNHAM

Lifeboat Inn
Sea Lane, 1½ miles off A149

Licensees: Nick & Lynn Handley
Tel: 048 526 236

A wonderful old pub on the edge of
the vast salt flats that lead to the sea
and across which smugglers struggled
with their contraband centuries ago.
The Lifeboat, a series of small
rooms, has low beams, five crackling
log fires in winter, oil and gas lamps
and pub games that include darts,
shove ha'penny and a penny-in-the-
hole bench. Although it can be cold
outside in winter, the pub has a
flourishing vine in a terrace at the
back. There are a few seats at the
front and the back garden has seats
among the trees, a climbing frame
and toys for children and a donkey.
Splendid bar food concentrates on

home-made dishes such as soups, ploughman's, pasta, cheese and onion quiche, sandwiches and home-made ice creams. The small candle-lit restaurant has à la carte meals that include local seafood and game. A fine place to stay, eat and drink and thoroughly deserving its place in *Classic Country Pubs*.

Beer: Adnams Bitter, Greene King IPA and Abbot Ale on handpumps and straight from the cask, plus guest beers.

Accommodation: 1 single, 1 double, 1 family room. B&B £14.50 per person. Weekend £26.50. Off-season terms on application. Children's room; children welcome to stay, no reductions.

a popular bar with a piano and good bar food. The separate restaurant has no less than four chefs and offers acclaimed French and English cooking. Wells is a delightful town to stroll in and is close to Blakeney, Holkham Hall, the North Norfolk Heritage Coast and Sandringham.

Beer: Adnams Bitter, Burton Ale, Marston Pedigree on handpumps.

Accommodation: 1 single, 13 doubles, 2 family rooms, 8 rooms with en suite facilities. B&B from £20 per person. Weekend from £52 for dinner B&B, Week from £182. Children's room; children welcome to stay, reductions on application. Credit cards: Access, Amex, Diners, Visa.

# WELLS-NEXT-THE-SEA

Crown Hotel
The Buttlands, off A149

Licensee; Wilfred Foyers
Tel: 0328 710209

The Crown, described in *The Times* as 'the sort of small hotel tired travellers dream about', is charmingly placed in this picturesque old sea port that is also a good hunting ground these days for buyers of antique furniture and paintings. The old coaching inn has

GRIFFIN HOTEL, ATTLEBOROUGH —
*see p 100*

# WOOD DALLING

Wood Dalling Hall
4 miles from B1149 Holt to Norwich road

Licensee: Brian Daws
Tel: 036 284 832

An opulent and impressive Elizabethan manor house, built in 1580 by William Bulwer, who also built the nearby Heydon Hall. A major and tasteful renovation programme in recent years has restored the rooms to their former glory. A tree-planting scheme has provided delightful gardens to stroll in with ponds stocked with carp and tench. The hall is a Grade II listed building and declared a house of Outstanding Interest by the Department of the Environment. There are beautiful beamed rooms and an original wooden spiral staircase. Accommodation is self-catering in 30 cottages that were once both Elizabethan and Victorian farm cottages. In the hall there are bar meals ranging from sausage and chips to venison and black cherries as well as full restaurant meals lunchtime and evening. There is an adventure playground for children in the garden.

Beer: Bateman XXXB, Hall & Woodhouse Tanglefoot, Marston Pedigree on handpumps.

Accommodation: 30 self-catering cottages: cottage for 4 £60 for 3 days, for 6 £70, for 8 £80. Each cottage has colour TV, fridge, oven, fitted carpets and gas heating. Further details on application. Credit cards: Access.

wholemeal loaves. In winter there is a carvery, too, with a hot roast. The lovely old village has stone and thatch cottages. The Gunpowder Plot was hatched in the manor, Althorp Hall.

Beer: Flowers Original, Marston Pedigree, Sam Smith's Old Brewery Bitter or Museum Ale on handpumps.

Accommodation: 1 single, 4 doubles, 2 family rooms, all with en suite facilities. B&B £27.50 single, £30 double. Children welcome, £5 per night.

## ASHBY ST LEDGERS

Old Coach House
Off A361 near Daventry; 4 miles from M1 junction 18

Licensees: Douglas & Frederika Jarvis
Tel: 0788 890349

Accommodation at the Old Coach House includes stabling for horses, recalling the time when the stone buildings were a farm and the front room was set aside as a bar. The Jarvises have been undoing a great deal of thoughtless modernisation in the 1960s and have discoverd wonderful old inglenooks and stone floors. The many small rooms have settle chairs, farm kitchen tables, old harnesses and hunting prints. Table skittles, darts and dominoes are played in the front bar. The spacious garden has a climbing frame and swings for children and there are barbecues in the summer. Bar food includes a 'pot luck' daily special, ploughman's with local cheese, game casserole, local trout, mackerel and such vegetarian dishes as vegetable crêpes or mushrooms baked in small

## BLAKESLEY

Bartholomew Arms
High Street, 3 miles off A5, near Towcester

Licensee: Tony Hackett
Tel: 03227 860292

A cheerful village local with, says Mr Hackett, no gimmicks — no pool, juke box, space invaders or plastic food. 'We offer good beer and company.' The beamed bars are packed with cricketing memorabilia, hams, guns and malt whiskies. The pub is the home of the National Soap Box Derby held every year in September. The championships were started by Tony Hackett and other villagers to raise funds for charity. Excellent bar food is served lunchtime (not Sundays) with a limited choice in the evening. All the guest rooms have colour TVs and central heating. The pub is a good base for Towcester, its race course and the Silverstone motor racing circuit.

Beer: Marston Pedigree on handpump.

Accommodation: 1 single, 4 doubles, 2 rooms with en suite facilities. B&B £12.50. Full board available. Children welcome, 40% reduction.

## ROTHWELL

### Red Lion Hotel
Market Hill, A6 near Kettering

Proprietors: Anne & Jim Tibbs
Tel: 0536 710409

The Red Lion is a welcoming 19th-century coaching inn with imposing gables and chimneys in Rothwell's market place. The lounge has many interesting brasses and the rare game of Northamptonshire skittles is played there. Bar food is served lunchtime and evening and includes home-made steak and kidney pie, ploughman's, salads and steaks. The separate evening restaurant has a wide range of dishes, including beef Wellington, steak chasseur, beef Stroganoff and trout with almonds. There is also a traditional Sunday roast, with children's portions. The guest rooms have TVs and tea and coffee making facilities. Rothwell is close to Rockingham Castle.

Beer: Charles Wells Eagle Bitter and Bombardier on handpumps.

Accommodation: 4 rooms, can be used as single, double or family. B&B £15 single, £25 double, £30 family. Weekend £55 per person in double/twin, including dinners and Sunday lunch. Special terms for honeymooners. Children welcome. Additional rooms in preparation.

# WEEDON

### Globe Hotel
High Street. Junction of A45 & A5. 3 miles from M1 exit 16

Licensees: Peter & Penny Walton
Tel: 0327 40336

The Globe is a modernised and extended 18th-century farmhouse on the junction of the A45 and Watling Street. The Waltons have launched a programme of careful and tasteful refurbishment to the lovely old buildings in order to offer the best of both the old and the new worlds, with first class cuisine and guest rooms with en suite facilities. There is a large garden with fine views of the rolling countryside. Families are welcome. Bar billiards and darts are played in the bar. There are lunchtime bar meals, an evening à la carte restaurant and a Sunday roast. Bar meals include soup, ploughman's, salads, pizzas and curries. The Globe is a good base for visiting the site of Naseby Civil war battlefield, Sulgrave Manor, Banbury and the brave new world of Milton Keynes.

Beer: Fuller London Pride, Marston Pedigree, Wadworth 6X on handpumps.

Accommodation: 2 singles, 11 doubles, 3 family rooms, all en suite. B&B £29 single, double £35, family room £41.50-£45. Weekend single £23.50, double £33.50, family room £38.50-£40. Credit cards: Access, Amex, Diners, Visa.

# ALLENDALE

Hare & Hounds
The Path, Haltwhistle Road,
A6303

Licensee: Geoff Smith
Tel: 043 483 300

A fine, old 18th-century coaching inn in beautiful countryside near the Cumbrian and Durham borders. The inn is vigorously old fashioned, with stone floors and open fires in the bar and the lounge. It is a good base for touring the wild and unspoilt Northumberland moors, commons and forests. The inn serves food lunchtime and evening, its bars are quiet and free from loud music, and there is a pleasant garden.

Beer: Webster's Choice on handpump.

Accommodation: 3 doubles. B&B £10.50 per person.

# ALNWICK

Oddfellows Arms
Narrowgate, off A1

Licensee: Anthony Copeland
Tel: 0665 602695

A cheerful and welcoming pub by the castle in this cobbled, historic town (pronounced 'Annick'), the centre of many long and bloody battles and sieges over the centuries. The Oddfellows offers coal fires, a public bar with darts and dominoes 'but no pool' and a comfortable lounge. The inn is a haven of quiet, without juke boxes and other distractions. Food is served lunchtime and evening in summer, lunchtime only in winter. *Accommodation in summer months only.*

Beer: Vaux Samson on handpump.

Accommodation: 2 doubles, 1 family room. B&B £10 per person.

# BAMBURGH

Victoria Hotel
Front Street, junction of B1340,
1341 & 1342

Licensee: Robert Goodfellow
Tel: 066 84 431

With a host named Goodfellow, the Victoria has a head start over most pubs and hotels, and emphasises the point by offering special rates for CAMRA members. The friendly hotel is in the heart of Bamburgh village in one of the loveliest coastal areas of Britain. Bamburgh was once the capital of the ancient kingdom of Bernicia and is now designated an area of outstanding beauty. The Victoria is a splendid base for touring the area, and visiting the Farne Islands, Holy Island, the Grace Darling Museum and the great castles of Bamburgh, Dunstanburgh and Lindisfarne. The hotel has a wide range of bar meals — toasties, ploughman's, home-made soups, fish and chips, burgers and children's portions — served lunchtime and evening, plus full meals in a separate dining room. There is a residents' lounge and all-day coffee shop.

Beer: Tetley Bitter on handpump with always one guest beer, usually Theakston Old Peculier or Marston Pedigree.

Accommodation: 25 rooms, 5 singles, 15 doubles, 5 family rooms, 18 rooms with private bath. B&B from £15 per person, £20 with bath. Children welcome, under 2 years £2, under 13 half price. Small charge for dogs. Bargain breaks: details on application. *Special rates for CAMRA members:* B&B £10, £15 with private bath, available 16 Sept to 15 May.

# CORBRIDGE

Wheatsheaf Inn
St Helens Street, off A69 & A68

Proprietors: Carol & Gordon
Young
Tel: 043 471 2020

A friendly inn in an ancient village with Roman connections, including the remains of a fort. The hotel has a comfortable bar and lounge with live music at weekends and a dominoes competition every Tuesday. Lunchtime bar meals include soup, farmhouse grill, chops and fish, sandwiches and children's meals. Full evening meals offer steak, fish, lasagne and a vegetarian dish.

Beer: Lorimer Scotch, Vaux Bitter and Samson on electric and handpumps.

Accommodation: 1 single, 3 doubles, 2 family rooms, 1 room with private bath. B&B from £12 per person. Off-season Weekend from £50. Children welcome, 30% reduction.

# FALSTONE

Blackcock Inn
Off A68

Licensee: Alexandra Brown
Tel: 0660 40200

The Blackcock really has a warm welcome, for Miss Brown has a collection of vintage coal fires. The fire in the bar was made in Newcastle at the turn of the century and first fitted in a house in Hexham. It is complete with oven and hot water tank. The lounge has a small stove made in Fife and called a 'Beatonette', presumably in honour of Mrs Beaton of Victorian home-hints fame. The dining room has a large open fire with a handsome black marble surround built for Allerwash Hall at Newbrough. The village-centre inn is more than 200 years old and was originally a single-storey thatched building. It has been extended and modernised over the years without losing its genuine character. The residents' lounge includes a grand piano and the dining room seats 30. Falstone, on the banks of the Tyne, is close to the largest man-made lake in Europe in Kielder Forest with its facilities for water sports, walking, fishing and pony trekking.

Beer: Vaux Samson on handpump.

Accommodation: 1 single, 1 double, 1 twin. B&B £10 single, £18 double. Children welcome, half price under 12.

# LOWICK

Black Bull Inn
4 Main Street, B6353

Licensee: Tom Grundy
Tel: 0289 88228

A delightful old village inn renowned for its welcome, good ale and bar food, served lunchtime and evening. It is fine base for visiting the Scottish borders, the Cheviots, the great castles of north Northumberland and the vast stretches of unspoilt beaches. Lowick is also handy for the main A1 to the south.

Beer: McEwan 70 and 80 shilling, Theakston Best Bitter on handpumps.

Accommodation: in self-catering cottage next to pub. Rates depend on number of guests and time of year: phone for details. Credit cards: Visa.

# NEWBIGGIN-BY-THE-SEA

Old Ship Hotel
Front Street, off A1189

Licensee: D Latimer
Tel: 0670 817212

The Old Ship is a coaching inn on the seafront of this delightful fishing village, once a major port in the 15th century. Fishermen still put to sea in their traditional 'cobbles' to catch salmon and lobster. The hotel offers a good welcome and good cheer, with an extensive menu in the Captain's Pantry, that includes soup, pâté, salads, omelettes, home-made steak and kidney pie, curry and scampi. Wansbeck Riverside Park and Woodhorn Lake are close to Newbiggin. St Mary's Church in Woodhorn is the oldest church on the Northumbrian coast and is now a museum and cultural centre.

Beer: Vaux Bitter and Ward Sheffield Best Bitter on handpumps.

Accommodation: 1 single, 6 doubles. B&B £12. Weekend £20. Week £70. Off-season Weekend from £10 per night. Children welcome, half price.

WHEATSHEAF INN, CORBRIDGE —
*see opposite*

# SEAHOUSES

Black Swan Inn
2 Union Street, off A1 between Craster & Bamburgh

Licensee: Billy Gillhom
Tel: 0662 720227

The Black Swan is a happy little stone-built backstreet pub in this famous seaside resort, with its harbour and fine beaches. The inn has bar snacks and accommodation at extremely reasonable rates. Seahouses is a good base for visiting Bamburgh Castle, Craster with its home-cured kippers, Holy Island and the Farne Islands.

Beer: Lorimer Scotch and Vaux Samson on handpumps *(Beers may change in 1988).*

Accommodation: 2 doubles, 1 family room. B&B £9.50 per person. Week £60. Children's room; children welcome to stay, half price.

# WOOLER

Anchor Inn
Cheviot Street, off A697

Licensee: Reg Sterne
Tel: 0668 81412

A striking two-storey building decked out with hanging baskets and pots of flowers in a pleasant old market town at the foot of the Cheviots in the Glendale Valley. It is a genuine family pub and is popular with people on walking holidays. Bar meals are served at lunchtime and evening and there are camping facilities nearby.

Beer: Vaux Samson on handpump.

Accommodation: 1 single, 1 double, 1 family room. B&B £8.50 per person. Week: 10% discount. Children welcome, reductions if sharing.

## WOOLER

**Ryecroft Hotel**
On A697 on northern edge of
town

Licensees: Pat & David McKechnie
Tel: 0668 81459

The Ryecroft is a warm and friendly
family-run hotel with log fires on
the outskirts of the town. Pat
McKechnie supervises the cooking
and discriminating diners come from
far afield for her meals that are based
on local produce and include fruits
of the sea, creamed mushrooms,
cheese soup, pork steaks braised in
cider and smoked salmon quiche.
The comfortable bar has strong local
support for enthusiasts of darts,
dominoes and quoits. The Ryecroft
has a residents' lounge and all the
guest rooms have en suite facilities.
The hotel arranges special bird-
watching and walking weekend
holidays with guides, from March to
May.

Beer: Marston Pedigree, Tetley
Bitter, Yates Bitter and guest beers
on handpumps.

Accommodation: 1 single, 8 doubles.
B&B £25 single, £20 per person
sharing. Weekend £58-£62. Off-
season Weekend £58. Children's
room; children welcome to stay, half
price, free if sharing with parents.
Bird-watching and walking weekends
£75 per person, including B&B,
dinner and packed lunches.

## HAYTON

**Boat Inn**
Main Street, 1 mile off A620

Licensee: Anthony Ralton
Tel: 0777 700158

The delightful Boat is on the banks
of the Chesterfield Canal, where it
has its own moorings and is a
popular stopping place for boating
people. The inn has a large car park
and spacious gardens that run down
to the water's edge. The rooms are
in converted cottages next to the
pub. Carvery meals are served in a
separate restaurant seven days a
week. There are facilities for
camping, too.

Beer: Whitbread Castle Eden Ale
and Trophy, John Smiths Bitter on
handpumps.

Accommodation: 3 singles, 5
doubles, 2 family rooms, 2 rooms
with private bath. B&B from £15
single. Children can stay in the
family rooms.

## HOVERINGHAM

**Marquis of Granby**
Main Street, 1½ miles S of A612

Licensee Ken Adlington
Tel: 0602 663080

The pub's tranquil village setting is
matched by the warm and relaxed
atmosphere of the well-furnished
interior. The high standards of the
bar are continued in the guest
rooms, all of which have colour
TVs. A substantial menu, based
mainly on English dishes, is available
lunchtime and evening every day
except Sunday. The Marquis is the
ideal base for walkers or anglers
visiting the River Trent.

Beer: Marston Pedigree on handpumps.

Accommodation: 2 singles, 2 doubles. B&B £16 single, £26 double. Children welcome, no reductions.

## KIMBERLEY

Nelson & Railway Inn
Station Road, off A610

Licensee: Harry Burton
Tel: 0602 382177

If you wonder what connection there is between Lord Nelson and the railway, the answer is that the pub's original name was 'the Lord Nelson Railway Hotel'. Although Kimberley is just a village, at the height of the railway boom it boasted two competing railway stations, both a few yards from the pub. The stations still exist, as Kimberley Ex-Servicemen's Club and as the offices of a local timber firm. It is now the brewery tap, for Hardy (no connection with Nelson) and Hanson's large and imposing brewery dominates the village and looms over the pub. Both the lively bar and more sedate lounge offer a friendly welcome to visitors. There are gardens front and rear, with swings for children. The pub has darts and long alley skittles. Bar snacks are served lunchtime and early evening and include chips, bacon, sausage and fried egg butties, jacket potatoes with choice of filling, burgers, home-made quiche, cottage pie, chilli and lasagne, ploughman's, gammon, steaks, omelettes and a children's menu. There is a roast Sunday lunch too. Kimberley is close to Eastwood and the D H Lawrence museum.

Beer: Kimberley Best Bitter on handpump.

Accommodation: 2 doubles. B&B £9.50 per person. Children welcome, no reductions.

## NOTTINGHAM

Queens Hotel
2 Arkwright Street, opposite railway station

Licensee: Robert Beavis
Tel: 0602 864685

The Queens is the ideal place for refreshment as you leave the railway station or head for Trent Bridge cricket and football grounds. There is a cheery basic bar with darts and pool plus a comfortable lounge where dominoes is played. There are bar snacks and full meals in a separate restaurant. The pub is just half a mile from Nottingham's city centre and is a good base for visiting the castle and another splendid hostelry, the Trip to Jerusalem.

Beer: Shipstone Bitter on handpump.

Accommodation: 6 singles, 6 doubles/twins. £12 single, £20 double.

## WALKERINGHAM

Brickmakers Arms
Fountain Hill Road, ½ mile off A161

Licensees: Michael & Colin Dagg
Tel: 0427 890375

The Brickmakers is a traditional old world pub with one bar and a restaurant with good value food. There are welcoming log fires in winter. The guest rooms have baths or showers, colour TVs and tea and coffee making equipment.

Walkeringham is well placed for visiting Wesley's house at Epworth, Mattersley Priory, and the Old Hall at Gainsborough.

Beer: Stones Best Bitter, Tetley Bitter on handpumps.

Accommodation: 3 singles, 4 doubles, 2 family rooms, all en suite. B&B £25 single, £30 double, £35 family room. Children wlecome, terms included in price of family room.

# OXFORDSHIRE

# BURFORD

Highway Hotel
117 High Street, off A361

Licensee: D N Cohen
Tel: 099 382 2136

A superb 16th-century inn in one of the loveliest of the Cotswold towns. The Highway, strikingly painted white with black woodwork and decked with hanging baskets, stands in the wide High Street that slopes down to the River Windrush. Old Cotswold stone houses and cottages huddle together in a town created by the Saxons in the 8th century. The Domesday Book recorded a population of 200 in 1086. The inn has log fires in winter in its comfortable rooms, many of which still retain their original beams. In warmer weather, guests may sit in a courtyard. The guest rooms all have colour TVs, tea and coffee making facilities. There is a four-poster bed in one room where the old beams vie with modern central heating. Superb food is served in a candle-lit restaurant.

Beer: Hook Norton Best Bitter, Wadworth 6X on handpumps.

Accommodation: 8 doubles, 2 family rooms, 8 rooms with en suite facilities. B&B from £22.50 per person. Weekend £31.50 with evening meal. Mini-breaks: any two nights B&B + evening meal from £60 per person. Credit cards: Access, Amex, Diners, Visa.

Lamb Inn
Sheep Street

Licensees: R M & C de Wolf & K R Scott-Lee
Tel: 099 382 3155

The Lamb delights in quoting the verse of H C Beeching

*O fair is Moreton in the Marsh*
*And Stow on the wide wold;*
*But fairer far is Burford town*
*With its stone roofs grey and old;*
*And whether the sky be hot and high*
*Or the rain falls thin and chill,*
*The grey old town on the lonely down*
*Is where I would be still ...*

And the mellow stone Lamb is the perfect spot to cherish the town to the full. Its origins are 14th century. The bar has flagstone floors and high-back settles while the spacious, beautifully furnished lounge has beams and panelled walls. The beer is dispensed for both bars from a remarkable old beer engine in a glass cabinet. Menus change daily but bar food may include home-made vegetable soup with crusty bread, coq au vin, fresh grilled sardines, tagliatelle, ploughman's and rolls. Dinner may include courgette, garlic and Stilton soup, poached mushrooms in port wine and blue cheese, roast duckling, local trout Grenobloise, and baked escalope of salmon doria. The inn has a lovely sunny, flower-filled garden.

Beer: Wadworth IPA and 6X on handpumps, Old Timer in winter from the cask.

Accommodation: Single £22.50, double/twin £21.50 per person, £25 with bath or shower. Winter Break: £58-£62 per person, plus dinner allowance.

# GREAT TEW

Falkland Arms
Off B4022, 5 miles E of Chipping Norton

Licensee: John Milligan
Tel: 060 883 653

A stunning old inn in one of the loveliest of Oxfordshire villages, the Falkland Arms dates back to the 15th century. Originally named the Horse & Groom, it was renamed in honour of the local lords of the manor. It has a partially thatched roof and a vast overhanging tree. Inside there is a panelled bar with high-back settles, flagstones, oil lamps and an enormous collection of pots and tankards hanging from the beams. Lunchtime food (not Monday) includes home-made soups, ploughman's, salads and such daily specials as thatched pie, vegetarian country pie, trawlerman's pie, beef stew and dumplings and lamb and leek casserole. The guest rooms have old iron bedsteads and pine furniture. A gallon of ale is offered to anyone who sees the ghost of Lord Falkland.

Beer: Donnington BB, Hook Norton Best Bitter, Theakston XB, Wadworth 6X and guest beers on handpumps.

Accommodation: 4 rooms, 2 with private showers. B&B £17 single, £25-£28 double.

# MOULSFORD-ON-THAMES

Beetle & Wedge Hotel
Ferry Lane, off A329

Licensees: David & Evelyn Tiller
Tel: 0491 651381/651376

Beetle and wedge are foresters' tools and the oddly named inn, a fine red-brick Victorian building overlooking a gentle stretch of the Thames, has featured in Jerome K Jerome's *Three Men in a Boat* and appeared as the 'Potwell Inn' in H G Wells's *History of Mr Polly*. Since the last issue of the guide, the hotel has been extensively updated by the Tillers. All the guest rooms are now en suite, with colour TVs and tea and coffee making facilities. The bars have fine copper tables, with an open fire in the main bar surmounted by a large mirror that gives a reflection of the Thames in all its moods. Bar snacks include home-made soup, ploughman's, salads, beefburgers, lamb stew, curries, jacket potato and cheese while the separate dining room offers oak-smoked trout, fillet steak Stilton, duck à l'orange, roast venison and vegetarian dishes such as aubergine au gratin.

Beer: Courage Best Bitter and Directors on handpumps.

Accommodation: 5 singles, 11 doubles/twins. B&B from £25 per person. Children welcome, no reductions. Half Board Weekend Breaks: 2 nights £60, 3 nights £90 per person sharing twin or double room.

## BISHOP'S CASTLE

Castle Hotel
Market Square off A488 & A489

Licensee: Michael Cullen
Tel: 0588 638403

The Castle is in the centre of this small, bustling Shropshire town. The bars are cheerful and welcoming, and the pub grub is excellent and includes dishes for vegetarians. Dogs are welcome, there are baby-minding facilities and fishing is available nearby. Another pub worthy of note in the town is the Three Tuns, a famous home-brew inn with a small tower brewery in the backyard that produces excellent ales. There is a traction engine rally in the town on August Bank Holiday.

Beer: Bass and Springfield Bitter on handpumps.

Accommodation: 5 doubles, 3 twins, 1 room with private bath. B&B £17 single, £29 double, £34 for en suite room.

CRAVEN ARMS, STOKESAY — *see opposite*

## CLUN

Sun Inn
On B4368

Licensees: Keith & Bunny Small
Tel: 058 84 559

'The quietest place under the sun,' said A E Housman of Clun but the small town's history is anything but quiet. It was the scene of protracted battles between Britons and Romans. Later skirmishes with the Welsh forced King Offa to build his dyke to contain them and Clun Castle was built in the 11th century in a further effort to keep back the marauding Welsh. The Sun Inn, dating from the 15th century, is a delightful place to stay and a good base for visiting the Iron Age forts, Offa's Dyke, the medieval saddleback bridge over the river Clun, the castle and the fascinating museum in the town hall. The inn has a wealth of exposed beams, a vast fireplace in the bar, flagstones and settles. The restaurant offers ploughman's, quiche and exotic dishes from around the world based on local produce. There are always vegetarian dishes. Residents have the use of a comfortable lounge with an open fire, beamed ceiling and TV. Accommodation is in the converted old bakery and old stables attached to the inn.

Beer: Banks Mild and Bitter, Davenports Bitter, Woods Special Bitter on handpumps.

Accommodation: 3 en suite doubles, 2 singles, I double, 1 family room. B&B £15 single, £30 double, £35 en suite. Winter Specials: 3 nights £20 per person per night including dinner.

# CRAVEN ARMS

Stokesay Castle Hotel
School Road, off A49

Licensee: Sydney Harris
Tel: 058 82 2304

Craven Arms *is* a town, not a pub. The local is the Stokesay Castle, an imposing small hotel with a friendly, family welcome, good accommodation, excellent food, a large garden and a residents' lounge with TV. Watch out for the unusual beer engine in the lounge bar. The town stages one of Britain's biggest sheep sales in the autumn, while Stokesay Castle, half stone and half timber, is one of the country's finest medieval fortified houses.

Beer: Davenports Mild and Bitter on handpumps.

Accommodation: 2 singles, 7 doubles, 2 family rooms. B&B from £9.50 per person. Half and full board available. Children welcome, £5 a night if sharing with parents.

# FRANKWELL

Swan Inn
On A458

Proprietors: Don & Shirley Reynolds
Tel: 0743 64923

The Swan is a small, cheery and comfortable inn in one of the oldest suburbs of Shrewsbury. There is excellent food in the inn's sea food restaurant, Neptunes. Close by is the impressive Fellmongers Hall, built in 1580, while Charles Darwin's birthplace is just a short walk away. A few minutes' stroll over the Welsh Bridge brings you into the heart of Shrewsbury with its wealth of half-timbered 16th century houses and the later Georgian and Queen Anne architecture. Shrewsbury Castle

guards the loop in the River Severn and the famous annual flower show is held in Quarry Park.

Beer: Ansells Mild and Bitter, Burton Ale, Marston Pedigree, Wadworth 6X on handpumps.

Accommodation: 1 double, 1 twin. B&B £15 single, £24 double.

# LUDLOW

Church Inn
Buttercross, off A49

Licensee: J M Hargreaves
Tel: 0584 2174

An extensively modernised inn, with a pleasantly painted pastel exterior, Church is the fifth name it has had in 500 years. There is a comfortable lounge bar and a separate restaurant. Bar food includes soup, stuffed mushrooms, steak and beer pie, trout, plaice and mackerel, fisherman's pancake and home-made sweets. The restaurant menu offers melon and port, salmon steak, duckling, prawn and melon salad, pork, and trout and grapefruit. The inn is close to the medieval castle where the unfortunate princes stayed before leaving for London to die at the hands of either Henry Tudor or Richard Plantagenet, depending on which conspiracy theory you prefer. Nearby is the parish church of St Laurence, burial place of the Shropshire poet, A E Housman.

Beer: Marston Burton Bitter and Pedigree, McEwan 80 shilling, Robinson Best Bitter, Wadworth 6X on handpumps.

Accommodation: 9 doubles, all en suite, with TVs and tea and coffee making facilities. B&B £20 single, £30 double. Children welcome. Credit cards: Visa.

# MARKET DRAYTON

Corbet Arms Hotel
High Street, off A53

Proprietors: John & Cynthia Beckett
Tel: 0630 2037/2961

The Corbet Arms is a creeper-clad, 16th-century coaching inn in the centre of the fine old Shropshire market town, mentioned in the Domesday Book and scene of a major battle in the Wars of the Roses. Present-day attractions include a safari park, the Shropshire Union canal, fishing and horse riding. The hotel has a separate restaurant that seats 50 and can arrange for vegetarian dishes. There are also bar snacks, a cold buffet and a 'friendly' lady ghost. The guest rooms all have colour TVs and tea and coffee making facilities.

Beer: Springfield Bitter on electric pump.

Accommodation: 12 rooms, 10 with private baths. B&B £23 single, £25 double let as single, £36 double, £45 family room. Winter Weekend: £42 single, £46 double let as single, £64 double, £80 family room for 2 nights. Credit cards: Access, Amex, Diners, Visa.

# AXBRIDGE

Lamb Inn
The Square, on A371, off A37

Licensees: Max & Jenny Wiggington
Tel: 0934 732253

The Lamb is a fascinating 18th-century coaching inn that has previously been named both the Holy Lamb and the Lamb and Flag. The Wiggingtons specialise in good plain cooking, a sensible range of ale and comfortable accommodation in rooms with TVs and tea and coffee making facilities. The inn stands in the square famous for St John's hunting lodge and Axbridge church. The handsome old town nestles on the southern slopes of the Mendips and is close to both Cheddar and its gorge and Wells with its magnificent cathedral.

Beer: Butcombe Bitter, Flowers Original, Fuller London Pride on handpumps.

Accommodation: 2 doubles, 1 family room. B&B £12-£16. 10% reduction for week's stay. Children's room; children welcome to stay half price. Full board available.

# BATCOMBE

Three Horse Shoes
1½ miles off A359

Licensees: Kim & Ann Argent
Tel: 074 985 359

The Three Horse Shoes is a 600-year-old coaching inn in lovely countryside overlooking the Somerset Levels. The Argents specialise in home cooking, with food available in the bar or separate dining room. It is a genuine locals' pub and you may be challenged to play darts, shove ha'penny or pool. The pub has a resident ghost named

George and is close to such attractions as Cheddar, Wookey Hole, Glastonbury Tor and Stourhead.

Beer: Wiltshire Stonehenge and Red Devil on handpumps.

Accommodation: 1 single, 2 doubles, 1 family room. B&B £11 single, £20 double, £22 family room. Children welcome, no reductions.

# BURNHAM-ON-SEA

Royal Clarence Hotel
31 Esplanade, 3 miles off M5 exit 22

Licensee: Paul Davey
Tel: 0278 783138

The Clarence is an old coaching inn with facilities that range from a skittles alley to a Regency suite. It has fine views over the beaches and sea and it boasts its own miniature brewery where Clarence Bitter is brewed. There are good bar meals while the elegant restaurant offers sole, rainbow trout, pork Normande in cream and cider, duck, carbonade of beef and a daily vegetarian dish.

Beer: Butcombe Bitter, Clarence Bitter, Wadworth 6X and guest beers on handpumps.

Accommodation: 3 singles, 10 doubles, 2 family rooms, 9 rooms with private baths. B&B £19 single, £35 double. Half and full board available. Children welcome, half price under 11.

# CASTLE CARY

White Hart
Fore Street, 6 miles from A303 at Wincanton

Licensee: Charles Anderson
Tel: 0963 50255

The White Hart is a coaching inn that dates back to the 17th century, with local Cary stone in the servery and the fireplace. The main bar has an old wooden block floor and there is a strong emphasis on traditional pub games, including skittles, darts, bar billiards, table skittles and shove ha'penny. Bar food includes sandwiches, home-cooked ham, burgers, steak and kidney pie, pork with onion and chives, omelettes, cod, plaice and scampi with chips and peas, ploughman's, and tuna salad, plus home-made apple pie and ice cream.

Beer: Courage Best Bitter and Directors on handpumps.

Accommodation: 3 doubles. B&B £10 per person. Half board available. Weekend £20, Week £63. Off-season Weekend £19. No children.

# EMBOROUGH

Old Down Inn
At crossroads of A37 & B3139

Proprietors: Penny & Gordon Marshall
Tel: 0761 232 398

The Old Down is a 17th-century posting house on the old Bath to Wells coach route. It had considerable importance in the great mail coach era and was accredited as a 'post town', the equivalent of a modern post office, with its own post mark. It handled the mail from the packet port of Falmouth in Cornwall as well as the inland post.

When Bradshaw's first railway guide was published, the Old Down had the distinction of being the only inn listed in the entire country. The inn today has two comfortable bars and a dining room, a children's and a games room and a residents' swimming pool in summer. There is a camping and caravan site opposite. Bar food includes sandwiches, ploughman's, bubble & squeak, steaks and home-made shepherd's pie.

Beer: Bass, Oakhill Farmer's Ale on handpump and straight from the cask, plus guest beers.

Accommodation: 3 doubles, 1 family room, 3 rooms with private showers. B&B + evening meal £10. Full board available. Children welcome, half price under 5.

## EXFORD

White Horse Hotel
Near Minehead, on B3224

Licensee: Mrs D S Lee
Tel: 064 383 229

A welcoming outpost in the middle of Exmoor where moorland folk descend to meet, talk, drink and eat. The pub and hotel, with some half-timbered upper storeys, has two children's rooms, a candlelit dining room and a Dalesman Bar full of local pictures. Bar food ranges from soup and shepherd's pie to sirloin steaks. The full pleasures of Exmoor — riding, fishing, walking and bird-watching — are on the doorstep. As well as the hotel accommodation (all with private baths, TVs and tea and coffee making facilities), self-catering is available in a cottage and flat attached to the hotel.

Beer: Bass, Golden Hill Exmoor Ale straight from the casks.

Accommodation: 1 single, 7 doubles. B&B £20 per person. Children welcome.

## FROME

Sun Inn
6 Catherine Street, off A361

Licensees: D J Hands & P H Foster
Tel: 0373 73123

Not so much a pub, more a permanent beer festival with seven real ales always available. The Sun is an old coaching inn and listed building with a vast and impressive fireplace dominating the building. There is excellent pub grub every day and a restaurant menu with a daily roast. The guest rooms all have colour TVs and Messrs Hands and Foster supply friendly ghosts at no extra charge. Frome is four miles from Longleat.

Beer: (from) Arkell BBB, Burton Ale, Butcombe Bitter, Gibbs Mew Bishop's Tipple, Hall & Woodhouse Tanglefoot, Halls Harvest Bitter, Marston Pedigree, Merrie Monk and Owd Rodger, Miner's Arms Own Ale, Oakhill Farmers Ale, Smile's Best Bitter and guest beers, all on handpumps.

Accommodation: 5 doubles, 2 family rooms. B&B £16.50 single, £9.75 per person in double room. Weekend £19.50, Week £68.25. Off-season Weekend £18 per person. Children welcome, 20% reductions.

# KEINTON MANDEVILLE

Quarry Inn
High Street, B3153 between
Lydford & Somerton

Licensees: Barry & Becky Goddard
Tel: 045 822 3367

This handsome, creeper-clad inn was
originally the house of the quarry
master from the local mine. When
times were hard he paid his
labourers with cider. In the 19th
century, the house was licensed and
became a hotel. It is now a free
house with a skittles alley and beer
garden. A full menu and bar snacks
are available seven days a week and
the Goddards have added a new
25-seat dining room. The inn is just
a few miles from Glastonbury,
Shepton Mallet and Yeovil.

Beer: Oakhill Farmers Ale, Ushers
Best Bitter, Wadworth 6X on
handpumps.

Accommodation: 3 doubles. B&B
£12 per person, £20 double.
Reductions for weekly bookings.

SHIP INN, PORLOCK — *see p 122*

# LUXBOROUGH

Royal Oak
Minor road off A39 at Washford;
at Luxborough turn right over
bridge OS SS 984377

Licensee: Robin Stamp
Tel: 0984 40319

A rural pub of great charm and
antiquity in Exmoor national park.
The inn, known locally as the
Blazing Stump, dates back to the
15th century and has stone-flagged
and cobbled floors, inglenook
fireplaces and a wealth of ancient
beams. There are three bar areas and
a charming garden. Quiz night is
Tuesday and music night Friday.
Fresh local produce is used for both
bar snacks and in the dining room.
Mr Stamp claims that 'when you
walk through the door you will
think you have stepped back two
centuries and you won't have
changed your mind when you leave'.
Except for the prices, but even they
are extremely reasonable by 20th-
century standards.

Beer: Eldridge Pope Dorset IPA,
Flowers Original and IPA, Golden
Hill Exmoor Ale on handpumps
plus local scrumpy cider.

Accommodation: 4 doubles. B&B
£10 per person. Weekend £18 for 2
days. Week £60. Off-season
Weekend £16 for 2 nights. Children
welcome.

## MIDDLEZOY

George Inn
Main Road, ¼ mile off A372
between Bridgwater & Langport

Licensees: Keith & Maureen
Waites
Tel: 082 369 215

The George is a 17th-century inn in a fascinating village on the Somerset Levels. The Wiltshire militia lodged here during the battle of Sedgemoor in 1685 and it was used by 'Hanging Judge' Jeffries during the subsequent trials. The inn today specialises in good home-made food, including some authentic Indian dishes. It stages twice-yearly real ale festivals.

Beer: Butcombe Bitter, Cotleigh Tawny Bitter, Oakhill Farmers Ale and twice-weekly guest beers, all on handpumps.

Accommodation: 2 doubles. B&B £11.50 per person.

## PORLOCK

Ship Inn
High Street, A39 (bottom of Porlock Hill)

Licensees: Mark & Judy Robinson
Tel: 0643 862 507

The Ship is a splendid place to stay and useful for drivers when their vehicles refuse to go up the dreaded hill, one of the steepest in England. The delightfully rambling thatched inn dates back to the 13th century and offers good food in the bar and dining room, a skittles alley and a beer garden with wonderful views of the surrounding Quantock and Brendon hills and the sea. The guest rooms have central heating, TVs and tea making facilities.

Beer: Bass, Cotleigh Tawny Bitter, Courage Best Bitter on handpumps.

Accommodation: 7 doubles, 4 family rooms, 5 rooms with en suite bathrooms. B&B from £13.50 per person. Children welcome, half price under 12 when sharing with parents. Dogs allowed.

## PRIDDY

New Inn
Priddy Green, 3 miles W of A39
Bristol to Wells road

Licensees: Anne & Doug Weston
Tel: 0749 76465

The inn was originally a 15th-century farmhouse owned by local alehouse keepers who moved their business to the present building to meet the demands of the bibulous lead miners in the area. The tavern remained largely unchanged until the 1970s when a lounge was added from the existing outhouses, the bar replaced an old staircase and a skittles alley and guest rooms were developed. The Westons concentrate on good food and ale. Bar meals include jacket potatoes with a wide choice of fillings, omelettes, home-made vegetarian dishes — chilli casserole, golden rissotto, Indian spiced beans — pasties, sausages, plaice, trout and grills. Priddy, surrounded by beautiful countryside, is an ideal base for walking, seeing local country crafts of cheese and cider making, and visiting Wells and its cathedral.

Beer: Eldridge Pope Royal Oak, Marston Pedigree, Wadworth 6X on handpumps.

Accommodation: 3 doubles, 2 twins, 1 family room. B&B £12.50 for 1 using double or twin, £20 double. Children welcome, 10% reduction under 9 years.

# SHEPTON MALLET

Kings Arms
Leg Square, off A37

Licensee: Peter Swan
Tel: 0749 3781

The Kings Arms, a pub of great charm that covers three sides of a courtyard, was built in 1660 and has been a pub since 1680. Today it has a main bar, a heritage bar, a skittles alley and a residents' lounge. The patio is a popular drinking spot in the summer.

Beer: Burton Ale, Halls Harvest Bitter, Wadworth 6X on handpumps.

Accommodation: 3 doubles. B&B £15.50 single, £26.50 double. Full and half board available. 10% discount for CAMRA members. No children.

# STOGUMBER

White Horse Inn
2 miles off A358, 4 miles S of Williton

Licensee: Peter Williamson
Tel: 0984 56277

The White Horse is a small, white-painted inn opposite a 12th-century church in a delightful conservation village near the Quantocks and Brendon Hills. The main bar has red tiles on the floor, a coal fire in winter and old settles. Skittles, darts, dominoes and shove ha'penny are played in a separate room. Bar food (lunchtime and evening) includes steak and kidney pudding, liver and bacon casserole, Somerset pork and walnut or treacle tart. The separate restaurant is the village's old market house now joined to the inn, with the village 'reading room' on the top

floor. There is a pleasant garden for sunny-weather eating and drinking.

Beer: Cotleigh Tawny Bitter, Golden Hill Exmoor Ale on handpumps.

Accommodation: 1 double, 1 family room, both with en suite facilities. B&B £18.50 single, £28 double. Week £85 per person. Half and full board available. Children welcome, terms according to age. Credit cards: Access.

# TAUNTON

Masons Arms
Magdalene Street, town centre, off M5 exit 25

Licensee: J J Leyton
Tel: 0823 288916

The elegant, three-storey building stands in the shadow of the superb St Mary Magdalene church and in an area of considerable historical interest. At the turn of the 19th century, the present broad street was a squalid alley called Blackboy Lane named after an inn whose landlord was accused of murdering a soldier and throwing his body into the River Tone. Because cursing and swearing often drowned the singing in the church, the authorities cleared this 'sink of iniquity' in 1864

OLD DOWN INN, EMBOROUGH — *see p 119*

and turned the hovels and tenements into Magdalene Street. The Masons Arms was formerly the house of the local rent collector and became a beer house in 1855. Today it offers a good selection of bar meals as well as fine ale: a wide range of salads, turkey pie, savoury flans, Cornish pasties, steak and kidney pie, curry and jacket potatoes. There is a traditional skittles alley. Accommodation is in a self-catering flat with colour TV, kitchen and bathroom.

Beer: Bass, Golden Hill Exmoor Ale and Exmoor Dark, Wadworth 6X and guest beers in winter, all on handpumps.

Accommodation: Self-service flat with 1 twin and 1 single room. £15 per person for 1 or 2 nights, discounts for longer stays. Children 10 and over welcome.

# WEST PENNARD

Red Lion
Newtown, A361

Licensees: Caroline & Bryan Channing
Tel: 0458 32941

The Red Lion, just three miles from Glastonbury, was built in 1678, probably as a farmhouse and retains much of its old charm with flagstone floors, low beams and log fires in

winter. Snacks and full meals are available lunchtime and evening. Accommodation is in a converted old barn and all the luxurious, carpeted rooms have private baths, colour TVs, central heating, direct dial telephones, and tea and coffee making facilities. The Red Lion is a good centre for walking and visiting Glastonbury Abbey, Wookey Hole, Cheddar, Bath, Longleat, the East Somerset steam railway and three of the new breed of English wine makers at Wooton, Pilton Manor and Coxley.

Beer: Bass, Butcombe Bitter and a house brew Red Lion Best Bitter on handpumps.

Accommodation: 6 doubles/twins, 1 family room. B&B from £18.50 per person. Weekend £50 including dinner. Week from £111. Children's room; children welcome to stay, 40% reduction.

# WILLITON

Foresters Arms
Long Street, on A39 Bridgwater to Minehead road

Licensees: Reg & Pauline Human
Tel: 0984 32508

The Foresters is a 17th-century building, though some parts may be considerably older. Its first name as a licensed house was the Lamb but this was changed to the Railway Hotel with the arrival of steam — the West Somerset railway is just five minutes away. It was renamed the Foresters Arms in 1984. Mr and Mrs Human have devoted themselves to extending the quality of the welcome, the food, the ale and the accommodation. There is a children's room and the spacious gardens have ornamental pools and patios. There is a fine range of lunchtime bar meals. A Sunday roast lunch and evening grills are served in a restaurant seating 20. There is a lady ghost seen twice by Mrs Human. Williton is well placed for touring the Quantocks and visiting the picturesque town of Watchet.

Beer: Bass, Cotleigh Tawny Bitter and weekly guest beer on handpumps.

Accommodation: 1 twin, 3 doubles, 1 family room, all with colour TVs and tea and coffee making equipment. B&B £10.50 per person: all rooms available as single according to demand. Half and full board available. Children welcome, no charge for babies, £8.50 under 12. Facilities for the disabled in pub and restaurant only. Credit cards: Access, Visa.

# WINSFORD

## Royal Oak Inn
Exmoor National Park, off A396 near Minehead

Licensees: Sheila & Charles Steven
Tel: 064 385 455

The Royal Oak is a stunning, 12th-century thatched inn in the heart of Exmoor. For many years it doubled as a farm as well as a licensed house. Members of the wool trade operated

THREE HORSE SHOES, BATCOMBE

— see p 118

from the inn, working with both local wool and Irish yarn. Tom Faggus, a 17th-century highwayman and *Lorna Doone* character, lived near the village. The inn today has cheery bars, a welcoming open fire, bar meals and an à la carte restaurant.

Beer: Flowers Original and IPA on handpumps.

Accommodation: 1 suite, 5 doubles, 2 twins in the inn, 5 doubles in adjacent cottage. B&B from £40 single, £50 double. Children welcome, charged only for meals if sharing parents' room. Details of off-season breaks on application. Dogs allowed in cottage only.

# STAFFORDSHIRE

# ABBOTS BROMLEY

## Coach & Horses
High Street, B5014 near Rugeley

Licensees: Bob & Shirley Haywood
Tel: 0283 840256

The Coach and Horses is an attractive 16th-century inn with a comfortable lounge and a bar with inglenook fireplaces where dominoes, darts and bar billiards are played. There is a residents' dining room, large car park and beer garden. Bar meals, from £1.50 to £4, are served every lunchtime. The guest rooms all have colour TVs and tea and coffee making facilities. The inn has a resident ghost and is a good base for visiting Alton Towers and Cannock Chase.

Beer: Burton Ale on handpumps.

Accommodation: 3 twins. B&B from £9 per person.

# BURTON UPON TRENT

Station Hotel
Borough Road, next to railway station

Licensee: Geoff Morley
Tel: 0283 64955

A cheerful, unpretentious pub five minutes' walk from the town centre with one lounge bar adorned with railway memorabilia. Bar food is served every lunchtime. The bedrooms have tea and coffee making facilities. Burton is the historic centre of the British beer industry, its roots going back to monastic brewing. Bass, Allied's Ind Coope, Marston and Burton Bridge brew in the town and both the Bass Museum and the Heritage Brewery Museum in the former Everard's plant have fascinating displays of the industry ancient and modern.

Beer: Ind Coope Bitter and Burton Ale on handpumps.

Accommodation: 1 single, 3 doubles, 2 family rooms. B&B £15 per person.

# BUTTERTON

Black Lion
Near Cauldon, on B5053, off A53

Licensees: Ron & Derek Smith
Tel: 053 88 232

The Black Lion is a characterful, stone-built 18th-century rural pub with several rooms off the main bar. Furnishings range from pretty sofas to settles and bar stools with back rests. There are beams, open fires, a kitchen range and a carefully restored dining room. Excellent bar food includes ploughman's, sandwiches, steak and kidney pie, lasagne and daily specials. Games to play include darts, dominoes and shove ha'penny. A pleasant terrace has tables and chairs for use in warmer weather and fine views of the hamlet of Butterton close to Dovedale and the Manifold Valley. Close at hand is the remarkable Yew Tree at Cauldon, a rambling old inn packed with grandfather clocks and a collection of working Victorian music boxes, including polyphons and symphonions. At the Black Lion, there is a residents' TV lounge while the guest rooms all have en suite facilities and tea and coffee making equipment.

Beer: McEwan 70 shilling and Younger No 3 on handpumps.

Accommodation: 2 doubles, 1 family room. B&B £13.80 single, £25.30 double.

# HULME END

Manifold Valley Hotel
Off A515 & B5054

Proprietors: John Todhunter & John Milner
Tel: 029 884 537

A delightful old village inn in a hamlet in the north Staffordshire Peak District close to the lovely Manifold Valley and the tourist centre of Hartington. The inn has one cheerful bar with an open fire, and a separate restaurant, with food served lunchtime and evening. The two large guest rooms both have private showers, colour TVs and tea and coffee making facilities. Both rooms have two sofas that convert into beds suitable for children under ten years. There is also a separate residents' lounge. Camping facilities are close by. The inn's beer range is unusual for the area.

Beer: Darley Dark Mild and Ward Sheffield Best Bitter on handpumps with occasional guest beers.

Accommodation: 2 doubles. B&B from £25 per person. No dogs.

# UTTOXETER

Roebuck Inn
37 Dovebank, A518, off A50

Licensee: Jane Hastain
Tel: 088 93 5563

A famous old unspoilt pub with roaring fires in the bar and quarry-tiled floors. Meals are cooked to order and Mrs Hastain concentrates on using fresh local produce. There are meals and snacks every lunchtime and evening. The guest rooms have colour TVs and tea and coffee making facilities. The Roebuck is distinguished not only by its handsome features but also by

the visits of a local medium and clairvoyant who considers the inn to be a fascinating place for ghostly hauntings. The inn is a good centre for visiting Alton Towers, the Potteries and Tutbury castle and glassworks.

Beer: Burton Bridge Bitter, Porter and Old Expensive, Marston Pedigree, John Smiths Bitter and a weekly guest beer on handpumps and straight from the cask.

Accommodation: 1 single, 1 twin, 2 doubles, 1 with en suite facilities. B&B £12.50 per person. £3 supplement for en suite room.

# SUFFOLK

# ALDEBURGH

Mill Inn
Market Cross Place, A1094, off A12

Licensee: Brian Horrell
Tel: 072 885 2563

The Mill is an attractive old pub close to the sea front of this famous old Suffolk resort with its powerful Benjamin Britten associations. Snape Maltings concert hall, founded by the composer, is just outside the town and *Peter Grimes* is based on a story about this part of the Suffolk coast. The inn has a public bar that attracts both local fishermen and the gentry while the lounge is small, cosy and sedate. There are lunchtime and evening grills (not Wednesday or Sunday evening). The guest rooms have TVs and tea and coffee making facilities. Booking is advisable for summer and the Aldeburgh Festival.

Beer: Adnams Bitter and Old (winter) on handpumps.

Accommodation: 1 single, 2 doubles, 1 twin. B&B £11.50 single, £22 double. Children 14 and over are welcome, no reductions.

# BRANDESTON

Queens Head
2 miles off B1120 at Earl Soham

Licensees: Ray & Myra Bumstead
Tel: 072 882 307

A welcoming rural pub with one opened-out bar with banquettes and old pews to sit on and coal fires in the winter. The Bumsteads concentrate on home-cooked food and bar meals offer ploughman's, sandwiches, steak and kidney pie, lasagne and salads. Crib, darts, dominoes, shove ha'penny and bar skittles are played. Children are well catered for in a family room and a play area in the large garden, which also provides tables for summer drinking and eating.

Beer: Adnams Mild, Bitter, Extra (summer), Old (winter) and Tally Ho (Xmas) on handpumps.

Accommodation: 3 doubles (let as singles if demand allows). B&B £10 per person. Children welcome, terms according to age.

# CAVENDISH

George Inn
The Green, A1092

Licensees: Mike & Jill Vincent
Tel: 0708 280248

The George is a 15th-century village pub overlooking the green in Cavendish. It has a tall, imposing chimney and a handsome, bow-windowed frontage. It has a cosy public bar and a spacious lounge and excellent food is available both lunchtime and evening. This is Constable Country and the pub is a splendid base for visiting Flatford and Dedham. Closer to Cavendish are a vineyard, a working priory and the Sue Ryder Foundation headquarters.

Beer: Ruddles County, Websters Yorkshire Bitter on handpumps.

Accommodation: 2 doubles, 1 twin, 1 room with shower. B&B £11 per person. Half and full board available. Children over 5 welcome, terms by arrangement.

# CHELSWORTH

Peacock Inn
The Street, B1115

Licensees: Lorna & Tony Marsh
Tel: 0449 740758

The Peacock is a polished country pub ten miles from the nearest market town of Sudbury and five miles from Lavenham, one of the finest examples of a preserved medieval town in England. The inn is opposite a tiny bridge over the narrow River Brett. It has five small guest rooms, most with exposed beams. The horseshoe bar divides into a stand-and-chat bar, a snug with a blazing open fire and a smart lounge with a permanent art gallery.

There is an extensive menu of home-made food, including roast beef cooked over a log fire on Sundays. The saloon has a piano and there is live music, usually jazz, on Fridays.

Beer: Adnams Bitter and Old (winter), Greene King IPA and Abbot Ale, Mauldon Bitter on handpumps.

Accommodation: 1 single, 3 doubles, 1 twin. B&B £16 per person. children by special arrangement only.

# CLARE

Bell Hotel
Market Hill, off B1092

Licensee: Brian Miles
Tel: 0787 277741

The Bell is an imposing, 16th-century posting house with a half-timbered façade, a panelled and beamed bar with an open fire, and wine bar hung with hunting prints. The splendid accommodation is furnished with period furniture and includes a four-poster bedroom. Bar food, seven days a week, includes soup, ploughman's, toasties, home-made lasagne and grills. There is a separate restaurant too. Summer barbecues are held in good weather on the terrace at the back. Clare has the remains of a castle and priory.

Beer: Adnams Bitter, Mauldon Bitter, Nethergate Bitter, Ruddles County on handpumps.

Accommodation: 18 doubles, 2 family rooms, 15 rooms with en suite facilities. B&B from £25 per person. Weekend £36.50. Children welcome, no reductions. Dogs by arrangement, £1 per night. Credit cards: Access, Amex, Diners, Visa.

# DUNWICH

Ship Inn
St James Street, 2 miles off B1125

Licensees: Stephen & Annie Marshlain
Tel: 072 873 219

The nautical bar of the Ship is, rather suitably, slightly sunken, for the village of Old Dunwich lies beneath the North Sea and the church bells can be heard tolling at night before a storm — or so legend, embellished by a few pints, claims. The bar of the Ship has a tiled floor, wood-burning stove and captain's chairs. Home-made bar food includes soup, locally caught fish with chips, cottage pie, salads, ploughman's and various puddings. The separate restaurant (open for lunch and dinner) has home-made boozy pâté, fish dish of the day, turkey Waldorf, battered mushrooms, ice creams and sorbets. There is a pleasant garden, terrace and conservatory, ideal for families. Children are allowed inside when the dining room is not in use.

Beer: Adnams Bitter and Old (winter), Greene King Abbot Ale on handpumps.

Accommodation: 1 single, 2 doubles, 1 twin, 1 family room. B&B £15 per person. Children welcome, terms negotiable.

# FLEMPTON

Greyhound
Off A1101, near Bury St Edmunds

Licensee: Anna Baggaley
Tel: 028 484 400

A large, lively and rambling local overlooking the green in this old Saxon village with its ancient forge. The Greyhound, which is featured on the pub weather vane, has a heavily windowed exterior and a charming, unspoilt interior with welcoming open fires. There is bar food lunchtime and evening and a walled garden for the summer months. The pub is a good base for visiting the village, the local abbey gardens and historic Bury St Edmunds, home of Greene King the brewers.

Beer: Greene King XX Mild, IPA and Abbot Ale on handpumps.

Accommodation: 2 singles, 2 doubles, 1 family room. B&B £9 per person. Week £60. Half board available. Children over 10 welcome, rates negotiable.

# GREAT GLEMHAM

Crown
2 miles off A12

Licensees: Mick & Sheila Berry
Tel: 072 878 693

The Crown is a wonderfully welcoming pub with a massive, dominating fireplace that provides heat from both logs and a wood-burning stove. The comfortable lounge has captain's chairs round kitchen tables and there are local paintings decorating the white walls. There are seats on the lawn in spring and summer and inside locals play darts, dominoes and crib. Bar food includes soup, ploughman's, omelettes, chilli with garlic bread, salads, steaks and curries. Families can use the dining room at lunchtimes during the week.

Beer: Adnams Bitter and Old (winter), Greene King IPA and Abbot Ale, Mauldon Bitter on handpumps.

Accommodation: 1 single with shower, 1 double, 1 family room, both with en suite bathrooms. B&B £15-£18 single, £25-£29 double. Children free in family room, charged £3 for breakfast.

GEORGE INN, CAVENDISH — *see p 128*

# IPSWICH

**Station Hotel**
Burrell Road, off A12 & A45

Tel: 0473 602664

Tolly Cobold, the local brewers, have dug deep to modernise and improve the hotel that stands immediately opposite the entrance to Ipswich railway station. The lounge and bar have been updated to offer warm and comfortable surroundings and a new brasserie is open for food all day every day, not just during 'permitted' hours. The pleasant guest rooms have colour TVs and tea and coffee making facilities. The hotel is a good base for visiting the town with its Anglo-Saxon origins and charming, old Dutch-style town hall. You have to persevere though, walking from the hotel past the football ground and through the garish new shopping complex to get to old Ipswich.

Beer: Tolly Cobold Mild, Bitter, Original, XXXX and Old Strong (winter) on handpumps.

Accommodation: 4 singles, 2 doubles, 5 twins, 1 room with en suite bathroom, most with showers. B&B £22 single, £27 with shower, £33 twin/double, £36.50 en suite. Children welcome, no reductions. Credit cards: Access, Visa.

# LONG MELFORD

**Crown Inn**
Hall Street, A134

Licensees: M J & M M Wright
Tel: 0787 77666

An historic inn, with a striking black-and-white façade embellished with hanging baskets, dating from 1610. It is a listed building and retains its Tudor cellars, exposed beams and a log fire. A stained glass panel in the lounge showing a scene from Shakespeare's *A Midsummer Night's Dream* is thought to be of great value. The Riot Act was last read in England in 1885 from the steps of the Crown when Liberal voters from nearby Glemsford clashed with Tory voters at Melford's polling station. Long Melford and the Crown are more peaceful places these days. The town boasts the longest village street in England and has no less than 30 antique shops. The Crown has bar meals and a 35-seater restaurant. Local produce is used in the cooking which ranges from roasts to vegetarian dishes. The delightful accommodation includes a four-poster bedroom.

Beer: Adnams Bitter, Greene King IPA, Mauldon Bitter, Nethergate Bitter, Tetley Bitter on handpumps.

Accommodationa: 2 singles, 9 doubles, 2 family rooms, 7 rooms with private baths. B&B £20-£25 single. Double £15-£17.50 per person, four-poster en suite £21 per person. Bargain Winter Breaks: single £47.25-£50.50 for 2 nights, double £42-£44 per person, including £6.50 dinner allowance. Credit cards: Access, Amex, Diners, Visa.

# ORFORD

Jolly Sailor
Quay Street, B1084, off A12, 12
miles from Woodbridge

Licensee: Patrick Buckner
Tel: 0394 450 243

The sea has receded from Orford
but has left this merry matelot
behind as a reminder of the town's
nautical days. Parts of the 16th-
century inn are built from the
timbers of old shipwrecked vessels.
Beer and food come from a central
hatch that serves the bar, lounge and
snug. Darts, dominoes, crib and
shove ha'penny are played by locals.
The bar is warmed by an old-
fashioned stove, there is a spiral
staircase and a collection of stuffed
miniature dogs thought to come
from Tudor times. There is also a
children's room. Bar food includes
hot daily specials, seafood platter,
ploughman's, steaks, sausages and
salads.

Beer: Adnams Bitter and Old
(winter) on handpumps.

Accommodation: 1 single, 3 doubles.
B&B £12 per person. Children
welcome, reductions if sharing with
parents.

# SOUTHWOLD

Crown Hotel
90 High Street, off A12

Manager: Stephen Bournes
Tel: 0502 722275

The green and cream Georgian hotel
announces Adnams' dominant
position in the town. The carefully
extended brewery lies behind the
Crown, which doubles as small
town hotel-cum-pub and, upstairs,
the brewery's fast-expanding and
much-praised wine business. The
food is outstanding and, like the
accommodation, is surprisingly
reasonably priced. Bar food includes
broccoli soup, warm fish flan, baked
cod with pesto sauce, marrow with
chèvre and pine nuts, sorbets and
apple crumble. Restaurant meals
(lunch and dinner £9-£13 per person)
are accompanied by recommended
glasses of wine for each course. The
wines are kept under nitrogen
pressure in a Cruover machine: the
only permitted form of gas pressure
in this guide. On Sunday mornings
there is a rolling brunch with Bucks
fizz and generous helpings of food,
including local kippers. The Crown
holds regular wine appreciation
weekends: details and prices from
Mr Bournes. You will not need a
course to appreciate the ale, though.

Beer: Adnams Bitter, Extra and Old
(winter) on handpumps.

Accommodation: 2 singles, 9
doubles, 1 family room, 9 rooms en
suite. B&B £22 single, £35 double,
£55 family room. Children welcome,
half price plus food. Dogs by prior
arrangement. Credit cards: Access,
Amex, Visa.

# SOUTHWOLD

Red Lion
2 South Green

Licensee: Alan Coleman
Tel: 0502 722385

The Red Lion has one of the best positions in this delightful Victorian seaside town whose origins date back to the 15th century, when it was granted a charter by Henry VII. The famous battle of Sole Bay was fought here in 1672 between the combined English and French fleets against the Dutch. The pub, with its striking figure of a red lion, welcomes you to the wide expanse of South Green, just a few yards from the sea and the wide shingle beach. Inside there is one long panelled bar with bench seats running round the walls below the windows. Fascinating old photos show Southwold as it was before the Victorians discovered the place. To the left of the bar is a large, comfortable family room, to the right a pleasant dining room with buffet lunches based on locally caught crabs and fish. Hot food is served in the evening and Mrs Coleman is renowned for her generous traditional breakfasts.

Beer: Adnams Bitter, Extra (summer) and Old (winter) on handpumps.

Accommodation: 3 doubles. B&B £13.50 per person. Off-season Weekend: £20 for 2 nights, £30 for 3. Children welcome, 25% reductions.

# STOKE BY NAYLAND

Angel Inn
On B1068, 5 miles off A12

Licensee: P G Smith
Tel: 0206 263245/6

The Angel is a 16th-century inn in Constable country on the Essex border in the heart of Dedham Vale. The village was much loved by the painter who immortalised its cottages and river banks on canvas. The lively inn has a garden, open fires, pub games and excellent bar food lunchtime and evening. There is a separate restaurant for evening meals. The guest rooms all have en suite facilities, colour TVs and tea and coffee makers.

Beer: Adnams Bitter, Greene King IPA and Abbot Ale, Mauldon Bitter, Nethergate Bitter on handpumps.

Accommodation: 6 singles, 6 doubles, 1 family room. B&B £30 single, £18.50 per person in double room. Children welcome, no reductions. Credit cards: Access, Amex, Diners, Visa.

# WALBERSWICK

Bell Hotel
B1387, off A12. Go right through village to green, turn right for pub

Licensees: M L & F A Stansall
Tel: 0502 723109

A wonderfully unspoilt old fishermen's inn in a village that has no truck with such modern refinements as pavements or street lighting. The Bell is 600 years old and the passage of feet has worn and bowed the old stone floors. There are high-backed settles in the main bar, photos of the village and some of the local characters in a smaller side bar and games of shove ha'penny and crib in another room. There is a vast back garden with hedges, trees and tables, ideal for summer Sundays when crowds descend for Adnams' ale and the Stansalls' buffet lunch of fresh sea food and salads. There is an inside dining room, too, for lunches and dinner. The Bell is a genuine local, to which fishermen stroll up from the mouth of the Blyth for a pint, a chat and general agreement that the pub's 'not a bad shed, boi'. For 6p the ferryman will row you across to the opposite bank from where you can buy fresh fish and crabs or walk into Southwold.

Beer: Adnams Mild, Bitter, Extra and Old (winter) on handpumps.

Accommodation: 1 single, 2 twins, 2 en suite doubles. B&B £16 per person, £18 in en suite room.

# WOOLPIT

Swan Inn
The Street, ½ mile off A45

Licensees: Joseph & Gillian Thompson
Tel: 0359 40482

The Swan is an imposing, 400-year-old red brick coaching inn in the centre of the village with one large L-shaped bar warmed by a log fire in the winter. There are excellent lunchtime bar snacks (not Sundays) and hearty breakfasts. The guest rooms are in an annexe off the main building and they all have colour TVs and tea and coffee making facilities. Cambridge, Norwich and the Suffolk coast are within driving distance and Bury St Edmunds and its gracious Georgian buildings are just down the road. Woolpit has two good restaurants and the best 'chippy' in Suffolk.

Beer: Ruddles County, Websters Yorkshire Bitter on handpumps.

Accommodation: 1 single, 1 twin, 1 double, 1 double/family room en suite. B&B £12-£13.50 per person. Children of all ages welcome at reduced rates.

# BLETCHINGLEY

Whyte Harte
Off A25 & A22, 2½ miles from M25 exit 6

Licensee: Geoff Parsons
Tel: 0883 843231

A 300-year-old inn with low beams, wood floors, an inglenook fireplace with an ominous looking beam, and settles and stools to sit on. The pleasant garden is bounded by a stone wall and old Tudor cottages and there are also seats at the front among the flower tubs. Home-made pub fare includes sandwiches, ploughman's and daily hot specials such as cottage pie, spaghetti bolognaise and plaice, plus vegetarian dishes.

Beer: Friary Meux Best Bitter and Burton Ale plus regular guest beer on handpumps.

Accommodation: B&B from £17 single, £34 double, £4 supplement for private bath.

# DORKING

## Pilgrim
Station Road, off A24, next to
Dorking West railway station

Licensee: A Stappard
Tel: 0306 889951

The Pilgrim is a cheerful old inn
tucked away from the town centre
and offering a traditional pub
alternative to the town's many
pricey hotels. The handsome town
of Dorking is close to the well-
known beauty spots of Leith Hill —
at 1,000 feet the highest place in the
South-east — and Box Hill. The
North Downs run along the
northern edge of the town. The
Pilgrim has a garden and serves bar
food lunchtime and evening.

Beer: Friary Meux Best Bitter and
Burton Ale on handpumps.

Accommodation: 5 doubles, 1 family
room. B&B £15 per person.

# GODSTONE

## Bell
128 High Street, B2236, 1 mile S
of M25 exit 6

Licensee: John Courtney
Tel: 0883 843133

The Bell is a splendid, 600-year-old
coaching inn with a large, beamed
bar warmed by open log fires and
decorated with a wealth of copper
and brass. Bar food is served
lunchtime and evening and there is
also a separate restaurant. Crib,
backgammon, dominoes and shove
ha'penny are played by the locals.
The Bell has a large garden and there
is a children's room equipped with
games. It is close to the village green
and pond and handy for visiting the
North Downs, Penshurst Place and
Hever Castle. Chartwell, with its

Winston Churchill connections, is in
the area. Guest rooms at the Bell
include a four-poster bedroom.

Beer: Friary Meux Best Bitter,
Burton Ale and Tetley Bitter on
handpumps with Benskins Best
Bitter or Taylor Walker Best Bitter
doubling as guest beers.

Accommodation: 3 doubles. B&B
£15-£25 per person.

# GOMSHALL

## Black Horse Inn
On A25

Tel: 048 641 2242

The Black Horse is an imposing,
three-storey building in the centre of
the village, formerly the brewery of
Reffell Brothers that was bought by
Young of Wandsworth in 1926. It
has a small games bar and a large
comfortable lounge with antique
furniture. The inn has a spacious
beer garden and there is a separate
restaurant. Bar food includes
sandwiches and toasties, jacket
potatoes with a choice of fillings,
home-made soup, steak and kidney
pie, local trout, ploughman's with
choice of cheese, and daily specials.
The Black Horse is a good pub for
traditional games and, against intense
competition, has appeared in every
edition of the *Good Beer Guide*.

Beer: Young Bitter, Special Bitter
and Winter Warmer on handpumps.

Accommodation: 1 single, 3 doubles.
B&B £16.20 single.

# HINDHEAD

Devils Punchbowl Hotel
London Road, A3

Licensee: Tony Atkinson
Tel: 042 873 6565

The grand hotel stands 900 feet above sea level with superb views of the Surrey Downs and the famous Devil's Punchbowl beauty spot from which it gets its name. The building was originally the country residence of the Hon Rollo Russell, son of Lord John Russell, the first Liberal Prime Minister. Tony Atkinson has beavered to turn it into a quality inn that retains a genuine pub atmosphere in the busy bar popular with locals. There is a lounge for morning coffee and afternoon tea while Broomsquire's restaurant offers a wide choice of à la carte meals. All the beautifully appointed guest rooms have en suite facilities, colour TVs and tea and coffee making equipment.

Beer: Hall & Woodhouse Badger Best Bitter, King & Barnes Sussex Bitter and Festive Bitter, Tetley Bitter, Wadworth 6X on handpumps.

Accommodation: 8 singles, 30 doubles, 2 family rooms. B&B £40 single, £50 double. Weekend £30 per person per day B&B + evening meal. Children welcome, half price.

# OCKLEY

Kings Arms
Stane Street, A29

Licensee: Mary Doyle
Tel: 0306 711224

The Kings Arms is an attractive old inn on an even older Roman road in a pleasant village with a large green. The hostelry successfully trebles as pub, hotel and restaurant, with good food served both lunchtime and evening and an outdoor drinking area for the warmer months. It is popular with people using Gatwick airport and booking is therefore essential.

Beer: Fuller ESB, Hall & Woodhouse Badger Best Bitter, King & Barnes Sussex Bitter, Pilgrim Progress, John Smiths Bitter and guest beers, all on handpumps.

Accommodation: 6 doubles. B&B £24 per person. Credit cards: Access, Amex, Visa.

# SOUTH CROYDON

Windsor Castle Hotel
415 Brighton Road, A23

Licensees: G R Wenham & P Pollard
Tel: 01 680 4559

It is claimed that there has been a licensed house on this site since 1235, making it possibly the oldest licensed site in Britain. The present pub has a small and extremely old cellar, three bars, including a games bar, and a Toby Grill restaurant seating 60. The service is friendly and informal. The hotel, which is on the London to Brighton road, is handy for Purley Oaks station and is an easy drive to both Gatwick and Heathrow airports.

Beer: Charrington IPA on handpump.

Accommodation: 22 twins, 2 doubles, 6 family rooms all en suite and with colour TVs. Price per room (breakfast extra) £41.50 single weekday, £31.50 weekend, £51.50 double weekday, £41.50 weekend. Children welcome, no charge for small children sleeping in cots. 14 rooms on ground floor. 8 non-smoking rooms.

Accommodation: 3 twins, 3 doubles, 3 with en suite facilities. B&B £32.50 double, £40 en suite. Credit cards: Access, Amex, Diners, Visa.

# ARUNDEL (WEST SUSSEX)

The Swan
High Street

Licensees: Diana & Ken Rowsell
Tel: 0903 882314

The Swan, which boasts a handsome façade, striking red window shades and a high dormer roof, is in the centre of this famous old Sussex town with its imposing castle. The Rowsells continue energetically to improve the facilities of the hotel and plan to upgrade the guest rooms in 1988 and to introduce additional dishes on the menu. The large L-shaped, partly timbered lounge serves good food based on local produce, including home-made soup, ploughman's, quiche and sandwiches. The separate restaurant offers grills, Sussex plaice and trout and a traditional Sunday roast. All the guest rooms have en suite facilities and tea and coffee making equipment.

Beer: Hall & Woodhouse Badger Best Bitter and Tanglefoot, Harvey BB and XXX, King & Barnes Sussex Bitter on handpumps and guest beers.

# ARDINGLY (WEST SUSSEX)

Ardingly Inn
Street Lane, off B2028

Licensees: Robert & Shirley Blatchford
Tel: 0444 892214

A large, village centre pub with a spacious and comfortable lounge and separate restaurant, with meals served lunchtime and evening. Table skittles, dominoes and cribbage are played. The pub has a real fire and a pleasant garden. It is close to Ardingly College, the South of England Showground and the Bluebell Railway at Horsted Keynes. The inn's guest rooms all have tea and coffee making facilities and the bar boasts the largest range of malt whiskies — 104, with ten on order — in the South-east. The excellent breakfasts include black pudding. If you need to ask the way, the village is pronounced 'Arding-lie'.

Beer: Adnams Bitter, Fuller London Pride, Gale HSB, King & Barnes Sussex Bitter, Theakston Best Bitter and regular guest beers on handpumps.

BELL INN, BURWASH — see p 138

Accommodation: 10 doubles. B&B
£35 single, £40 double. Week £250.
Off-season Break: £80 B&B +
evening meal for 2 people, 2 nights.
Children welcome, 2 rooms suitable
for families, £7.50 per child sharing.
Credit cards: Access, Amex, Visa.

# BURWASH (EAST SUSSEX)

Bell Inn
High Street, A265

Licensees: Bruce & Maureen
Townsend
Tel: 0435 882304

The Bell dates back to 1609 and has
exposed beams and a sloping floor.
Ale and wine are mulled on the
open log fire and you can try your
hand at ring the bull, one of the
oldest pub games. The comfortable
lounge has old photos of the area,
which includes Batemans, not a
brewery but the former home of
Rudyard Kipling. Bar food (limited
range on Tuesdays) includes onion
soup, deep fried mushrooms with
garlic dip, ploughman's, cottage pie,
chilli, aubergine and mushroom
lasagne, grilled trout, home-made
steak and kidney pie cooked in
brown ale, and many puds, including
apple pie and cream, and sorbets.

Beer: Harvey BB and XXXX
(winter) on handpumps and a guest
beer.

Accommodation: 1 single, 3 doubles,
1 twin. B&B £15 single, £12.50 per
person in double room. Children
welcome, terms by arrangement. No
pets.

# MANNINGS HEATH (WEST SUSSEX)

Dun Horse
Brighton Road, A281 near
Horsham

Licensee: N Goodhew
Tel: 0403 65783

A homely pub south of Horsham
with comfortable bars and guest
rooms and fine windows dating back
to the days of the Rock brewery.
The Dun Horse has open fires, a
garden, excellent pub grub lunchtime
and evening and traditional games in
the public bar.

Beer: Chester's Best Bitter, Flowers
Original, Strong Country Bitter and
Wethered Winter Royal (seasonal)
on handpumps.

Accommodation: 2 singles, 1 double,
1 family room. B&B £12.50 per
person.

SWAN, ARUNDEL — *see p 137*

# DUDLEY (WEST MIDLANDS)

Station Hotel
Castle Hill, junction of Trindle
Road, A461

Manager: R Stephenson
Tel: 0384 53418

The hotel, which dates back to 1898, was extensively rebuilt in the 1930s. It is stone built and crescent shaped and was once the haunt of theatre-goers to the Dudley Hippodrome in the heyday of regional theatre and music hall. It is close to Dudley Zoo and Castle and the Black Country Museum. The hotel has a traditional lounge bar with a daily hot buffet lunch (not Sundays), cocktail bar, a young people's music bar called Trax, and an à la carte restaurant open Tuesday, Wednesday and Thursday evenings and for Sunday roast lunch. A solarium and gym were due for completion early in 1988. Dudley is built on the highest hill in the Black Country and is surrounded by villages created by the Industrial Revolution.

Beer: Banks Mild and Bitter on electric pumps.

Accommodation: 13 singles, 10 doubles/twins, 6 family rooms, 1 de luxe suite, many with en suite facilities, all with colour TVs and tea and coffee makers. B&B £34.50 single, £42 double/twin, £52 family room. Weekends £27 single per night, £37 double, £47 family room. Weekend Special (2 or 3 nights) £23.50 single per night, £31 double, £41 family. Credit cards: Access, Visa.

# KENILWORTH (WARWICKSHIRE)

Clarendon House Hotel
Old High Street, off A452

Licensee: Martyn Lea
Tel: 0926 57668

Kenilworth and the hotel are steeped in the history of the English Civil War. The hotel was once the Castle Tavern and was used by Cromwell's troops during the siege of the town. The present hotel has Cromwellian armour and other artefacts of the Civil War period. The original pub was built in 1538 around an old oak tree that today still supports part of the main roof. There is a comfortable bar and a restaurant in the converted stables with a full à la carte menu. There are lunchtime bar snacks, too, and a Sunday roast.

Beer: Flowers Original, IPA and Sam Whitbread Strong Ale, Hook Norton Best Bitter and guest beers, all on handpumps.

Accommodation: 12 singles, 12 doubles, 1 family room, all with private baths. B&B from £30 per person. Weekend from £55. Children welcome, terms negotiable.

## KINGSWINFORD (WEST MIDLANDS)

Old Court House
High Street, A4101, ½ mile from
A491

Licensee: Clive Burke
Tel: 0384 271887

The Old Court, with its attractive
cream and green façade and red-tiled
roof and porch, was built as a court
building in 1790 and still stands on
the village green in this pleasant
hamlet near Dudley. There is one
lounge bar serving bar meals (not
Sundays), a separate restaurant and a
new conservatory café bar.

Beer: Banks Mild and Bitter, Burton
Ale on handpumps.

Accommodation: 1 single, 1 double,
2 twins, all with en suite facilities.
B&B £28 per person. Credit cards:
Access, Amex, Diners, Visa.

## LONG ITCHINGTON (WARWICKSHIRE)

Jolly Fisherman
The Green, A423, opposite village
green

Licensee: Peter Hewitt
Tel: 092 681 2296

The Jolly Fisherman is a large pub
set back from the road across from
the village green and pond. The pub
has a large public bar, which sports a
photo of the pub in 1903, and a
comfortable lounge, which stages
live music on Saturdays. A games
room offers pool, Japanese 'noise
boxes', darts and dominoes. Food,
including bar snacks, is traditionally
English in style. There is a large
garden for use on sunny days.

Beer: Ansells Mild and Bitter on
handpumps.

Accommodation: 1 double, 2 family
rooms. B&B £10 per person. Half
and full board available. Children's
room; children welcome to stay.
30% reductions according to age.

## NETHERTON (WEST MIDLANDS)

Saltwells Inn
Saltwells Road, Quarry Bank,
Brierley Hill, just off A4036

Licensees: Gill & Alan Stewart
Tel: 0384 69224

The inn is in the Saltwells woods
and nature reserve in the heart of
the Black Country. It has a smart
1930s appearance from the outside,
with tall chimneys placed unusually
either side of the main entrance. The
interior has been extensively
redecorated in 'modern Tudor', with
ceiling beams and many old photos
and advertising prints on the walls.
The Stewarts offer a genuinely
hospitable welcome and good food
at reasonable prices: there is bar
food lunchtime and evening —
steaks, scampi, plaice, salads, pizzas
and pasties plus a children's menu —
and Sunday lunch. The large garden
is surrounded by trees, has a
children's amusement area and is
floodlit at night. There is a large
family room with camera link and
all the guest rooms have colour TVs
and tea and coffee making
equipment.

Beer: Banks Mild and Bitter on
electric pumps.

Accommodation: 5 singles, 5
doubles, 1 family room, 6 with en
suite facilities. B&B £15 single, £28
double. Credit cards: Access, Visa.

# WALL HEATH (WEST MIDLANDS)

**Prince Albert Hotel**
High Street, on A449 at village crossroads

Licensee: John Miller
Tel: 0384 287411

A sizeable turn-of-the-century mock Tudor pub in the centre of an urban village at the edge of the Black Country and close to the Staffordshire countryside and Broadfield House glass museum. The Prince Albert has good hot lunchtime bar meals every day (evening meals by arrangement), public and lounge bars and traditional games.

Beer: Hansons Mild and Banks Bitter on electric pumps

Accommodation: 3 singles, 2 doubles, 1 family room. B&B £11 per person.

# WARWICK

**Wheatsheaf Hotel**
54 West Street, near town centre, A429

Licensees: Keith & Rachel Hinton
Tel: 0926 492817

The Wheatsheaf, near the centre of this fascinating and historic town with its castle, doll museum and medieval Shire Hall, has a most

TROBUS ARMS, AMESBURY — *see p 142*
141

attractive three-storey exterior with white-painted brickwork and striped awnings. Keith Hinton, a self-confessed 'amiable nutter', and his wife run a small dining room that serves lunch, dinner and a traditional Sunday roast. Darts and dominoes are played in the lounge bar. The delightful guest rooms all have central heating, colour TVs and tea and coffee making facilities. One room has a four-poster bed.

Beer: Ansells Bitter, Burton Ale, Gibbs Mew Wiltshire Bitter, Tetley Bitter on handpumps.

Accommodation: 2 singles, 6 doubles, 3 family rooms. B&B £18 single, £28 twin, four-poster £32. 10% discount for weekly stay. Children welcome, 10% reduction under 12 years. Credit cards: Access, Amex, Diners, Visa.

# WOLVERHAMPTON (WEST MIDLANDS)

**Wheatsheaf Hotel**
Market Street, town centre

Licensee: Brian Hall
Tel: 0902 24446

A town-centre pub near the bus and rail stations, with public and lounge bars and a beer garden. It gets busy at weekends but is quiet at other times. There is a residents' TV lounge and morning tea or coffee are brought to the guest rooms. Breakfast is the only meal provided but there are many inexpensive restaurants close to the Wheatsheaf.

Beer: Banks Mild and Bitter on electric pumps.

Accommodation: 8 singles, 3 doubles. B&B £12 per person. Children welcome to stay, no reductions.

## AMESBURY

Antrobus Arms
15 Church Street, ½ mile off A303

Licensee: Mrs P B Stammers
Tel: 0980 23163

The Antrobus Arms is in the heart of Salisbury Plain, close to Stonehenge. The pub is beautifully furnished with fine antiques; the bar has a cheerful, friendly atmosphere and the restaurant has a deserved reputation for quality cooking. The garden has a cedar tree that is more than 400 years old and a Victorian pond and fountain. The guest rooms have colour TVs, phones and tea and coffee making facilities.

Beer: Bass, Wadworth Devizes Bitter and 6X on handpumps.

Accommodation: 8 singles, 12 doubles, 1 family room, 11 rooms with private bath. B&B £25 single, £30 with bath, £42 double, £46 with bath. Off-season £108 for 2 people for 2 nights. Children welcome, charged £10 for additional bed in room.

## BARFORD ST MARTIN

Green Dragon
Junction of B3089 & A30, 6 miles W of Salisbury

Licensees: David & Judy Southgate
Tel: 0722 742242

The Green Dragon has a traditional, oak-panelled bar with a log fire in winter and a games bar where darts, dominoes, shove ha'penny and pool are played. There is a play area for children. Meals are served in both bars and include soup, ploughman's and hot dishes of the day. The guest rooms are in a separate wing of the building, giving residents access at all times. The rooms have tea and coffee making facilities.

Beer: Hall & Woodhouse Badger Best Bitter and Tanglefoot on handpumps.

Accommodation: 1 single, 3 doubles, 1 family room. B&B £12 per person. Children welcome, one-third reduction.

## BURTON

Plume of Feathers
B4039, off A46 and M4 exits 17 & 18

Licensees: June & Peter Bolin
Tel: 045421 251

The Plume is a splendid 400-year-old listed building between Chippenham and Chipping Sodbury and close to Castle Combe and Badminton. The pub has a resident ghost, allegedly a young woman but, according to Mr Bolin, acts like a young man 'with a racy sense of humour'. Mr Bolin, a former civil and military pilot from Australia, and his wife offer a vast range of hot and cold food, bar snacks and full meals, seven days a week, supported by good ale and some fine Antipodean wines. Just a glimpse of the formidable menu finds mushrooms sautéed in port, smoked trout, Cornish tiddy oggies, ploughman's, home-made steak and kidney pie, lasagne verde, and vegetarian dishes. Authentic oriental food reflects the host's work in the east: beef and potato curry, Indonesian lamb curry and Burmese pork curry, for example, with rice, raita and sambals.

Beer: Usher Best Bitter on handpump.

Accommodation: 2 doubles, both en suite. B&B £20 single, £25 double.

# DOWNTON

Kings Arms
9 High Street, B3080, 1 mile off
A338

Licensee: Colin Ludwell
Tel: 0725 20446

A lively village pub near Salisbury
and the New Forest. Parts of the
building date back to the 14th
century and there are beams and
open fires. Darts and pool are played
indoors while boules brings a Gallic
influence to the large garden. The
Kings Arms enjoys a reputation for
its splendid home-cooked bar snacks
and full meals.

Beer: Gibbs Mew Wiltshire Bitter
and Bishop's Tipple on handpumps.

Accommodation: 2 doubles, 1 family
room. B&B £9.50 per person.
Weekend £18. Half board available.
Children welcome, one-third
reductions.

# EVERLEIGH

Crown
A342 between Andover and
Devizes

Licensee: Jim Earle
Tel: 026485 223

The Crown is a handsome 17th-
century dower house with the
addition of two 18th-century bays. It
stands in extensive walled gardens, in
which there are also geese, goats,
ducks, chickens, a great dane, two
labradors and a spaniel. The fowls
provide eggs for the hotel. The top
bar is relaxed and comfortable with
log fires in winter, armchairs and
sporting prints on the wall. The
downstairs public bar, popular with
stable lads and farm workers, has
darts on a century-old board, crib,
dominoes and shove ha'penny and
there is also a family room with
games and a piano for children.
Food in the Crown is based on
home-cooking and local produce.
The public bar offers river trout,
barbecued spare ribs, burgers,
sandwiches, soup, salads and
ploughman's, while the lounge may
offer such delights as casserole of
venison, local wood pigeon or hare,
fish and grills. Children's menus are
always available. The cellar of the
Crown is 36 feet below the bar; Mr
Earle can't pull his beer that far
with a beer engine, which explains
the unusual dispense for the area.

Beer: Wadworth IPA and 6X on
electric pumps.

Accommodation: 2 singles, 6
doubles, 2 family rooms, 3 with
private bath. B&B £16 single, £25
double, £28 en suite. Children
welcome, terms by arrangement.

# FONTHILL GIFFORD

Beckford Arms
2 miles off A303, 1 mile off B3089
near Tisbury

Licensees: Paul & Susan Connolly
Tel: 0747 870385

The Beckford Arms is a rural 18th-
century inn on a crossroads between
the villages of Hindon and Tisbury
in the middle of the former
Beckford's Fonthill estate. The pub

has a large garden and there are lakeside and woodland walks to enjoy. The pub has two bars, both with log fires and high ceilings. The bars are linked by the stillage where the beer is drawn staight from wooden casks. Food includes sandwiches, home-made soup, ploughman's, home-cooked smoked ham and pâté. No chips are served.

Beer: Wadworth IPA, 6X and Old Timer (winter) straight from the cask.

Accommodation: 1 double, 1 family room. B&B £12 per person. Weekend £20, Week £60. Children welcome, one-third reductions.

## FOVANT

Cross Keys
On A30

Licensee: Pauline Story
Tel: 0722 270 284

This fascinating old coaching inn was built in 1485 and nestles in the village beneath the Fovant Badges carved on a ridge of hills and depicting the emblems of British and ANZAC regiments in the First World War. The Cross Keys, once a haunt of highwaymen, is homely and welcoming but people of average height have to watch their heads to avoid contact with the low beams. The inn is a warren of nooks and crannies, has old open fires, a garden, camping facilities and splendid bar food served both lunchtime and evening.

Beer: Gibbs Mew Wiltshire Bitter, Wadworth 6X on handpumps.

Accommodation: 1 single, 2 doubles, 1 family room. B&B £10-£15 per person. Credit cards: Visa.

## HINDON

Grosvenor Arms
High Street, B3089

Licensees: A J & A A Pitcairn
Tel: 074 789 253

The Grosvenor is an old coaching inn that once stood proud on the London to Exeter road, offering ale, bed and victuals to travellers. It performs the same valuable functions today, though the guests arrive by different, mechanical means. The inn offers a vast fireplace ablaze with light and warmth on cold days, a host of traditional games — bar skittles, darts, shove ha'penny, solitaire — a garden, camping facilities, horse riding and good bar meals lunchtime and evening (not Monday lunch). Hindon is steeped in history: the Agricultural Riots broke out here in 1830 and, earlier in 1754, the Great Fire of Hindon wiped out many of the village's 13 ale houses.

Beer: Wadworth Hindon Bitter (a house brew) and 6X, Marston Pedigree on handpumps.

Accommodation: 1 double, 1 family room. £15-£25 per person.

PLUME OF FEATHERS, BURTON — see

## PORTON

Porton Hotel
1 mile N of A30, ½ mile S of
A338

Licensees: Peter & Lynne Yeats
Tel: 0980 610203

The Porton is an Edwardian railway
hotel on high ground in a village
five miles from Salisbury. The trains
no longer stop there but the London
to Exeter line runs nearby. The
hotel has a comfortable lounge with
pub games in the bar. Hot meals are
available lunchtime and evening (not
Sunday evening) and range from
soup to steaks, taking in the local
butcher's jumbo sausages. The
Porton offers a TV lounge,
children's room, a beer garden and
ample parking. It is a good base for
Stonehenge and the New Forest.
Finsbury Rings, an ancient earth
site, is only five miles away.

Beer: Gibbs Mew Wiltshire Bitter,
Salisbury Best Bitter and Bishop's
Tipple (winter) plus Bulmer
traditional cider on handpumps and
from the cask.

Accommodation: 2 singles, 6
doubles. B&B £14 single, £12 double
per person. Weekend £28, Week £98.
Children welcome, no reductions.
Credit cards: Access, Visa.

## SALISBURY

Old Mill
Town Path, West Harnham, just off
A3094

Licensee: Jerry Sugh
Tel: 0722 27517

A breathtakingly ancient hostelry
dating back to 1135 and built from
brick, flint and stone on the River
Nadder across the water meadows
from the awesome cathedral. The
mill was used to store church
ornaments when the cathedral was
being moved from Old to New
Sarum and has also served as a
nunnery and a leper colony. It
became a restaurant in 1983 and its
low-beamed interior offers
traditional English cooking,
including game in season. Lunch and
dinner, morning coffee and tea are
served but in winter it is closed
Sunday evenings and all day
Monday. The hotel section was
originally a store house for the mill
and was divided into accommodation
early in this century. The building
includes a residents' TV lounge and
a small groundfloor bar popular
with locals.

Beer: Palmer IPA, Wadworth 6X
and Old Timer (winter) on
handpumps and straight from the
cask.

Accommodation: *1 April - 30 Nov
only*. 2 singles, 4 doubles/twins, 1 en
suite family room. B&B from £15
per person. Reductions for weekly
stays. Credit cards: Access, Amex,
Diners, Visa.

## SALISBURY

Red Lion Hotel
Milford Street

Proprietor: Michael Maidment
Tel: 0722 23334

The Red Lion is a superb, 13th century inn rooted in the history of this magnificent cathedral city. It became an extended coaching inn in the hey-day of horse-drawn road travel but its earlier origins are evident from the wealth of exposed beams, wattle-and-daub, hand-painted medieval plasterwork and brass and copper decorations. Among the many antiques is a remarkable skeleton organ clock in which the skeletal figures ring the hours: it is thought to have been carved by Spaniards taken prisoner after the defeat of the Armada in 1588. The half-timbered exterior is partially covered by a fine Virginia creeper. The dining room specialises in tradtional English cooking and includes venison and jugged hare in season, local trout and roast beef. Sumptuous accommodation includes several four-poster bedrooms.

Beer: Bass, Courage Best Bitter, Usher Best Bitter, Wadworth 6X and guest beers on handpumps.

Accommodation: 10 singles, 45 doubles,.4 family rooms, all en suite. B&B £40 single, £60 double, £64 four-poster, £67.50 family room plus children's breakfasts. Spring & Summer Breaks £70 per person for 2 nights including lunch or dinner. Credit cards: Access, Amex, Diners, Visa.

## TISBURY

South Western Hotel
Station Road, off A30 & A303

Licensee: R C Short
Tel: 0747 870160

A large and imposing pub 200 yards from the Wiltshire Brewery. The South Western has one L-shaped bar and a small games area where darts, crib and bar billiards are played. The small dining room seats 20 and is supervised by Mr Short, a trained chef. Bar food includes soup, home-made pâté, grills, curries, shepherd's pie, chilli, burgers and — a thoughtful touch — good value specials for senior citizens such as fish, chips and peas for £1.50. The restaurant offers seafood pancake, avocado and smoked bacon salad, chicken and asparagus, fruits de mer, game, vegetarian dishes, trout and curries. The guest rooms all have tea and coffee making facilities.

Beer: Wiltshire Regency Best, Stonehenge Bitter and Old Devil plus such regular guest beers as Adnams Bitter and Wadworth 6X, all on handpumps.

Accommodation: 1 double, 4 twins, 1 with private shower. B&B £12.50 per person. Weekend £32.50, Week £70. Off-Season Weekend £10 per night. Children welcome, half price under 5. Credit cards: Visa.

# WHITEPARISH

Fountain Inn
The Street, A27 between Romsey
and Salisbury

Licensee: Martin Mount
Tel: 07948 846

A cheerful, 300-year-old inn with
beamed bars and dining room and
open fires. Locals mix happily with
visitors here. Mid-week breaks
organised by Mr Mount include
excursions to historic buildings and
places of interest in the locality,
including Salisbury, the New Forest,
Romsey and the home of the
Mountbatten family.

Beer: Hall & Woodhouse
Tanglefoot, Marston Pedigree, Tetley
Bitter, Wadworth 6X and guest beers
on handpumps and from the cask.

Accommodation: 1 single, 5 doubles,
all en suite. B&B £18 per person.
Weekend £32, Week £100. Evening
meals available. Children welcome,
10% reductions.

# ABERFORD
# (W YORKS)

Swan Hotel
Centre of village on old A1

Licensees: Otto & Ann Kreft
Tel: 0532 813205

The Swan is a former coaching inn
on the Great North Road in an
attractive village now by-passed by
the new A1 road. The hotel has
some interesting outbuildings that
date back to coaching days while
inside the main building there are
two bars linked together, a games
room and a separate restaurant. Bar
meals and full meals are served

lunchtime and evening. The guest
rooms all have colour TVs and tea
and coffee making facilities and the
double rooms have their own
showers. The Swan has a pleasant
garden to enjoy in good weather and
is a good base for visiting such
interesting local places as Hazlewood
Castle.

Beer: Whitbread Trophy and Castle
Eden Ale on handpumps.

Accommodation: 2 singles, 4
doubles. B&B £10-£15 per person.
Credit cards: Access, Amex, Visa.

# APPLETREEWICK
# (N YORKS)

New Inn
2 miles off B6160 at Barden Tower
or Burnsall OS 051601

Licensee: John Pitchers
Tel: 075 672 252

The New Inn is a cheering sight
from the riverside Dales Way
footpath. It stands at the foot of the
village street in an area of great
historic and scenic beauty. The
welcoming inn received fame and
notoriety under its previous tenant
who banned smoking and decorated

the place with warnings against the Evil Weed. Mr Pitchers has a more even-handed approach, supplying both ash trays and air purifiers. The inn is a fine Dales pub and the view may be enjoyed from the horseshoe chairs and benches outside. Mr Pitchers wisely retains the inn as a genuine local and not a tourist trap. As well as his good draught ale, he has a world-wide collection of bottled beers, inlcuding some bottle-conditioned Trappiste monastery brews from Belgium. There is good lunchtime bar food (the other village inn, the Craven Arms, has evening meals). Appletreewick and its environs are packed with interest: the Earls of Craven supplied a Lord Mayor of London in 1610, Mock Beggar Hall was a shelter for the homeless while Percival Hall dates back to Tudor times. Bolton Abbey and Strid Woods are nearby. Trollers Gill is haunted by a barguest, not an itinerant toper but a spectral hound of Baskerville proportions.

Beer: John Smiths Bitter, Younger Scotch Bitter on handpumps.

Accommodation: 1 single, 3 doubles. B&B £10-£15.

## ATLEY HILL (N YORKS)

Arden Arms
B1263 near North Cowton

Licensee: Bob Lamb
Tel: 032 578 678

Arden Arms is a 400-year-old inn with open log fires, a cosy public bar and a pleasant, comfortable lounge. It overlooks Richmond to the west and the Cleveland Hills to the east. Bar meals are served lunchtime and evening. Children are welcome and can use the lounge at lunchtimes. There is a pleasant patio garden for sunny days. The bar has memorabilia of Beverley's Wakefield brewery, taken over by Watney in 1967. The pub is an excellent base for visiting Richmond, Northallerton and Heriot country.

Beer: Theakston Best Bitter, XB and Old Peculier on handpumps.

Accommodation: 1 single, 1 double, 1 family room. B&B £8.50 per person. Children welcome. Reductions for weekly stays.

## BRADFORD (W YORKS)

Victoria
Bridge Street, opposite transport interchange

Licensee: Richard Lay
Tel: 0274 728706

The Victoria is a city-centre, three-star hotel in a good position for Bradford's growing tourist industry. It is an imposing stone building dating from 1880 and was originally named the Great Northern Hotel when it stood opposite the now defunct Exchange railway station. The Victoria has a quiet residents' lounge and meals lunchtime and evening. Colour TVs and tea and coffee making facilities are available in all the guest rooms. Bradford's Barber Shop Singers regularly sing for their suppers in the plush public bar. The Victoria is next door to St George's Hall, which holds concerts and many other events, and is close to the National Museum of Photography, Film and Television, and the revamped Alhambra theatre.

Beer: Tetley Bitter, Websters Green Label Best on handpumps.

Accommodation: 29 singles, 30 doubles (doubles can be converted to family rooms), all rooms with private baths. B&B £30 per person midweek. Weekend £26 per night (minimum 2 nights stay), Week from £133. Children welcome, terms negotiable. Credit cards: Access, Amex, Diners, Visa.

## West Leigh Hotel
30 Easby Road, A647 towards Halifax, ½ mile from city centre

Licensee: John Jowett
Tel: 0274 727089

The West Leigh is a spacious and comfortable pub that was once three separate Victorian houses. It has a cheerful, comfortable bar with a pool table and a separate residents' lounge. It has a wide selection of bar meals and excellent-value, three-course meals in the restaurant. The guest rooms have colour TVs and central heating. The hotel is handy for the city centre, the university, Bradford's famous curry houses and pubs. A short journey will take you to Haworth, with its Brontë connections and steam railway centre.

Beer: McEwan 80 shilling, Younger Scotch Bitter and No 3 on handpumps.

Accommodation: 11 singles, 11 twins, 8 doubles, 2 family rooms, 9 rooms with private baths. B&B £16 single, £28 twin/double, £5 extra for bath. Children welcome, terms by agreement. Dogs allowed.

# BOROUGHBRIDGE (N YORKS)

## Three Horseshoes Hotel
Bridge Street, off A1

Proprietors: R S & B S Porter
Tel: 090 12 2314

The Three Horseshoes is an impressive hotel rebuilt between the wars and retaining a homely, 1930s flavour. The lounge has an unusual tiled fireplace and a wealth of wood panels and leaded glass. There is a basic public bar, a separate dining room and a lounge. Boroughbridge is an historic market town on the old A1, offering leisurely boating trips on the River Ure and visits to the stately home of Newby Hall.

Beer: Vaux Samson on electric pump.

Accommodation: 5 singles, 5 doubles/twins, 2 family rooms, 3 rooms with private baths. B&B £12.50 per person. Children welcome, terms according to age. Limited facilities for the disabled; easy access to pub.

# DALTON (N YORKS)

## Jolly Farmers of Olden Times
Off A168, A19 & A168, 4 miles S of Thirsk

Licensees: Norman & Patricia Clark
Tel: 0845 577359

A lively and much-loved small country inn, 200 years old with some of the original beams and a welcoming coal fire, in the heart of Heriot country below the white horse cut in the chalk of the Hambleton Hills. The Clarks are enthusiasts — for the pub, for real ale (they are CAMRA members) and for organising rambles in the dales and on the moors. The inn offers a games room, bar and lounge, a fine garden with trees, and a welcome for families. Local produce is used for bar meals and the restaurant. Food in the bar includes steaks, chops, chilli, haddock and mackerel, rainbow trout and vegetarian dishes. Meals in the restaurant (lunch and dinner) offer soup, ham cooked in wine, mushroom and cheese sauce, casserole supreme and curried lamb. There is a traditional Sunday roast lunch, too — good value at £3.95 per person, 1987 price.

Beer: Websters Yorkshire Bitter and Choice, Wilsons Original Bitter on handpumps with regular guest beers.

Accommodation: 1 double, 1 family room. B&B £12 per person, £11 for more than 1 night. Weekend £22, Week £77. Children welcome.

# DEWSBURY (W YORKS)

Railway
Bradford Road

Licensee: Geoffrey Moore
Tel: 0924 465598

The Railway is a typical Tetley urban local, a popular pub that makes a good overnight resting place for weary travellers. It is just off the inner ring road and close to Dewsbury's open market place. It is close — but not too close — to the M1 and M62. The pub has been given a thorough overhaul and offers all modern amenities while retaining its 'Heavy Woollen' area character.

Beer: Tetley Mild and Bitter on handpumps.

Accommodation: 1 single, 6 doubles, 1 family room. B&B £15 single, £25 double, £35 family. Evening meals available.

# EASINGWOLD (N YORKS)

George Hotel
Market Square, off A19 York-Thirsk road

Licensee: Mrs E Johnson
Tel: 0347 21698

The George is an 18th-century coaching inn in a cobbled market square with handsome, white-painted bow windows, porch and shutters on the top storey. It has all modern amenities such as central heating, colour TVs and tea and coffee making facilities in the pleasant guest rooms but retains its old charm with beams, open fires and wood panelling in the bar and candlelit dining room. Mrs Johnson — and more power to her elbow — resolutely turns her back on 'juke boxes and pin ball machines that distract your enjoyment'. Lunchtime bar snacks include home-made steak and kidney pie, ham, chicken and mushroom pie, sandwiches and salads. The dining room offers an extensive à la carte menu in the evenings. The hotel is a splendid base for visiting York, the east coast and the moors. An 18-hole golf course is close at hand.

Beer: Younger Scotch Bitter and IPA on handpumps.

Accommodation: 1 single, 14 doubles, 2 family rooms, all en suite. B&B from £17.50. Off-Season Weekend £49, 2 nights B&B + evening meal. Children welcome. Facilites for the disabled. Credit cards: Visa.

# GOOSE EYE
# (W YORKS)

Goose Eye Hotel
Minor road from Oakworth to
Laycock, 2 miles SW of Keighley.
OS SE 029406

Licensee: Bryan Eastell
Tel: 0535 605807

The hotel and Mint Bar are part of
the Goose Eye brewery complex
that also includes the Turkey Inn.
Hotel and bar are in an old mill that
previously produced such diverse
products as banknotes and
motorbikes. Set in a quiet valley $2\frac{1}{2}$
miles from Keighley, Goose Eye is
approached by steep and winding
roads and is well placed for visiting
Brontë country and the Worth
Valley Railway. Bryan Eastell is
brewer, restaurateur and hotelier and
has plans to extend the hotel with a
swimming pool and additional bar.
There are full meals in the restaurant
while bar meals offer home-made
soups, sandwiches, ploughman's,
chilli, fish and chips, pies and peas,
and curries. Among the beers on
offer, Mr Eastell's Pommies·
Revenge, at 6% alcohol, is a liquid
insult to pale, insipid fake-Aussie
lagers.

Beer: Goose Eye Bitter, White Rose
Bitter and Pommies Revenge,
Thwaites Best Mild and Bitter on
handpumps.

Accommodation: 3 singles, 4
doubles, 1 family room, all with en
suite facilities and tea and coffee
makers. B&B £20 single, £28 double.
Half and full board available.
Children welcome, no reductions.
Bargain breaks are being planned:
please enquire. Limited facilities for
the disabled: fire exit avoids stairs.

# GRASSINGTON
# (N YORKS)

Foresters Arms
Main Street, near Skipton, off A65

Licensee: W A Chaney
Tel: 0756 752349

The Foresters is a superb, welcoming
pub in a lovely old Wharfedale
village with a cobbled square. The
lively bar offers darts, dominoes and
pool and the contented chatter of
the village locals. Bar food includes
home-made soup and steak and
mushroom pie, grills, home-cooked
ham and pork, haddock, plaice and
scampi, ploughman's and a choice of
sweets. The pub has a residents' TV
lounge and the guest rooms have tea
and coffee making facilities. Satisfied
visitors single out the 'terrific'
breakfasts for particular praise.

Beer: Tetley Mild and Bitter on
handpumps.

Accommodation: 1 single, 5 doubles,
2 family rooms. B&B £11 per
person. Off-season Weekend £30.
Children's room; children welcome
to stay.

# HAWORTH (W YORKS)

Brontë Hotel
Lees Lane, near junction with
A6033

Licensee: G Bailey
Tel: 0535 44112

A new pub and hotel, built some
seven years ago, in the village heavy
with Brontë connections. It is a mile
from the Brontë parsonage (now a
museum) where Anne, Charlotte and
Emily penned, despite their genteel
surroundings, the novels of great
power and passion, such as
*Wuthering Heights* and *Jane Eyre*.
The hotel, with a comfortably furnished lounge bar, has all the amenities of a modern hotel, serving meals
lunchtime and evening. It is also a
handy base for visiting the moors
and the Keighley and Worth Valley
Light Railway (Haworth station).

Beer: Stones Best Bitter, Tetley
Bitter on handpumps.

Accommodation: 3 singles, 5
doubles, 3 rooms with en suite
facilities. B&B £15-£25 per person.
Half and full board available. Credit
cards: Access, Visa.

# HELMSLEY (N YORKS)

Crown Hotel
Market Square, off A170

Licensees: Mr & Mrs B J Mander
Tel: 0439 70297

The Crown is a 16th-century
coaching inn that dominates one side
of the square of this picturesque old
market town with its eerie and
awesome castle ruins, fine parish
church, a miniature Albert Memorial
and, nearby, Rievaulx Abbey. There
are darts in a small bar and an
imitation log fire blazes in a cosy
lounge bar where there are
comfortable bench seats. The
pleasant Jacobean restaurant serves
lunch, high tea and dinner (last
orders 8pm) using traditional English
cooking and fresh local produce.
Some of the guest rooms in this
listed building have exposed beams
and all have colour TVs and tea and
coffee making equipment. There is a
TV lounge for residents.

Beer: Cameron Best Bitter and
Strongarm on electric pumps.

Accommodation: 6 singles, 7
doubles/twins, 2 family rooms, 14
rooms en suite. Two ground floor
rooms permit dogs. B&B £20 single,
£22 with bath. Half and full board
available. Winter Break: £49.80 per
person 2 nights B&B + evening
meal. Children welcome, child in cot
charged only for meals; if in separate
bed in parents' room, £2 per day
plus meals. Credit cards: Access,
Visa.

# HEPTONSTALL (W YORKS)

Cross Inn
Towngate, 1 mile off A646, near
Hebden Bridge

Licensees: Gerald & Joan Fisher
Tel: 0422 843833

The Cross is a welcoming 17th-century inn built on the site of a previous licensed building and with a later Victorian frontage. There is a large games room at the back, morning coffee, lunches and evening meals. It stands in the main street of a picturesque and historic hill-top village overlooking Hebden Bridge and set in wonderful Pennine scenery.

Beer: Timothy Taylor Golden Best and Best Bitter on handpumps.

Accommodation: 1 twin, 1 double. B&B £12 per person. Children welcome, terms according to age.

# HUBBERHOLME (N YORKS)

George
Off A684, 1 mile from Buckden on Hawes road. OS SD 926782

Licensee: John Frederick
Tel: 075 676 223

There are many claims on the title, but the George is probably *the* Dales pub. It dates back to at least the 18th century, was once the village vicarage, and has stone-flagged floors, low beams, mullioned windows and antique furniture. There are blazing fires in winter. On New Year's Day, the local parliament of 'House of Lords' (vicar and churchwarden) and 'House of Commons' (local farmers) negotiate the letting of nearby pasture land in aid of poorer

parishioners. The George has a separate restaurant. Bar meals include French bread with choice of fillings, ploughman's, pâté and hot dishes of the day such as steak and kidney pie. There are a few outside seats with stunning views of the moors rising all around. The village is named after the viking Hubba who settled there. It remains an attractive huddle of church, bridge, inn and a few scattered farms and cottages. The road through the hamlet is the highest in Yorkshire, reaching 1934 feet on its way to Hawes.

Beer: Younger Scotch Bitter and IPA on handpumps, occasionally Trough Wild Boar.

Accommodation: 5 doubles/twins. B&B £14 per person. Week £84. Winter Break £38 for 2 nights B&B + evening meal. Children over 8 welcome, no reductions.

# HUDDERSFIELD (W YORKS)

Albion
164 Manchester Road, Longroyd Bridge, A62

Licensee: James Dutton
Tel: 0484 531199

Life ticks over at a sedate, suburban pace in this welcoming, 200-year-old pub half a mile from the centre of Huddersfield. It stood once on the main Yorkshire to Manchester coaching route and still has some beams in its rooms and bars. There is good lunchtime bar food and sandwiches are available in the evening.

Beer: Wilsons Original Mild and Bitter on handpumps.

Accommodation: 5 twins. B&B £8.50 single, £15 double.

## JACKSON BRIDGE (W YORKS)

Red Lion
Sheffield Road, A616

Licensee: Mrs J Oscroft
Tel: 0484 683499

This is *Last of the Summer Wine* territory near Holmfirth. The success of the TV series draws visitors but cannot detract from the outstanding and unspoilt character of the countryside and its small towns and villages. The Red Lion is a delightful old inn with a cosy bar, open fire and beer garden. Food is served lunchtime (not weekends) and evenings (residents only). The guest rooms all have colour TVs and tea and coffee making facilities. The Red Lion has a ghost named Chippy Brook, a former landlord of the inn.

Beer: Marston Pedigree, Tetley Mild and Bitter on handpumps and guest beers straight from the cask in winter.

Accommodation: 2 twins, 4 doubles, 3 en suite. B&B £16 single, £18 en suite, £28 double, £32 en suite. £2 reduction for weekend stay.

WHITE HORSE, JACKSON BRIDGE

White Horse
Scholes Road, off A616 3 miles from Holmfirth

Licensee: Ron Backhouse
Tel: 0484 683940

This is the heart of the *Summer Wine* saga, for this splendid old stone-built Yorkshire pub features prominently in the series and is adorned with a multitude of TV memorabilia. But it retains its character — and its genuine local characters, too. The pub is popular with walkers and offers open fires in winter, a large and attractive garden, a games room with darts and dominoes and pub food lunchtime and evening. The guest rooms have tea and coffee making facilities.

Beer: Stones Best Bitter on handpumps.

Accommodation: 2 doubles, 3 family rooms, may be used as singles according to demand. B&B £10-£15 per person.

## KIRBY HILL (N YORKS)

Shoulder of Mutton
2 miles from A66 W of Scotch Corner

Licensee: Hylton Pynner
Tel: 0748 2772

The Shoulder of Mutton is a country inn in a superb hillside setting near Richmond, overlooking lower Teesdale and the ruins of Ravensworth Castle. It was built in 1800, possibly as a farmhouse, and converted to licensed premises some 50 years later. It is in a village of great antiquity. The church dates back to 1200 while the handful of cottages stem from the 15th century. The inn has two bars, traditional pub games and a separate restaurant. Bar food ranges from steak and kidney pie to gammon and steaks, local trout, lasagne and jacket potatoes with a choice of fillings. The guest rooms all have showers, colour TVs and tea and coffee making facilities.

Beer: Theakston XB, Websters Choice, Younger No 3 on handpumps.

Accommodation: 2 doubles, 1 twin. B&B £11.25 single, £13.50 with shower, 3 days or more £10.50 or £12.50 with shower per day. Half board £20.50 en suite.

# LEEDS (W YORKS)

Brookfield
11 Brookfield Terrace, Hunslet Road

Licensees: Mike & Pauline Page
Tel: 0532 451851

Brookfield is a solidly built pub in an industrial area on a busy main road, noted for good value food lunchtime and evening. It is a typical early 20th century Tetley pub built when industry was developing in the area. It is still surrounded by factories ancient and modern and is close to the M1, the city centre and Tetley's brewery.

Beer: Tetley Mild and Bitter on handpumps.

Accommodation: 2 doubles. B&B £9.50 per person. Reductions for stays of a week or more. Families are welcome, particularly at weekends: special rates on application.

Eagle Tavern
North Street, Sheepscar, A61

Licensee: Keith Pearson
Tel: 0532 457146

The Eagle is a cheerful pub on the northern side of Leeds ten minutes walk from the city centre. It is a plain but welcoming listed building, dating from the 1820s, with a large public bar where darts and pool are played, and a small, plush lounge. Live music is played at weekends. There is an outside drinking area and bar meals are served at lunchtime.

Beer: Theakston XB, Timothy Taylor Best Bitter, Landlord, Porter and Ram Tam, Trough Wild Boar on handpumps.

Accommodation: 8 twins. B&B £10-£15 per person, reductions for longer stays.

# MASHAM (N YORKS)

Kings Head Hotel
Market Place, A6108 near Ripon

Licensee: David Richards
Tel: 0765 89295

The Kings Head is a stately, three-storey stone building in the home town of Theakston's Brewery, where tours can be arranged with prior notice. The hotel has been extensively improved and has a large marble fireplace, cast-iron tables, a profusion of plants and a shelf of pottery figures. Excellent bar food includes salads, Yorkshire pudding with mince, sausage and egg, steak and kidney pie, and Old Peculier hot pot. There are a few seats in a courtyard in fine weather.

Beer: Matthew Brown Lion Mild, Theakston Best Bitter, XB and Old Peculier on handpumps.

Accommodation: 5 singles, 9 doubles/twins, 5 rooms with private baths. B&B £22.50 single, £34.50 double.

# MIRFIELD (W YORKS)

Black Bull
130 Huddersfield Road, A644

Licensee: Tony Woods
Tel: 0924 493180

The Black Bull was built in 1850 as a railway hotel — it is still handy for Mirfield BR — but it has come a long way since its inception. Mr Woods runs a lively regime with a disco and cabaret yet it retains some of its true local character. It has bar meals lunchtime and restaurant meals in the evening.

Beer: Tetley Mild and Bitter on handpumps.

Accommodation: 9 rooms, 4 doubles, 3 twins, 2 family rooms. B&B £15 single, £25 double/twin, £35 family room. Discounts for long term stays. Credit cards: Access, Amex, Visa.

# OAKENSHAW (W YORKS)

Richardsons Arms
Bradford Road, A638, ½ mile from M62 exit 26

Licensee: Tony Maskill
Tel: 0274 675722

Richardsons is a lively pub with a strong emphasis on entertainment — it has live music on Thursday to Sunday evenings and jazz Sunday lunchtimes. The lounge is open plan and bar meals are served lunchtime and evening. The well-appointed guest rooms all have TVs and tea and coffee making facilities. Oakenshaw is a village that is being subsumed into Bradford's outskirts and is close to the M62 and M606.

Beer: Whitbread Trophy on handpump.

Accommodation: 5 singles, 4 doubles. B&B £12.50 per person.

# OSSETT (W YORKS)

Crown
20 Horbury Road, 1 mile S of town centre

Licensee: David Roberts
Tel: 0924 272495

The Crown is a small, traditional, stone-built pub with panelled rooms and a collection of dolls in a cabinet. Pub games include darts, dominoes and ring the bull. There are two lounge bars where lunches are served every day except Sunday. The specialities of the house are Yorkshire puddings eight inches in diameter filled with beef stew, plus many other home-made dishes including braised steak and onions, steak and kidney pie, chilli, sandwiches and toasties. The guest rooms are in an adjoining building with a separate entrance. Each room has colour TV and tea and coffee making facilities.

Beer: Tetley Mild and Bitter on handpumps.

Accommodation: 2 singles, 2 doubles, 1 family room. B&B £15.50 single, £25.50 double. Weekend £13.50 per person per night, Week £14.50 per night. Children welcome, charged only for meals if sharing parents' room.

# OSWALDKIRK (N YORKS)

Malt Shovel Inn
Off B1363 & B1257 S of Helmsley

Licensee: Ian Pickering
Tel: 043 93 461

The Malt Shovel is a 17th-century listed coaching inn, formerly a manor house, in a village mentioned in the Domesday Book. The inn has imposing staircases, log fires in winter, and old photos, miners' lamps and clay pipes in the beamed rooms. The busy bar has an imposing fireplace and many traditional pub games, including darts, dominoes and shove ha'penny. A lounge, where children are allowed to eat, has a surprising collection of Expressionist paintings. Both bar food and the separate restaurant use local produce in the imaginative dishes. You may find home-made soup, hot poached pear with blue cheese dressing, black pudding cooked in Dijon mustard, open sandwiches on granary bread, 'shovel bun' — an individual cottage loaf filled with home-made curried chicken and Indian pickles — vegetarian roast of hazelnuts and fresh vegetables, whole lemon sole, sea trout steak, grills and salads.

There are separate menus for children. The lawns are used in the summer months.

Beer: Sam Smith Old Brewery Bitter and Museum Ale on handpumps.

Accommodation: 1 twin, 2 doubles, all with tea and coffee making facilities. B&B £15 per person. Children welcome, £10 per night under 10. No pets.

# OTLEY (W YORKS)

Black Horse
Westgate, town centre

Licensee: Geoffrey Cutts
Tel: 0943 461047

The Black Horse is a substantial and imposing building in the heart of the small, picturesque market town. The pub is of Victorian origin with lounge and public bars and meals lunchtime and evening (no evening meals Monday). Guest rooms have tea and coffee making facilities.

Beer: Tetley Mild and Bitter on handpumps.

Accommodation: 2 singles, 6 doubles, 1 family room. B&B £10 per person. Half board available. Business breakfasts arranged.

## SHELLEY (W YORKS)

Three Acres Inn
Roydhouse, Drinker Lane, off A637
& exit 38 of M1 OS 216125

Partners: Derrick & Neil Truelove &
Brian Orme
Tel: 0484 602606

Three Acres is a substantial country
pub and restaurant beautifully
situated in the rolling scenery of
Emley Moor, close to the TV mast.
It has spectacular views of the moors
yet is within easy reach of the
motorway, Huddersfield and the
Holmfirth area. It has a cheerful bar
with beams and brasses, a more
sedate cocktail bar and a restaurant
concentrating on quality English and
Continental cuisine. Lunch and
dinner, including bar meals, are
available every day. The inn offers
facilities for families and disabled
people. The splendid guest rooms all
have private baths or showers,
colour TVs, and tea and coffee
making facilities.

Beer: McEwan 80 shilling, Tetley
Mild and Bitter, Younger Scotch
Bitter, IPA and No 3 on handpumps.

Accommodation; 3 singles, 5
doubles, 1 family room. B&B £32
single, £43 double. No charge for
children sharing with parents.
Weekend £36 single for 2 nights, £54
for 3, £60 double for 2 nights, £90
for 3. Half and full board available.
Credit cards: Access, Amex, Visa.

FOX & HOUNDS, STARBOTTON

## SLAITHWAITE (W YORKS)

White House
B6107 Meltham to Marsden road,
6 miles from Huddersfield

Licensee: Gillian Sykes
Tel: 0484 842245

The White House's official address is
Slaithwaite but it is actually in the
tiny hamlet of Holthead, near the
open moors of the East Pennines.
The cheerful, spacious old rural pub
has retained much of its original
charm, with open fires, two bars,
facilities for families and bar food
and full meals in the separate
restaurant. There is a traditional
roast lunch on Sundays. The guest
rooms all have en suite facilities and
tea and coffee making equipment.

Beer: Tetley Mild and Bitter,
Younger Scotch Bitter and IPA on
handpumps.

Accommodation: 1 single, 3 doubles.
B&B £20 single, £30 double, £28 for
single occupancy in double room.
£25 double per night at weekends.
Half and full board available. Credit
cards: Access, Amex, Diners, Visa.

## STARBOTTON (N YORKS)

Fox & Hounds
B6160, 2 miles N of Kettlewell

Licensee: Ann Wilkinson
Tel: 075 676 269

The Fox & Hounds is set in a lovely
limestone village in upper
Wharfedale. The stone-built Dales
pub has a vast fireplace, beams,
flagstone floors, settles and other old
and comfortable furniture. Bar food
includes soup and sandwiches, home-
made steak and kidney pie, game

and trout. Darts and dominoes are played and there are tables and benches outside in warm weather with stunning views of the hamlet and the hills.

Beer: Timothy Taylor Landlord, Theakston Best Bitter and Old Peculier, Younger Scotch Bitter on handpumps.

Accommodation: 3 doubles, 2 twins. B&B £10-£15 per person. Credit cards: Access, Visa.

# WENTWORTH (S YORKS)

Rockingham Arms
Main Street, B6090, 3 miles from
M1 exit 36

Licensee: Cyril Ayscough
Tel: 0226 742075/742198

The Rockingham Arms is a traditional old pub in an unspoilt village between Rotherham and Barnsley. It has a main bar with log fires and comfortable furnishings. The barn bar has live music three nights each week. Bar food is available lunchtime and evening and includes ploughman's, sandwiches, steak pie and grills. The pub has an orchard beer garden and a bowling green. The guest rooms all have tea and coffee making facilities and TVs.

Beer: Younger Scotch Bitter, IPA and No 3 on handpumps.

Accommodation: 12 rooms, 4 with en suite facilities. B&B from £18 per night.

# WALES

PONT-Y-PAIR HOTEL, BETWS-Y-COED — *see p 172*

# GLYNDYFRDWY

Berwyn Arms
A5 between Llangollen & Corwen

Licensee: David Thomas
Tel: 049 083 210

The Berwyn Arms is a fine old coaching inn with welcoming open fires in winter, superb views of the Dee valley and 1¾ miles of salmon fishing. Darts and dominoes are played in the bar, food is served lunchtime and evening, there is a beer garden and facilities for families. Camping can be arranged in the village.

Beer: Burtonwood Bitter on handpump.

Accommodation: 3 singles, 2 doubles, 4 family rooms, 4 rooms with private showers. B&B £10-£15 per person. Half board available.

# HANMER

Hanmer Arms
¼ mile off A539, near Whitchurch
OS SJ 459399

Proprietors: Trevor & Lesley Hope
Tel: 094 874 532

The Hanmer Arms is in superb border country between Wales and Shropshire and overlooks the lovely Hanmer Mere. The village is dominated by the ancient church of St Chad's while Chirk Castle is nearby. The pub has a bar used mainly by young people, a lounge with a brick fireplace and range, where hot and cold bar meals are served, plus a bistro bar and separate restaurant. Both the pub and the accommodation are in buildings converted from a former inn and farmhouse. The guest rooms have British Tourist Board 4 crown ratings and surround a cobbled courtyard; two rooms have been specially converted for use by disabled people. All the rooms have colour TVs, video programmes, baby listening and private baths.

Beer: Border Mild, Marston Pedigree, Tetley Mild and Bitter on handpumps.

Accommodation: 1 single, 9 doubles, 2 family rooms. B&B £25-£30 per person, £17.50-£25 if sharing double. Weekend Break: 2 people 2 nights (Fri, Sat or Sun) £12.50 per person per night. Half and full board available. Credit cards: Access, Visa.

# LLANGOLLEN

Bridge End Hotel
Abbey Road, A539, near Dee Bridge

Proprietor: B Coulthard
Tel: 0978 860634

The Bridge End is an extensively modernised, lively and welcoming hotel that is close to the canal and has fine views of Llangollen and the river. Fishing can be arranged for anglers. Meals are available lunchtime and evening with both bar snacks and an à la carte restaurant.

Beer: Robinson Best Bitter on handpump.

Accommodation: 3 singles, 7 doubles, 1 family room. B&B £15 per person, £12.50 in winter. Children's room; children welcome, half price.

# LLANGOLLEN

Hand Hotel
Bridge Street, 400 yards off main road

Licensee: Derick Evans
Tel: 0978 860303

The Hand is a bright and cheerful small hotel with a large open-plan lounge bar and fine views of the 8th-century castle and the river. It provides an excellent buffet lunch with both hot and cold dishes and there is a separate restaurant too. The guest rooms all have colour TVs and tea and coffee making facilities.

Beer: McEwan 70 shilling on handpump.

Accommodation: 22 singles, 10 doubles, 6 triples, 3 family rooms all with en suite baths or showers. B&B £15-£25 per person. Weekend and bargain breaks: terms on application. Credit cards: Access, Amex, Diners, Visa.

# RUABON

Wynnstay Arms
High Street, junction of old A483 & A539 Wrexham-Whitchurch roads

Licensees: Marie & Paul Skellon
Tel: 0978 822187

The Wynnstay is an imposing, stone-brick and ivy-clad building with a wood-panelled lounge and popular back bar where darts and dominoes are played. It is an old coaching inn that has refound peace and tranquillity with the opening of a new bypass. It takes its name from the estate of Sir Watkin Williams Wynn: the houses of the estate workers flank the road past the hotel. Bar lunches and the restaurant concentrate on local produce and meals may include coq au vin, duckling, Welsh lamb, steak and kidney pie, curries, poached salmon, choice of salads and open sandwiches. The comfortable guest rooms all have TVs and tea and coffee making facilities. Ruabon has an ancient church with wall paintings and is a good base for visiting Llangollen, Chester and the Shropshire meres.

Beer: Robinson Best Mild and Best Bitter on electric pumps.

Accommodation: 1 single, 8 doubles, 3 with private baths. Doubles can provide family accommodation. B&B £22 single, £32 double. Credit cards: Access, Amex, Visa.

# RUTHIN

Wynnstay Arms
20 Well Street, off A494 & A525

Licensee: Hugh Meikle
Tel: 082 42 3147

Not to be confused with the previous entry, the Ruthin Wynnstay Arms is a comfortable 16th-century inn with a cheerful locals' bar and separate, attractively timbered lounge. Bar meals are served lunchtime and early evening and there is also a separate restaurant. The inn, with tea and coffee making facilities in the guest rooms, is an excellent base for visiting the Clwydian Hills, Offa's Dyke, Horseshoe Pass and Ruthin's 13th-century court house and castle.

Beer: Burtonwood Bitter on handpumps.

Accommodation: 2 singles, 4 doubles, 2 family rooms, 2 rooms with en suite facilities. B&B £10-£15 per person. Children welcome.

# ABERPORTH

Headland Hotel
2 miles off A487

Licensee: D Watterson
Tel: 0239 810 501

The Headland is a popular small hotel with spectacular views of the sea and the Cardigan coastline. The hotel has a lively locals' bar, a residents' lounge and beer garden. Meals are served in the bar as well as the separate dining room. As well as the coast, the area around Aberporth offers unspoilt countryside, salmon rivers and woollen mills and local crafts.

Beer: Bass, Hancock's HB on handpumps.

Accommodation; 3 doubles. B&B £12 per person. Children welcome.

# LLANGADOG

Castle Hotel
Queen Square, 5 miles from Llandovery on A4969

Licensee: Alastair Dye
Tel: 0550 777377

The Castle is a 500-year-old inn in a village nestling at the foot of the Black Mountains on the edge of the Brecon Beacons national park. Later extensions used original ship's timbers from vessels of Nelson's times. The inn has a 20-seater restaurant with a menu making use of such local produce as fresh salmon. Bar meals are served in the lounge and saloon bars. The light and roomy guest rooms are on the first floor and have pleasant views over the town square.

Beer: Flowers Original, Marston Pedigree and occasional guest beers on handpumps.

Accommodation: 3 singles, 2 doubles, 2 family rooms. B&B £13.50 per person. Weekend £27, Week £94.50, Off-season Weekend £25. Children welcome.

# TAL-Y-BONT

White Lion Hotel
A487 near Aberystwyth

Licensee: John C Davies
Tel: 097 086 245

The White Lion dates back to the 16th century and retains some original characteristics in spite of many alterations over the years. It has an impressive façade with dormers in the roof, a balcony above the porch and fine bay windows on the ground floor. The hotel has coal and log fires in winter and, according to Mr Davies, a 'ghost that goes *bonk* in the night' ... but there is no extra charge for this service. Darts, pool, dominoes and cribbage are played in the bar and meals are served there lunchtime and evening. Food includes fresh poached salmon and local trout, home-cooked ham, cannelloni, salads, jacket potatoes, steaks, sandwiches, toasties, curries, and burgers and fish fingers for children, plus apple pie, trifle and raspberry or lemon torte. Guest rooms all have tea and coffee making facilities. The area offers sandy beaches and golf courses and narrow gauge railways at Rheidol, Tal-y-Llyn and Ffestiniog.

Beer: Banks Mild and Bitter on electric pumps.

Accommodation: 1 single, 3 doubles, 1 family room, 3 rooms with showers. B&B £11.50 per person. Off-season Weekend £10 per night. Children welcome, 20% reduction. Credit cards: Access, Visa.

## WOLF'S CASTLE

Wolf's Castle Inn
On A40 near Haverfordwest

Licensees: Fritz & Judy Neumann
Tel: 0437 87662

The inn is a 200-year-old stone building with a slate roof and a welcoming halo of roses, hanging baskets and trees. Inside there is a cheerful bar with a tiled floor where darts and dominoes are played, a comfortable lounge and a conservatory doubling as a restaurant and a delightful garden for the summer months. Bar food includes soup, farmhouse pâté, local smoked trout, ploughman's, fish and chips and a wide range of salads. Dishes from the restaurant can also be eaten in the bar: you can choose from smoked salmon, fresh rainbow trout, chicken chasseur, grills, salads and a splendid sweet trolley that includes ice creams and sorbets. Children are made particularly welcome. The area offers beaches, windsurfing and walks and the inn is a good resting place to and from the Irish ferry. The accommodation is one self-contained suite with a kitchenette that includes a fridge and tea and coffee making facilities but no cooker.

Beer: Felinfoel Double Dragon on handpump.

Accommodation: 1 double with bed for a child, with shower. B&B £12.50 per person. Weekend £25, 7 days £75. Children welcome, half price under 11 years. Credit cards: Access, Visa.

## COWBRIDGE (S GLAMORGAN)

Bear Hotel
High Street, off A48

Licensees: H P Lewis & J Davies
Tel: 044 63 4814

The Bear is a cheery 12th-century inn with a ramble of small rooms and beamed ceilings, a flagstoned public bar and carpeted lounge, plus a grill room and up-market cocktail bar. Good value bar food includes scampi, lasagne, steak and kidney pie and ploughman's. There is a separate restaurant in an impressive vaulted room. Two of the attractive guest rooms have four-poster beds and all the rooms have colour TVs and tea and coffee making facilities.

Beer: Bass and Welsh Hancock's HB, Brains Dark, Bitter and SA, Flowers IPA plus guest beer of the week on handpumps.

Accommodation: 13 singles, 23 doubles, 1 family room, 34 rooms with private baths. B&B £29 single, £39 double. Weekend £62 double. Children welcome, no reductions.

WHITE LION HOTEL, TAL-Y-BONT —

# NOTTAGE (MID GLAMORGAN)

Rose & Crown
Heol-y-Capel, A4299, 2½ miles
off M4 exit 37

Manager: J W Rout
Tel: 065 671 4850

The Rose and Crown is a white-painted hotel with a stone porch, hanging baskets and outdoor trestle tables in a village near Porthcawl. The bar has some original beams and stone walls, a separate restaurant and beautifully appointed guest rooms with private bathrooms, tea and coffee trays and colour TVs. The restaurant offers pâté, smoked mackerel, roast beef and Yorkshire pudding, desserts and a children's menu. There are facilities for sea fishing, sailing and golf in the area.

Beer: Ruddles County, Ushers Best Bitter, Websters Yorkshire Bitter on handpumps.

Accommodation: 2 singles, 6 doubles, 1 family room. B&B £30 single, £40 double. Weekend £37 per person for 2 nights. Babies free, children 3-12 sharing with parents £5 per night inc. breakfast. Credit cards: Access, Amex, Diners, Visa, Grand Met.

# OGMORE-BY-SEA (MID GLAMORGAN)

Sea Lawn Hotel
Overlooking beach near river mouth and castle, off A48

Proprietor: Verdun Moore
Tel: 0656 880311

Mr Moore has strong views about food: his breakfasts will 'set you up for the day — they're not a roll and jam' and other meals are made from fresh produce 'not from plastic bags'. The Sea Lawn is a small, family-run hotel with stunning views of the sea and the heritage coastline. The area offers sea and river fishing, golf, beaches and walks. The guest rooms have colour TVs and tea and coffee making facilities. Lunch and dinner are served and the food may include fillets of sole, tornados Rossini, noisette of lamb, cod mornay, fillets of plaice and desserts.

Beer: Bass and Welsh Worthington Dark and BB on handpumps.

Accommodation: 1 single, 8 doubles, all en suite. B&B £20 single, £34 double. Weekend (3 nights) £54 B&B + evening meal.

# ABERGAVENNY

Llanwenarth Arms
Brecon Road, A40 midway between Abergavenny & Crickhowell

Licensee: D'Arcy McGregor
Tel: 0873 810550

The Llanwenarth Arms is a combination of 16th-century inn and modern hotel on the banks of the River Usk and with hills and mountains forming a backdrop. The pub has a welcoming frontage, with its awnings over the windows and tubs of flowers on the forecourt. Inside there are two superb bars with beamed ceilings and bar meals, while the dining room that overlooks the river has an à la carte menu. All the well-appointed guest rooms have baths or showers, colour TVs and tea and coffee making facilities.

Beer: Robinson Best Bitter, Wadworth 6X on handpumps.

Accommodation: 18 doubles. B&B £38 single, £45 double. Weekend £17.50 per person per day for any 2 nights. Children welcome, half price. Facilities for the disabled. Credit cards: Access, Amex, Diners, Visa.

# CAERLEON

## Rising Sun
Ponthir Road, 3 miles from M4 exit 25. Watch for Caerleon/Ponthir signpost: go through Caerleon village, turn left, inn ½ mile on left.

Proprietors: Brian & Judith Ansen
Tel: 0633 420534

The Ansens offer a warm welcome at this cheerful old inn with an entrance decked with hanging baskets. It is a splendid base for visiting the ancient Roman fortress in Caerleon, no less than six castles within a 15 minutes' drive, the Brecon Beacons and the Wye Valley. Meals are available in the dining room both lunchtime and evening every day and the restaurant makes use of the new change in the law to sell drinks with food outside normal licensing hours.

Beer: Brains SA with a minimum of 5 guest cask beers always on handpumps.

Accommodation: 1 single, 5 doubles, 2 family rooms, 2 en suite (extra rooms planned for 1988). B&B from £12.50 per person. Half and full board available. Children welcome, from no charge to half price depending on age. Credit cards: Access, Amex, Diners, Visa.

# CHEPSTOW

## Coach & Horses
Welsh Street, off A48

Licensee: Mr L Bell
Tel: 029 12 2626

A one-bar, split-level pub at the end — or the beginning — of Offa's Dyke, with a strong emphasis on sport. The pub boasts three darts teams, a crib team and a Rugby side, plus regular quiz nights. The locals are friendly and always keen to discuss Rugby on the firm understanding that Wales has the best national team. There are bar snacks at lunchtime and many nearby restaurants offer evening meals.

Beer: Brains SA, Ruddles County, Usher Best Bitter, Websters Yorkshire Bitter on handpumps.

Accommodation: 3 singles, 3 doubles, 1 family room, 3 rooms with private baths. B&B £16 per person. Children welcome, no reductions.

# LLANTHONY

## Abbey Hotel
Off A465, near Crucorney

Licensee: Ivor Prentice
Tel: 087 32 487

A stunning and ancient inn set amid the ruins of a Norman priory with the backdrop of the Black Mountains. The priory was established in 1108 by William de Lacy; his task was to put down rebellious Welsh in the area but he tired of the bloodshed and settled for the monastic life instead. The inn is part of the original prior's lodge and was restored in 1811. It has a stone-flagged and vaulted bar and a dining room with an impressive oak-backed settle and a profusion of brass. The guest rooms, reached by a stone spiral staircase, includes a four-poster bedroom. The restaurant is open Tuesday to Friday evenings. Bar food, available every lunchtime and every evening except Sundays, includes soup, home-made pâté, chilli, vegetable lasagne, vegeburgers and sweets. *The hotel is usually closed from December to Easter: phone to check availability.*

Beer: Brain Bitter, Flowers Original and IPA, Ruddles County on handpump. Welsh whisky is also available.

Accommodation: B&B from £15-£25 per person.

# LLANTILIO CROSSENNY

Hostry Inn
B4233 by White Castle, between Monmouth & Abergavenny
Licensees: Mike & Pauline Parker
Tel: 060 085 278

The Hostry is a 15th-century village inn on Offa's Dyke and owned since 1459 by the descendants of Sir David Gam, knighted by Henry V for saving his life in battle. It has a free-standing inn sign and tubs of flowers, benches and seats by the entrance. There is a superb 300-year-old banqueting hall and long alley skittles. Bar skittles, darts and dominoes are played in the bar. A vintage Rolls-Royce is available for hire. Bar food includes soup, crab au gratin, home-made steak and kidney pie, lasagne, chicken, grills, plaice with cheese and broccoli and trout plus an enterprising range of vegetarian dishes such as mushroom and aubergine lasagne, pasta Florentine and smoked haddock pasta with prawns and mushrooms.

Beer: Bass, Smiles Exhibition, Usher Best Bitter on handpumps.

Accommodation: 1 single, 2 doubles, 1 family room. B&B £10 per person. Half and full board available. Children's room, children welcome to stay, half price. Facilities for the disabled.

# TREDEGAR

Cambrian Hotel
The Circle, A65
Licensees: Neil & Val Breeze
Tel: 0495 711107

The Cambrian is a street-corner, mining-valleys local dating back to 1810. It has Chartist connections in a town associated with Nye Bevan, post-war architect of the National Health Service. The lively pub has log fires in winter, live music on Tuesdays and Thursdays and a Sunday charity quiz. Bar food includes rolls and sandwiches, ploughman's, jacket potatoes with choice of fillings, sausage, egg and chips and a daily special. Full meals are available in a separate restaurant. Water sports are available in Bryn Bach park, there are some remaining working mines and a mountain railway.

Beer: Bass and Welsh Hancock's HB, Brain Bitter and SA, Flowers Original on hand and electric pumps.

Accommodation: 3 doubles, 1 en suite. B&B £10-£12 per person. Children welcome.

# ABERDARON

Ty Newydd Hotel
Centre of village, off A4413

Licensee: Mrs B Jones
Tel: 075 886 207

Ty Newydd is a large, comfortable pub, with commanding views of the beaches and sea in a village on the furthest point of the Lleyn peninsula, which is also the port for Bardsey Island (Ynys Enlli), the Isle of Saints. The hotel has several large rooms, including a comfortable lounge with sea views. There are real fires in winter, traditional games in the bar, meals lunchtime and evening, facilities for the disabled, and camping close by.

Beer: John Smiths Bitter on handpump.

Accommodation: 4 singles, 12 doubles, 1 family room, 9 rooms en suite. B&B £15 single, £28 double. Bargain Breaks: terms on application. Credit cards: Access, Visa.

# ABERSOCH

St Tudwal's Hotel
Main Street, off A499

Licensee: John Page
Tel: 075 881 2539

A popular pub with locals and tourists, St Tudwal's has a smart, comfortable lounge and large public bar. The hotel offers open fires in winter, a welcome for families, a garden, pub games and good food both lunchtime and evening. Abersoch, on the Lleyn peninsula, has a good harbour and fine beaches and is the home of the South Caernarfonshire Yacht Club, one of the biggest in Britain.

Beer: Robinson Best Mild, Best Bitter and Old Tom (winter) on electric pumps and straight from the cask.

Accommodation: 2 singles, 6 doubles, 1 family room, 5 rooms with en suite facilities. B&B £15-£25. Credit cards: Access, Visa.

# BANGOR

Union Hotel
Garth Road, off A55

Licensee: John E Duggan
Tel: 0248 2462

The Union has tiny bars awash with a vast collection of glass, china, copper, brass, ships' wheels, lights, floats, anchors and binoculars. John Duggan is a former merchant navy captain and has brought a strong nautical air to the pub that backs on to the bay close to the pier. There are traditional pub games, a garden and lunchtime bar food. Bangor is a good base for touring the North Wales coast, with Snowdonia a few miles to the south and Anglesey just across the Menai Strait. Accommodation in the Union is remarkably good value in well-furnished rooms served by a bathroom with a shower.

Beer: Burtonwood Bitter and JBA Premium on handpumps.

Accommodation: 3 doubles. B&B £8 per person.

# BEAUMARIS (ANGLESEY)

## Bold Arms
Church Street, off A545

Licensees: Ray & Pat Lewis
Tel: 0248 810313

The Bold Arms has a nautical flavour with many old photographs and prints of ships and the sea. There is a small beer garden for warm days, a public bar and a lounge with adjoining dining room. Traditional pub games are played and bar meals are served lunchtime and evening. The pub is just off the centre of an interesting old town with a 13th-century castle built by Edward I to control the entry from Conwy Bay into the Menai Strait. Sea fishing and sailing can be arranged in the town. All the guest rooms in the pub have tea and coffee making facilities.

Beer: Burtonwood Bitter on handpump.

Accommodation: 5 doubles, including 2 family rooms. B&B £12.50 per person. Children welcome, terms by arrangement.

## Old Bull's Head
Castle Street

Proprietors: Keith Rothwell & David Robertson
Tel: 0248 810329

You are in distinguished company here for those two itinerant travellers and boozers, Dr Johnson and Charles Dickens, stayed here in the original posting house of the borough, established in 1472 and rebuilt in 1617. It is a grade two listed building and is packed with fascinating antiques, including brass and copper ware, china, armour and weapons. There is a 17th-century water clock, and a high-backed chair in the beamed bar that used to be the town's ducking stool for law breakers. Access to the enclosed courtyard at the rear of the inn is through the original stage coach entrance which has the largest single-hinged door in Britain. Bar food includes soups, sandwiches, ploughman's, sausages and sauerkraut, and local salmon salad. Experienced restaurateur Keith Rothwell uses his skills in the beamed dining room to produce dishes based on such local produce as turbot, sole, salmon and hare. There is a residents' lounge and morning tea is brought to your bedroom.

Beer: Bass on handpump.

Accommodation: 9 singles, 8 doubles, 1 family room, 5 rooms with en suite facilities. B&B £15.50 single, £16.50 with bath, £26.50 double, £27.50 with bath. Children welcome, one-third reduction if sharing. Credit cards: Access, Visa.

# BEDDGELERT

## Prince Llewelyn
By bridge over river, off A498 & B4085

Licensee: Mr Morton
Tel: 0766 242

A fine old three-storey, brick-built inn in a wonderfully peaceful setting, of rushing streams and quiet meadows, by a river in the Snowdon mountains. The spacious inn offers a genuinely warm welcome with open fires, facilities for families, disabled people and campers, and good lunchtime bar meals.

Beer: Robinson Best Mild and Best Bitter on electric pumps.

Accommodation: 2 singles, 6 doubles, 2 family rooms, 3 rooms with en suite facilities. B&B £10-£15 per person. Half board available. Credit cards: Access, Visa.

# BENLLECH (ANGLESEY)

Glanrafon Hotel
Benllech Bay, A5025

Licensee: Jim Robinshaw
Tel: 024 885 2364

The Glenrafon is a gracious, black and white fronted hotel with superb views from Moelfre Bay of the Irish Sea and Ormes Head at Llandudno. The beaches of Benllech Bay are just minutes away; there are opportunities for fishing, boating and golf on the island, while Snowdonia is just across the bridge on the mainland. The hotel has a lively public bar and quiet lounge. Darts and dominoes are played. There is a separate residents' TV lounge and a restaurant with table d'hôte menu. Bar snacks are also available. Most of the bright and airy guest rooms have fine sea views.

Beer: Lees Bitter on handpump.

Accommodation: 8 doubles, 4 twins, 5 family rooms, 12 with private baths. All rooms let as single when available. B&B from £13.50 per person, £20 with dinner. Weekend from £33 half board, Week £91

B&B, £132 half board. Children's room; children welcome to stay, 25-95% reductions according to age.

# BETWYS-Y-COED

Pont-y-Pair Hotel
Town centre, A5

Licensees: Steve & Phyllis Harley
Tel: 06902 407

The Pont-y-Pair is a solid, stone-built hotel with bay windows and an impressive dormer roof in a famous Welsh village that remains something of a Victorian inland resort and institution. The surrounding countryside is beautiful and the village straddles the A5 as the road follows the rushing and tumbling rivers Lledr and Llugwy as they pour into the Conwy north of Betwys. The hotel has open fires in winter, a welcome for families in the garden, and regular quiz and live music nights. Bar meals are available at weekends and throughout the summer. There are evening snacks for residents or the hotel arranges discounts at local restaurants. The guest rooms all have colour TVs with video programmes, tea and coffee making facilities and baby-listening service.

Beer: Younger Scotch Bitter, IPA and No 3 on handpumps.

Accommodation: 2 singles, 8 doubles, 3 family rooms. B&B £10-£15 per person. Off-peak breaks available: terms on application. Limited facilities for the disabled: assistance up steps.

# BODEDERN (ANGLESEY)

Crown Hotel
B5109, 1 mile off A5

Licensees: Reg & Candy Bryant
Tel: 0407 740734

The Crown is a fine example of a traditional village pub and is a good base for both the beaches of Anglesey and the port of Holyhead. It offers good and reasonably priced accommodation and food, with bar meals — home-baked pies, jacket potatoes and basket meals — available both lunchtime and evening. The bars have beamed ceilings and stone fireplaces. Darts and dominoes are played in the public bar. There is a children's room and a separate small restaurant. The Crown offers plenty of live entertainment, with quizzes on Sunday nights, regular parties, fancy-dress and charity fund-raising events.

Beer: Burtonwood Bitter on handpump.

Accommodation: 1 single, 1 twin, 2 doubles, 2 family rooms, all rooms with TVs. B&B from £11.50 per person. Children welcome, terms by arrangement.

# BULL BAY (ANGLESEY)

Trecastell Hotel
On A5025, near Amlwch

Licensees: Arthur & Iris Leese
Tel: 0407 830651

The Trecastell Hotel overlooks the rocks at Bull Bay and has magnificent views over the Irish Sea. It is next door to an 18-hole golf course. There is a comfortable lounge bar with sea views, a cocktail bar, games rooms and residents' lounge and restaurant. Food ranges from bar snacks to grills. Arthur Leese is a motor sport enthusiast and his daughter 'grows' her own sweaters: she breeds Angora rabbits, spins their wool and then knits with it. Most of the guest rooms have private baths and tea makers and all have superb sea views.

Beer: Robinson Best Bitter on electric pump.

Accommodation: 9 doubles, 3 family rooms, doubles let as singles when available. B&B £18 single, £30 double. Off-season Breaks: details on application. Children welcome, 25% reduction 10-15 years, half-price 2-10.

# CAERNARFON

Castle Hotel
Castle Square, off A487

Licensee: John Fairbanks
Tel: 0286 2640

The Castle is a friendly pub near the famous and dominating castle. There is a busy locals' bar and a quiet, smart lounge. Bar food is available both lunchtime and evening with the accent on home-cooking and local produce. The guest rooms are spacious and comfortably furnished and have tea and coffee making facilities. The town offers a small maritime museum, a Roman fort and walks by the River Seiont.

Beer: Bass and M&B Mild on handpumps.

Accommodation: 1 single, 3 doubles, B&B £10 per person.

# CAPEL CURIG

**Bryn Tyrch Hotel**
On A5 at eastern edge of village

Licensee: P Davis
Tel: 06904 223

This is the final oasis before you hit 'Dry-on-Sunday' Wales; Bryn Tyrch is the last watering hole until Llanberis or the aptly named Llanfrothen. The cheerful hotel on the A5 has a comfortable lounge with superb views across the valley to Moel Siabod, and a small public bar where darts and pool are played. There is an enterprising range of bar food lunchtime and evening, plus a separate restaurant. The hotel offers real fires in winter, a welcome for families, a garden and camping. Mr Davis plans both a tennis court and a photographic dark room: the latter facility must, when in situ, be unique among British pubs and small hotels.

Beer: Whitbread Castle Eden Ale and Flowers IPA on handpumps.

Accommodation: 2 singles, 9 doubles, 2 family rooms, 4 rooms en suite, all rooms with tea and coffee making equipment. B&B £10-£15 per person, discounts for group bookings. Credit cards: Access, Amex, Diners, Visa.

**Cobden's Hotel**
On A5, 1 mile E of village

Licensee: Mrs S Wetton
Tel: 06904 243

Cobden's is a lively and welcoming smart country hotel with a comfortable lounge and a climbers' bar. It offers facilities for families and disabled people, a garden and excellent bar food both lunchtime and evening. It is a popular resting

place for visitors who enjoy the surrounding countryside or who energetically clamber up the encircling peaks.

Beer: Tetley Bitter, Websters Yorkshire Bitter, Younger Scotch Bitter on handpumps.

Accommodation: 4 singles, 12 doubles, 2 family rooms, 9 rooms with en suite facilities and TVs. B&B £15-£25 per person. Half and full board available. £50 per person for 2 days full board. Group discounts. Credit cards: Access, Visa.

**Tyn-y-Coed**
On A5, 1 mile E of village

Licensee: G Wainwright
Tel: 06904 231

Thousands of visitors know the Tyn-y-Coed as the pub with the stage coach in the car park. The prominent landmark, more arresting than any pub sign, stands opposite the liveliest hotel in Capel. At weekends the bars are bursting with thirsty walkers and climbers, while residents can relax in more peaceful lounges and the restaurant. There are open fires in chilly weather, a garden with a welcome for families, and good bar food and full meals lunchtime and evening. Pen-y-Pass

CROWN HOTEL, BODEDERN — *see p*

and Nant Ffrancon, two landmarks of Snowdonia, are just a few miles away and there are gentler walks and climbs for the less energetic all around. The guest rooms in the hotel all have private baths or showers as well as tea and coffee making equipment.

Beer: Whitbread Castle Eden and Flowers IPA on handpumps.

Accommodation: 10 doubles, 3 family rooms. B&B from £18 per person. Half and full board available. Bargain Breaks £14 per person, £23 with evening meal. Credit cards: Access, Visa.

## CLYNNOG FAWR

St Beuno
Off A499

Licensee: S P Williams
Tel: 028 686 212

St Beuno is a comfortable and spacious old inn in a quiet village. Its origins date back in the mists of time to AD 616 and there is still an outstanding perpendicular church dedicated to St Beuno, who died in AD 630, and an impressive neolithic burial chamber. The inn has open fires, a garden, a lively public bar and bar food lunchtime and evening.

Beer: Bass on handpump.

Accommodation: 9 doubles, 3 family rooms. B&B £10-£15 per person. Credit cards: Access, Amex, Diners, Visa.

## LLANBEDR-Y-CENNIN

Olde Bull Inn
Off B5106. OS 761695

Licensees: Phillipe & Brenda de Ville Forte
Tel: 049 269 508

The Olde Bull is a 16th-century inn on the slopes of the Conwy valley. The old stone bar has beams, settles and log fires, one in a vast inglenook. There is a residents' lounge, separate dining room with beams from an old Spanish galleon, and a patio with wonderful views of the lowering mountains. Cheap and plentiful food includes soup, sandwiches, jacket potatoes, flans, salads and grills. Darts, dominoes and crib are played. As well as the guest room there is a six-berth caravan for hire.

Beer: Lees GB Mild and Bitter on handpumps.

Accommodation: 1 family room. B&B £15-£18 per person. Children welcome, terms by arrangement. Credit cards: Access, Diners.

## LLANBERIS

Padarn Lake Hotel
High Street, off A4086

Licensees: Robert & Sheila Elton
Tel: 0286 870260

The hotel overlooks Padarn Lake and has magnificent views of Snowdonia. There is a public bar with darts and pool, a lounge bar with a stage and live entertainment three evenings a week, and a cocktail bar next to the restaurant. There is a wide range of bar food lunchtime and evening and the restaurant menu includes local produce and game whenever possbile. The excellent accommodation has lake and mountain views, private baths or showers and tea and coffee making equipment. The hotel is a fine base for the Snowdon Mountain Railway, Llanberis Lake Railway, the Welsh Slate Museum and Padarn Country Park where you can fish, sail or row. Dinorwig Power Station, known as the 'Underground Giant' as it is contained within the heart of the mountain, is the largest pumped storage power station in Europe.

Beer: Bass and Stones Best Bitter on handpumps.

Accommodation: 21 doubles/twins, 3 family rooms. B&B £19.50 single, £35 double. 10% reductions for more than 3 nights. Two-day Breaks including dinner: £49 single, £90 double. Credit cards: Access, Amex, Diners, Visa.

# LLANDUDNO

## Gresham
143 Mostyn Street

Licensee: S G Capes
Tel: 0492 76120

The Gresham is a small, cheerful, one-bar pub in this famous Welsh seaside resort. The lounge is decorated with old pictures and prints and a lower area is reserved for darts enthusiasts and pool players. There is frequent live music, aided by a piano, with singalongs most evenings in summer and at weekends in winter. The guest rooms all have tea and coffee making facilities; the pub has a garden and lunchtime bar food in summer. The North Shore beach is just 200 yards away.

Beer: Tetley Bitter on handpump.

Accommodation: 1 single, 1 double, 4 family rooms. B&B £10-£15 per person. Half board available.

## Sandringham Hotel
West Parade

Licensee: D Kavanagh
Tel: 0492 76513

The Sandringham is a small, family-run hotel just 30 yards from the West Shore beaches. The décor has a naval theme: there are many seascapes and sailors' hats. Pool, dominoes, draughts and cards are played in the bar. There is a garden with splendid views of Conwy Bay and Snowdonia. Bar meals are served lunchtime and evening. The well-furnished guest rooms all have en suite baths or showers and tea and coffee making facilites.

Beer: Burtonwood Bitter on handpump.

Accommodation: 3 singles, 9 doubles/twins, 5 family rooms. B&B £15-£25 per person. Credit cards: Access.

## Snowdon Hotel
11 Tudno Street

Licensee: R G Corris
Tel: 0492 75515

The Snowdon is close to the North Shore and the Great Orme tramway station. It has a spacious, open-plan lounge bar decorated with old photos of the pub, old mirrors and whisky jugs. One of the original Victorian windows has been preserved and hangs framed above the fireplace. One section of the lounge is reserved for the local lifeboat crew. Its walls are decorated with lifeboat memorabilia and there is also a scale model of one of the old Llandudno boats. The small public bar is a haven for darts players: the pub has three teams. The Snowdon serves bar meals every lunchtime except Sundays. The neat guest rooms have colour TVs, tea and coffee making facilities and, a nice touch, bowls of fresh fruit.

Beer: Bass on handpump.

Accommodation: 4 doubles, 2 en suite. B&B £10 per person, £12 en suite.

# MENAI BRIDGE (ANGLESEY)

The Anglesey Arms Hotel
On A5025

Licensee: Alex Honeyman
Tel: 0248 712305

Cross the Menai Strait by Telford's famous suspension bridge and on the left at the far end you will find the Anglesey Arms. The hotel has an interesting collection of photos showing the Britannia bridge, which is farther along the coast, in its various stages of construction. The white-painted hotel with dormer windows is set in lovely tree-guarded gardens with panoramic views of Snowdonia. There is an extensive bar snacks menu while the restaurant offers both table d'hôte and à la carte meals. The spacious and comfortable guest rooms all have private baths or showers, tea and coffee making facilities and colour TVs.

Beer: Lees Bitter on electric pumps.

Accommodation: 4 singles, 4 doubles, 9 twins. B&B from £19 per person. Weekend from £23 half

board per person per night, Week from £115. Children welcome, terms depend on age.

# MORFA NEFYN

Cliffs Inn
Beach Road, off A4417 & A497

Licensees: Glynne & Mary Roberts
Tel: 0758 720 356

This popular seaside pub is famous for its superb bar meals (lunchtime and evening) and separate lounge and dining room. There is a lively public bar with frequent live music, a garden, facilities for disabled people and camping nearby. Morfa Nefyn is in a superb seaside setting and has a long sandy beach and the natural harbour of Porth Dinllaen. The accommodation is in self-contained flats, loft and studio.

Beer: Whitbread Castle Eden Ale on handpump.

Accommodation: 2 flats, 1 loft room, 1 studio room. Flat 1 has 1 twin & bunk beds, flat 2 has 1 double, 2 twin rooms, the loft has 1 twin, 1 double, the studio has 1 twin. All have kitchens and bathrooms; bed linen supplied. Weekly rates range from £80 for the loft to £120 for the larger flat: details on application.

# PENMAENMAWR

**Red Gables Hotel**
Bangor Road, A55

Licensees: Maureen & Malcolm
Stuart
Tel: 0492 623722

Red Gables was originally a private
residence and has been carefully
converted into a comfortable hotel
while retaining many of the original
features, including wood panels and
fireplace surrounds, a conservatory
and an imposing staircase to the
upper floor. It is on the main
Conwy to Bangor road but has a
secluded rear garden and magnificent
views of the Menai Strait, Anglesey,
Puffin Island, Conwy Bay and the
Great Orme. Excellent bar meals are
served lunchtime and evening. The
spacious and well-furnished guest
rooms all have tea and coffee making
facilities. Families are welcome,
including well-behaved dogs.

Beer: Websters Yorkshire Bitter and
Choice, Wilsons Original Mild on
handpumps.

Accommodation: 1 single, 3 doubles
including 1 family room. 1 room en
suite. B&B £10 per person. Children
half price up to 14 years.

# RED WHARF BAY (ANGLESEY)

**Min-Y-Don Hotel**
1 mile off A5025 between
Pentraeth & Benllech

Licensee: Diana M Kitchen
Tel: 0248 852596

There is a warm, friendly
atmosphere in this pleasant black
and white hotel overlooking the
cliffs and the sea. The guest rooms
are small but well equipped, with tea

making facilities on request, and
most of them have fine views of the
sea. Local produce features in the
restaurant and bar meals. Pool, darts
and dominoes are played and there is
a comfortable lounge where the Bass
comes straight from the cask. The
hotel has regular live entertainment
and is a good base for wind-surfing,
sailing, boating, fishing and
exploring Anglesey and Snowdonia.

Beer: Bass and Stones Best Bitter,
Burtonwood JBA on handpumps
and straight from the cask.

Accommodation: 4 singles, 6
doubles, 4 twins, 3 family rooms, 3
rooms with private baths. B&B £15
single, £28 double. Children's rooms;
children welcome, cot in family
room £1.50, £5-£7 up to 14 years.
All year reductions for parties of 10
or more.

# ROEWEN

**Ty Gwyn**
Follow signs to village from B5106
Conwy Valley road.
OS SH 759720

Licensee: A Mitchell
Tel: 0492 650232

The Ty Gwyn is a small, beamed
Welsh village pub with a tempting
easy-going atmosphere, nestling at
the foot of the low range of hills
and mountains that run down to the
sea at Penmaenbach. The pub is a
cheering sight to many a weary
walker who has completed the 13
peaks. It offers open fires, a welcome
to families, a garden and good
lunchtime bar food. There are
camping facilities in the village. The
pub is a TV star, having featured in
'Family at War' as well as the
'Home Brew' series when several

local characters became celebrities overnight.

Beer: Lees GB Mild and Bitter on handpumps.

Accommodation: 2 singles, 2 doubles. B&B £10-£15 per person.

# TRAWSFYNYDD

White Lion
Top of the hill in centre of village, off A470

Licensee: Mrs M Kreft
Tel: 076 687 277

The White Lion is a homely, unspoilt moorland village inn with solid brick walls and three small rooms, in a beautiful setting between Porthmadog and Dolgellau in the hills south of Snowdonia and just ten minutes' drive from Blaenau Ffestiniog, its steam railway and slate museum. The pub has brasses and fascinating old photos on the bar walls, darts, dominoes and cards are played by locals and visitors and bar meals are available lunchtime and evening.

Beer: Burtonwood Dark Mild and Bitter on handpumps.

Accommodation: 1 single, 3 doubles, 1 family room. B&B £10-£15 per person.

# BRECON

Gremlin Hotel
The Watton, A40

Proprietors: Stuart & Eleanor Harwood
Tel: 0874 3829

The Gremlin is just outside the centre of Brecon and is a fine base for visiting the national park where canoeing, sailboarding, pony trekking, golf, fishing and canal boating are available. Parts of the building date back more than 400 years. It is a genuine popular local with open fires, a garden, and a public bar where darts and quoits are played. Food ranges from sandwiches and home-cooked snacks to full meals in the small restaurant. The Gremlin claims to be haunted by a piano-playing ghost named Hilda.

Beer: Robinson Best Bitter, Wem Best Bitter on handpumps with regular guest beers.

Accommodation: 2 singles, 5 doubles, 2 family rooms. B&B £10 per person. Children welcome.

# ERWOOD

Erwood Inn
A470

Licensee: P J Lewis
Tel: 098 23 218

A happy-go-lucky old coaching inn in a village on the Cardiff road in the Wye Valley. The writer Henry Mayhew, one of the founders of *Punch* magazine, worked in the inn. The pastel-coloured exterior is prettily decked with hanging baskets and window boxes. There are a few seats and tables at the front and a garden at the rear with fine views of the valley where salmon and trout fishing are available. The inn has a lounge and public bar, visitors'

PRINCE LLEWELYN, BEDDGELERT — *see p 171*

lounge and good, plentiful bar food lunchtime and evening. The guest rooms have tea and coffee making facilities. Petrol and oil are available 24 hours a day on the forecourt.

Beer: Flowers Original, Wadworth 6X (summer) and guest beers on handpumps.

Accommodation: 2 singles, 2 doubles, 1 family room. B&B £9 per person. Half and full board available. Weekend £28, Week £90. Children welcome.

# GLASBURY-ON-WYE

Harp Inn
B4350, off A438

Licensees: David & Lynda White
Tel: 04974 373

The Post Office thinks the pub and Glasbury are in Herefordshire but they are firmly and geographically in Wales. The inn is a former 18th-century cider house, now with a full licence, in the beauty of the Wye Valley and the Black Mountains. In summer, you can soak up the surroundings from the back terrace and lawn that slopes down to the Wye. Inside there is a strong emphasis on games with shove ha'penny, cribbage, cards, dominoes and pool played in a separate room that overlooks the river. The lounge has brick walls and a log fire in winter. Bar food includes home-made soup, ploughman's, sandwiches and rolls, hot-pot, jacket potatoes and vegetarian dishes. The Whites welcome children and sensibly ask that parents as well as off-spring are well-behaved. The inn is a splendid base for walking, fishing, riding, golfing and canoeing. Hay-on-Wye, with its famous second-hand book shops, is close by.

Beer: Flowers Original and IPA, Robinson Best Bitter on handpumps.

Accommodation: 2 twins, 1 double, 2 rooms en suite. B&B £9.50 per person. Week £60. Children welcome, 40% reductions.

# LLANDRINDOD WELLS

Llanerch
Off Waterloo Road, near BR station

Proprietors: John & Kenneth Leach
Tel: 0597 2086

The Llanerch is a fine old inn in the county town of Powys and once an important coaching inn in old Radnorshire. Llanerch is a shortened version of 'Llanerchderion' — 'resting place by the glade for coaches'. The inn was built in the 16th century and still has old beams, an inglenook fireplace and superb Jacobean staircase. It stands in spacious grounds with a beer garden, terrace and children's play area. Darts, dominoes, pool and boules are played and golf, fishing and pony trekking are available in the area. There is a residents' TV lounge. Food is available from the bar or in the brasserie and includes onion soup with croutons, steak, kidney and mushroom pie, curry, rainbow trout, vegetarian pancakes, grills, toasties, filled baps, jacket spuds, fisherman's pie, lasagne, omelettes, and children's dishes. The inn is a splendid base for visiting the Elan Valley, Powis Castle, the Wye Valley and the neighbouring English towns of Ludlow and Shrewsbury.

Beer: Bass and Welsh Worthington Best Bitter, Robinson Best Bitter on handpumps.

Accommodation: 3 singles, 7
doubles/twins, 2 family rooms, 6
rooms en suite. B&B £13-£18 per
person. 2 day break from £37
includes dinner. Week from £80.
Children welcome, terms negotiable.
Credit cards: Access, Visa.

# LLANFAIR CAEREINION

Goat Hotel
¼ mile off A458 Welshpool road

Licensees: Richard & Alyson
Argument
Tel: 0938 810428

The Goat is a handsome country inn
in old Montgomeryshire near the
town of Welshpool: Llanfair and
Welshpool are linked by the narrow
gauge steam railway that operates in
the summer months. The inn offers
old-fashioned comfort with crackling
fires, polished brasses and deep
armchairs, with central heating and
tea makers in the guest rooms. Bar
meals include soups, ploughman's,
jacket potatoes, casserole of the day,
ham, sausages, chicken, curry, fish,
and beef and kidney pie. The menu
offers smoked mackerel fillet, grills,
Welsh lamb cutlets, duckling and
rainbow trout. The area is rich in
history and places of interest,
including Powis Castle, St Mary's
church and well in Llanfair, the
working weaving mill at Dinas
Mawddwy, and Montgomery Castle.

Beer: Bass and Welsh Hancock's HB
on handpumps.

Accommodation: 5 doubles, 1 family
room, 4 rooms with en suite
facilities. B&B £9-£12 per person.
Week £52.50-£70. 10% discount if
you carry a CAMRA guide.
Children's room; children welcome
to stay, half price.

# LLANFYLLIN

Cain Valley Hotel
High Street, A490

Licensee: John Hankin
Tel: 069 084 366

The Cain Valley Hotel is an
imposing, small market town hotel
with a multi-windowed, stucco
frontage and beams and log fires in
the interior. The hotel dates back
more than 350 years and has every
comfort in its wood-panelled bars,
lounges and well-appointed guest
rooms, all of which have private
bathrooms and tea and coffee
makers. Mr Hankin and his staff
have a growing reputation for good
food: meals may include home-made
soup, chicken chasseur, plaice fillets,
pork chop garni, home-made apple
pie and pears in red wine. As well as
draught beer and wine there is an
interesting selection of imported
lagers. Fishing by boat at Lake
Vyrnwy and along the River Cain
can be arranged. Places of interest
include the Berwyn Mountains, Lake
Bala, Chirk and Powis castles and
the waterfalls at Llanrhaeadr.

Beer: Bass, Ind Coope Bitter,
Marston Pedigree on handpumps.

Accommodation: 11 doubles, 3
family rooms. B&B £18 per person.
Weekend £25.50 including dinner,
Week £165. Off-season Weekend
£20.50 per person per day with
dinner. Children welcome, half
price. Credit cards: Access, Visa.

# LLANGADFAN

Cann Office Hotel
A458

Licensee: G Lewis
Tel: 0938 88202

A large pub set back from the road
and with trees and bushes guarding
the entrance, the Cann Office dates
from the 14th century and offers
facilities for all ages. There is a
games room with pool, a juke box
and video machine, a bar where
darts and dominoes are played, a
cocktail bar and a family lounge.
Food, mainly home-cooked, ranges
from egg and chips to a T-bone
steak. Welsh singing often breaks
out spontaneously on Saturday
nights.

Beer: Marston Pedigree on
handpump.

Accommodation: 2 singles, 4
doubles, 2 family rooms. B&B £10
per person. Children welcome, 40%
reductions.

# LLANGURIG

Blue Bell Inn
A44, near Llanidloes

Licensees: Bill & Diana Mills
Tel: 05515 254

The Blue Bell is a 16th-century
fishing inn, two buildings knocked
into one with an impressive double-
porch façade, a fine resting place for
touring mid-Wales. The hotel will
arrange for permits for fly fishing on
the Clywedog reservoir and there
are also facilities for golf, pony
trekking, bird watching and walking
in the beautiful surrounding
countryside. The Blue Bell has a
welcome for families, open fires in
winter, a public bar, full restaurant

meals, hot and cold bar snacks and
packed lunches if required. Llangurig
is 1,000 feet above sea level and has a
14th-century monastic church and a
craft centre. Five miles away is
Llanidloes, an historic market town
at the confluence of the rivers
Severn and Clywedog. The
Plynlimon mountains, Elan Valley
and Claerwen lakes are all within
easy reach.

Beer: Flowers Original, Sam Powell
Best Bitter on handpumps.

Accommodation: 4 singles, 5
doubles, 1 family room, 1 en suite.
B&B £13.50 per person. Children
welcome.

# LLANWRTYD WELLS

Neuadd Arms Hotel
The Square, A483

Proprietors: Gordon & Di Green
Tel: 0591 3236

The Neuadd Arms is a splendid
19th-century hotel by the river in
the smallest town in Britain, whose
Georgian and Victorian architecture
has been carefully restored. There
are log fires, the obligatory ghost
and good cooking. The traditional
back bar has a good local
atmosphere where quoits, darts and
shove ha'penny are played. There is
Welsh singing at weekends. Gordon
Green is an enthusiastic CAMRA
member, organises the Mid-Wales
Beer Festival every November and
Real Ale Rambles in the forests. The
Greens will also attempt to order
any guest beers that visitors request
and will arrange visits to Buckley's
and Felinfoel breweries. For visitors
of a less bibulous nature, there are
pony trekking, horse riding, fishing,
mountain cycling and bird watching
facilities all around.

Beer: Felinfoel Double Dragon, Greene King Abbot Ale, Welsh Worthington Best Bitter on handpumps.

Accommodation: 7 singles, 7 doubles, 1 family room, 7 en suite. B&B £13.50 per person. Weekend £41, Week £145. Details of beer festival and other ale-activities on request. Children welcome, up to 50% reductions. Credit card: Visa.

# MACHYNLLETH

Dyfi Forester
4 Heol-y-Doll

Licensee: John Smith
Tel: 0654 2004

The pub is more than 100 years old and Mr Smith says he is determined not to move too much with the times; he offers his record collection as evidence of old-fashioned tastes. He has allowed a pool table in but retains such traditional pub games as darts, dominoes and crib. Piano players are welcome to tinkle the resident ivories. Food in the single, large bar is mainly home made and includes chilli con carne and lasagne. The pub is popular with steam-railway enthusiasts and plays host to the crews of the railway which runs along the glorious Cambrian coast.

Beer: Marston Border Mild, Bitter, Pedigree and Owd Rodger (some beers seasonal) on handpumps.

Accommodation: 1 single, 2 doubles (also let as family rooms). B&B £11 per person. Weekend (3 nights) £30 per person, Week £65. Children welcome, half price if sharing with parents.

# PENYBONT

Severn Arms Hotel
Junction of A44 & A488

Proprietors: Geoff & Tessa Lloyd
Tel: 059 787 224

The Severn Arms is a splendid old coaching inn with ancient roots and a more recent, stunning Georgian frontage: Penybont, or Pont Rhyd-y-Cleifon as it was first known, dates from medieval times when it served as the fortification of Castle Cefn Llys. An inn by the bridge over the River Ithon has existed for centuries and was known as the Fleece or New Inn until 1814, when it became known as the Severn Arms. It was moved, lock, stock and barrels, to its present site in 1840 and retains a wealth of old beams and log fires, with a traditional bar and a residents' TV lounge. Residents can use the fishing rights on the river and pony trekking is available locally. The inn is in a superb location and a good base for border hopping between Wales and Shropshire. There are bar snacks and full meals in the beamed dining room.

Beer: Bass on handpump.

Accommodation: 4 doubles, 6 family rooms, doubles let as singles when available. B&B £18 per person. Weekend £52.60, Week £140 including dinner. Children welcome, up to half price depending on age. Credit cards: Access, Visa.

## PONTDOLGOCH

Mytton Arms
A470 9 miles W of Newtown

Licensee: Mrs Lyn Taylor
Tel: 0686 84 8919

The Mytton Arms is a half-timbered, black and white country pub with a bright, modern interior, a family room, garden, open fires and a public bar. Bar meals and restaurant meals use fresh local produce while the guest rooms have colour TVs and tea making equipment. Pony trekking and fly fishing are available and the Plynlimon mountains and Clywedog reservoir are close by.

Beer: Sam Powell Original and Samson, Tetley Bitter on handpumps.

Accommodation: 4 doubles, 1 family room, 1 room en suite. B&B £15 per person. Half and full board available. Weekend £45 half board, £55 full. Week £140 half board, £180 full. Children welcome, free if sharing, charged for meals.

## PONTROBERT

Royal Oak Hotel
2 miles off A495 from Meifod

Licensees: Francis & Dulcie Jones
Tel: 093 884 474

The Royal Oak stands in magnificent scenery and is built of Welsh stone. It has exposed beams and log fires in winter. The locals' bar has a snug with a dart board and a pool area. The lounge is spacious and comfortable and there is a separate family room where bar meals can be enjoyed as well as a restaurant that seats 24. Bar food includes soup, grills, home-made lasagne, chilli, cottage pie and curry, with trout, seafood pasta, steak and kidney, ploughman's and a children's menu. Outside there is a landscaped garden with a children's play area and tables in warm weather.

Beer: Marston Pedigree on handpump.

Accommodation: 1 single, 3 doubles. B&B £8 per person. Children welcome.

## TALGARTH

Tower Hotel
The Square A479

Licensees: J Poole & M J Barnes
Tel: 0874 711253

The Tower is in the centre of town and offers excellent, family-run accommodation and food. The bar has a large log fire in winter, a pool table and home-made bar snacks lunchtime and evening. The lounge has a TV for residents and children, while the separate dining room is open seven days a week. The guest rooms have tea and coffee making facilities. The surrounding area offers gliding, hang gliding, canoeing, sailing, fishing, hill walking and golf.

Beer: Flowers Original and IPA on handpumps, with regular guest beers.

Accommodation: 1 single, 6 doubles, 2 family rooms. B&B £12.50-£14.50 per person. Weekend £24.75 per person, Week £77.50-£91. Children welcome, reductions by arrangement.

# SCOTLAND

Scottish pub hours are standard: 11-2.30 and 5-11, Sunday 12.30-2.30 and 6.30-11. Many pubs have regular afternoon and evening extensions that allow them to open all day, often until midnight or later. Not all pubs open on Sunday but hotels serve drinks to residents.

ROYAL HOTEL, FORRES — *see p 196*

# BROUGHTON

Greenmantle Hotel
On A701

Licensee: Rena Anderson
Tel: 089 94 302

A roadside hotel in the middle of this pleasant Lanarkshire village near Biggar. It has a bar and lounge, two open fires in winter and a sitting room for residents. Families are welcome and there are bar meals and full meals lunchtime and evening. Broughton is the home of the small independent brewery of the same name, set up in 1980 by a former Scottish & Newcastle executive with the splendid brewing name of David Younger. In a country dominated by two giant groups, he has had surprising but welcome success.

Beer: Broughton Greenmantle Ale on air pressure.

Accommodation: 6 doubles, 1 en suite, all rooms with colour TVs. B&B £15-£25 per person. Half and full board available. Credit cards: Access, Amex, Diners, Visa.

# CARLOPS

Alan Ramsey
On A702

Licensee: Anthony Swift
Tel: 0968 60258

A 200-year-old inn with blazing log fires in winter and stone-flagged floors. There is a bar, food lunchtime and evening, family facilities and an outdoor area for picnics and barbecues in warm weather. Carlops is a tiny Borders village in wonderful walking country.

Beer: Belhaven 70 and 80 shilling, Theakston Best Bitter on handpumps.

Accommodation: 2 singles, 4 doubles. B&B £10-£15 per person. Half board available. Credit cards: Amex. Visa.

# COLDSTREAM

Newcastle Arms
50 High Street, A697

Licensees: R W & M E Atkinson
Tel: 0890 2376

Trip and you fall into England in this famous old Borders town with its strong military connections — there is even a Coldstream Guards Museum. The Newcastle Arms is family run and offers a warm welcome in its bars. There is a separate dining room that serves meals at most times of the day. You may be close to the border but the licensing hours tell you that you are definitely in Scotland: the bar is open all day Monday to Saturday until midnight and is also open Sunday afternoon and evening.

Beer: Arrol's 70 shilling on electric pump.

Accommodation: 1 single, 3 doubles, 1 family room. B&B £13.50 per person. Children welcome, half price.

# INNERLEITHEN

Traquair Arms
Traquair Road, off A72

Licensee: Mr Anderson
Tel: 0896 30229

A quiet and comfortable hotel in a quiet Borders town that is popular with hill walkers and anglers. Traquair Arms has open fires, a family welcome, a garden and excellent food lunchtime and evening: Mr Anderson is a trained chef. The hotel is close to Traquair House, the stately house that keeps its main gates shut until a Stuart returns to the throne. To keep himself occupied while awaiting this unlikely event, the laird, Peter Maxwell-Stuart, brews the famous, strong bottled-fermented beer named after the house and has recently added a draught beer too. Brewing is in an 18th-century brew house. Visits can be arranged.

Beer: Broughton Greenmantle Ale, Traquair Bear Ale on handpumps.

Accommodation: 2 singles, 7 doubles, 1 family room, 4 en suite. B&B £15-£25 per person. Half and full board available. Off-peak and weekend breaks: terms on application. Credit cards: Access, Diners, Visa.

# KELSO

Black Swan
Horsemarket, A689

Licensee: Mr Henderson
Tel: 0573 24563

The Black Swan is a cheerful old pub in a typical small Borders town. It has an atmospheric public bar and a comfortable lounge and serves good lunches and suppers. Darts and dominoes are played but there is no intrusive piped music. There are some facilities for the disabled and camping can be arranged nearby. The pub is open all day Monday to Saturday and Sunday afternoons.

Beer: Tennent 80 shilling on handpump.

Accommodation: 1 single, 1 double, 1 family room, all en suite. B&B £10-£15 per person. Half and full board available. Credit cards: Visa.

# OXTON

Tower Hotel
Off A68 near Lauder

Licensees: George & Ann Scott
Tel: 05785 235

The Tower is a picturesque old country inn with a striking black and white exterior, stained glass windows, public and lounge bars and a separate dining room. The public bar has a traditional gantry and a blazing fire on cold days. It is a genuine local, with a strong emphasis on darts and dominoes. All the guest rooms have TVs and tea and coffee making facilities. Food ranges from bar snacks to full meals and is available until 9.30 every day.

Beer: Arrol's 70 shilling on handpump.

Accommodation: 3 family rooms.
B&B £11 per person. Half and full
board available. Children welcome.
Family room charged at £27.50 B&B
on a room basis.

# PEEBLES

Kingsmuir Hotel
Springhill Road, off A72

Proprietors: Elizabeth & Norman
Kerr
Tel: 0721 20151

The Kingsmuir is a century-old
stately house in leafy grounds on the
south side of the Royal Burgh of
Peebles. There is a pleasant, parkland
walk to the High Street. The guest
rooms in the hotel have been
extensively refurbished and all have
colour TVs, private bathrooms and
tea makers. The popular bar is one
of the busiest in town. It has
retained its original thick walls that
stress the quality of 19th-century
workmanship. Traditional Scottish
food is served in the bar and the
dining room and its quality has won
'Taste of Scotland' awards in 1987
and 1988. Bar food includes soup,
steak pie, haggis, neeps and mashed
tatties, mince with skirlie pudding,
vegetarian casserole, and sandwiches.
Dinner may offer such dishes as
lentil soup, smoked salmon cornets,
smoked haddock in Mornay sauce,
lamb curry and roast chicken with
skirlie stuffing. Peebles is famous for
its many tweed and woollen shops
and there is also an 18-hole golf
course, pony trekking and fishing.

Beer: Broughton Greenmantle Ale
and Merlin's Ale on handpumps.

Accommodation; 2 singles, 6
doubles, 2 family rooms. B&B £22
per person sharing. Off-season
Weekends £18 per night. Children
welcome, no charge under 6.

# ST MARY'S LOCH

Tibbie Shiels Inn
A708 Moffat to Selkirk road

Licensees: Shanks & Hildegard
Fleming
Tel: 0750 42231

An historic and remote lochside inn
named after a local character who
married the mole catcher after being
in service to the family of James
Hogg, the shepherd poet of Ettrick.
Tibbie is a diminutive of Isabella.
Her photograph hangs in the back
bar, an original part of the old stone
building. A modern extension has
waitress-served meals. There is a
strong emphasis on home-cooking.
Local produce and food include
home-made soup, haddock, chips
and peas, Yarrow trout, home-made
chilli con carne, ploughman's,
burgers and sandwiches plus a daily
vegetarian special such as bulghur
wheat and walnut casserole. Evening
meals are served in the summer and
there is also a splendid afternoon
high tea. The loch offers sailing and
windsurfing and the inn is a good
base for visiting Grey Mare's Tale
waterfall, Bowhill, home of the
Duke of Buccleuch and Abbotsford,
the former home of Sir Walter Scott.

Beer: Caledonian 80 shilling plus a
guest beer on handpumps.

Accommodation: 5 doubles, 1 family
room. B&B £11.50 per person.
Children welcome, £9 per night
under 7 years if sharing with
parents. Facilities for the disabled: 5
bedrooms on the ground floor with
wheelchair access to bathrooms. The
inn has an all-day licence in summer
months.

## STOW

Manorhead Hotel
168 Galashiels Road, A7

Licensee: John Pickles
Tel: 057 83 201

A splendid 19th-century coaching inn in 1¼ acres of beautifully kept gardens. Mr Pickles is an enthusiastic host and offers superb food both lunchtime and evening. There are pub games, an open fire and a welcome for families.

Beer: Caledonian 70 shilling, 80 shilling, Stout and Strong Ale on handpumps.

Accommodation: 1 single, 5 doubles, 1 family room. B&B £10-£15 per person.

## TOWN YETHOLM

Plough Hotel
Main Street, B6352 near Kelso

Licensee: Ian P Angus
Tel: 057 38 2215

A remote old country hotel in the Border hills at the end of the Pennine Way, where there is salmon fishing on the Tweed and visits arranged to Floors Castle. The Plough has open fires, a garden and a bar with darts and dominoes. There is an extensive range of bar snacks. Lunches and suppers are served in the dining room. Meals include home-made pâté, sardine salad, soup, haddock, prawn nuggets, chicken and ham salad and sweets.

Beer: Arrol's 70 shilling on handpump.

Accommodation: 1 single, 2 doubles, 1 family room. B&B £12.50 per person, £21 double. Weekend £25, Week £75. Half and full board available. Children welcome, 25% reduction.

## TWEEDSMUIR

Crook Inn
A701 near Biggar & Moffat

Licensee: Bill MacDowell
Tel: 089 97 272

The Crook is a former drovers' halt in wooded hills. Dating from 1604, it is thought to be Scotland's oldest licensed premises. It was a clandestine meeting place for the 17th-century Covenanters and takes its name from the landlady named Jeanie o' the Crook who hid a fugitive from the dragoons in a peat stack. Robert Burns wrote his poem *Willie Wastle's Wife* in the kitchen of the inn and John Buchan was born nearby. The inn has a lounge with an open fire and an old stone-flagged bar with a stone fireplace and lots of carved wood. Bar food includes soup, ploughman's and steak and kidney pie. Darts, dominoes and crib are played in a separate room. There is a pleasant garden and a children's play area with climbing frame and slide.

Beer: Broughton Greenmantle Ale on handpump.

Accommodation: 1 single, 7 doubles, 6 rooms with private baths. B&B £26 per person, £44 double. Children welcome, 20% reduction sharing with parents.

## YARROW

Gordon Arms Hotel
Junction of A708 & B709

Licensee: Harry Mitchell
Tel: 0750 82222

A delightful old inn by the bridge at Yarrow Water. It was an ale house for drovers and traders and later was the meeting place for such noted local writers as Sir Walter Scott and

James Hogg, the Ettrick poet. When proposed by Hogg, it was granted a full licence by Scott the magistrate, perhaps not a good example of the even-handed nature of the law. The hotel today has a cheerful bar, lounge and dining room. Food ranges from bar snacks to high tea and full dinner. Fresh trout is always available and residents can enjoy free fishing on the Yarrow and Ettrick rivers. The hotel has an all-day licence seven days a week.

Beer: Broughton Greenmantle Ale on handpump.

Accommodation: 6 doubles. B&B £13.50 per person, £23 double. Children welcome, half price. Dogs allowed. Good access to the hotel for disabled people.

# CENTRAL

## BRIDGE OF ALLAN

Queens Hotel
24 Henderson Street, 1 mile from end of M9 at Dunblane roundabout, 2 miles from Stirling

Licensee: Douglas Ross
Tel: 0786 833268

The Queens is an impressive, Victorian sandstone building on the main road of this picturesque village. Douglas Ross ensures a warm family welcome for tourists and business people in well-appointed guest rooms, all with colour TVs and tea and coffee making facilities. There are two bars, with the lounge selling a renowned pint of IPA. The cellar bar has a wide range of international beers. Bar snacks are served throughout the day and the bars are licensed until 1am. The Queens has a beer garden and a new basement restaurant serving dinners was due to open in the spring of 1988.

Beer: Arrol's 70 shilling and 80 shilling, Younger IPA on handpump and air pressure.

Accommodation: 2 singles, 6 doubles, 2 family rooms. B&B from £15 per person. Half and full board available. Children welcome, half price if sharing. Credit cards: Access, Amex, Visa.

## CALLANDER

Bridgend House Hotel
Bridge End, A81, just off A84

Proprietors: Bill & Pauline Thomson
Tel: 0877 30130

The Bridgend is a friendly, welcoming country hotel at the foot of Ben Ledi, the gateway to the Trossachs. The hotel has a Tudor façade and luxurious furnishings inside. The emphasis is on quality and tradition; most of the guest rooms have private baths and colour TVs and there are a few rooms with four-poster beds. An extensive menu offers Scotch smoked salmon and trout, pasta carbonara, rib of beef, duck, steaks, salads (including vegetarian) — all served until 9.30pm. The hotel is close to the banks of the River Teith and is handy for Stirling Castle, Rob Roy's grave and Loch Katrine. TV nostalgists will recognise Callander as Dr Finlay's 'Tannochbrae'.

Beer: Broughton Greenmantle Ale, Harvieston 80 shilling on handpumps.

Accommodation: 7 doubles, 1 family room, 5 with private bath. B&B from £10 per person, £20 with bath. Half and full board available. Weekend Friday night to Sunday lunch £65. Children welcome, half price 12 and under.

## DRYMEN

Salmon Leap Inn
19 Main Street, just off A811

Proprietors: A, P & S MacDonald
Tel: 0360 60357

The inn was first known as the Plough and opened in 1759, the year of Robert Burns' birth. It was an ale house for cattlemen and farmers and the oldest part of the building, now called the Poachers' Rest, retains the original Hamilton Oak fireplace with wood etchings from Hampden Palace. The name changed in honour of the great salmon leaps at the nearby Pots of Gartness. The inn has a lively bar with a large collection of bric-à-brac, the Poachers' Rest lounge and dining room and a third bar that serves the beer garden in summer where barbecues are held. Food is served in all three bars and includes home-made soup, local smoked salmon, home-made steak pie, pork in cider pie, seafood pie, pasta dish of the day, grilled trout, ploughman's, jacket potatoes, toasties, daily blackboard specials and desserts. The guest rooms all have showers, colour TVs and tea and coffee making equipment.

Beer: Belhaven 80 shilling on air pressure.

Accommodation: 4 doubles, 1 family room (1 double has four-poster bed). B&B from £17.50 single, £28.50 double. Family room (2 adults, 1 child) from £33.50. Four poster room £37.50.

## KINLOCHARD

Altskeith Hotel
B829 off A81 & A821, near Aberfoyle

Proprietor: Priscilla Heaton-Armstrong
Tel: 087 77266

The hotel's lawns sweep down to beautiful Loch Ard, deep in Rob Roy country, with Ben Lomond glowering over the glen. The Altskeith is a lively, fun-loving hotel with weekend ceilidhs and a wide range of sporting activities. There are lounge and public bars, a residents' lounge and a candlelit dining room. Bar meals are served, too. The area is ideal for fishing, walking, golf, sailing, windsurfing, pony trekking and visiting Stirling Castle, Doune Motor Museum and Glengoyne Distillery.

Beer: McEwan 70 shilling and 80 shilling on handpumps.

Accommodation: 5 doubles/twins, 1 family room, 2 rooms with showers. B&B from £12.50 per person. Children's room; children welcome to stay, 20% reduction for children under 12 sharing. Credit cards: Access, Amex, Diners, Visa.

## DUMFRIES & GALLOW

## CANONBIE

Riverside
Signposted from A7

Licensees: Robert & Susan Phillips
Tel: 054 15 512/295

A lovely old inn in beautiful wooded countryside by the River Esk: the Phillips can arrange for fishing permits. There is an old beamed bar reached through an archway from the lounge, cheerful open fires in winter, old pictures of the area on the walls, stuffed wildlife, a long case clock and comfortable seats. Food in the bars and dining room is imaginative and widely praised: sample home-made beef or lentil broth, quiches, including vegetarian, fresh salmon with onion and ginger sauce, selection of salads, steaks and delicious sweets including date pudding and butterscotch meringue. There is a splendid range of local fish in the restaurant. Visitors praise the breakfasts, too.

Beer: Broughton Merlin's Ale, Theakston Best Bitter on handpumps.

Accommodation: 4 twins, 2 doubles, rooms can be let as singles. B&B from £22 per person. Credit cards: Access, Visa.

# LOCKERBIE

Kings Arms Hotel
29 High Street, town centre, ½ mile off A74

Licensee: Ian Guthrie
Tel: 05762 2410

The Kings Arms is a welcoming, 17th-century coaching inn in the heart of Burns country — 'bonny, bonny Galloway' as Burns described the magnificent scenery. The hotel offers substantial good value bar snacks and restaurant meals. It is the ideal base for coarse fishing on the river or loch and there are no less than six golf courses within a half hour's drive.

Beer: McEwan 80 shillings on air pressure.

Accommodation: 3 singles, 6 doubles, 5 twins, 1 family room. B&B £10.50 per person, £19 double. Children welcome, up to 50% reduction.

# MOFFAT

Black Bull
1 Churchgate, 1 mile off A74

Licensees: Jim & Lynda Hughes
Tel: 0683 20206

The Black Bull is a fine old 16th-century inn but its roots go back much further. There was a monastery on the site and a papal bull gave the monks permission to build an ale and rest house for pilgrims. The tiled lounge bar of the inn today has old coaching notices and prints while the bar across a courtyard has much memorabilia of the more recent age of steam: the defunct Caledonian Railway ran close to the inn. Between 1682 and 85 the inn was the headquarters of Graham of Claverhouse ('Bonnie Dundee'): his dragoons ruthlessly put down religious rebels in the area. Robert Burns was a frequent visitor to the Black Bull and scratched his *Epigram to a Scrimpit Nature* on a window pane (it is now in a museum in Moscow). Excellent bar food offers soup, shepherd's pie, cheese, potato and bacon hot pot, haggis, fish pie, quiche and salads.

Beer: Broughton Greenmantle Ale and Merlin's Ale, McEwan 80 shilling and Younger No 3, Theakston Best Bitter on air pressure and handpumps.

Accommodation: 3 singles, 3 doubles all with TVs and tea and coffee makers. B&B £15 single, £27.50 double. Children welcome. Facilities for the disabled.

## ABERDOUR

Aberdour Hotel
High Street, A92

Proprietors: Mike & Pat Taddei
Tel: 0383 860325

The hotel is a 17th-century coaching inn with a quaint bar famed for its friendly atmosphere and cheery coal fire in winter. The emphasis is on wholesome home-cooked food, including vegetarian dishes: Mr and Mrs Taddei are vehemently opposed to 'junk food'. There is fresh game plus fish and crabs caught locally in the hotel's own pots. Fresh vegetables and herbs come from the garden. There are bar snacks and full meals in the restaurant. The guest rooms all have TVs and tea and coffee making facilities. Aberdour is a good base for visiting the local castle, Inchcombe Abbey and the nearby beaches.

Beer: Belhaven 70 shilling and 80 shilling on handpumps.

Accommodation: 1 single, 1 double, 3 twins, 2 family rooms. B&B £12 per person. Weekend £24, Week £84.

## LARGOWARD

Staghead Hotel
A915/B940

Licensee: Sheelagh Gulbrandsen
Tel: 033 484 205

The Staghead is an old world village pub in beautiful countryside close to St Andrews, the home of golf, and picturesque East Neak fishing village. The hotel has a public bar with darts, dominoes and pool, and the lounge leads to a comfortable sitting room with an open fire and interesting antiques.

Beer: McEwan 80 shilling on air pressure.

Accommodation: 1 twin, 1 double, 1 family room. B&B £15 per person. Children welcome, half price if sharing.

## ST ANDREWS

Russell Hotel
The Scores, off A91

Proprietors: Angus & Jennifer Mitchell
Tel: 0334 73447

The Russell is a small, friendly hotel overlooking St Andrews Bay and close to the Old Course of the Royal and Ancient golf club. The hotel's cosy Victorian Bar has a unique atmosphere in which locals, undergraduates, young and old mix freely. The hotel is renowned locally for its splendid bar lunches while the restaurant serves fresh local produce, including seafood, game and Aberdeen Angus beef. The hotel is a fine base for the golf course, the castle, medieval cathedral and shopping centre.

Beer: Broughton Greenmantle Ale on handpump.

Accommodation: 6 doubles, 1 family room, 5 rooms with private baths. B&B from £20 per person. Off-season Weekends available: terms on application. Children welcome, free under 12 if sharing, charged for meals 12-16.

BLACK BULL, MOFFAT — *see p 193*

# ABERDEEN

**Brentwood Hotel**
101 Crown Street

Licensee: Jim Byers
Tel: 0224 595440

The Brentwood is a stylish modern hotel near the town centre that avoids the plastic, 'have a nice day' style of the big hotel chains. The emphasis is on quality and individual attention. Carriages Brasserie is part of the hotel designed as a traditional eating and drinking place with a good choice of food and ale. It is open seven days a week, lunchtime and evening, and children are welcome. Food includes home-made soup, smoked salmon, lasagne, pasta piccanti with chilli sauce, home-made steak and kidney pie, curry, vegetarian dish of the day, burgers, salads and grills.

Beer: Whitbread Castle Eden Ale and Wethered Bitter on handpumps plus a regular guest beer.

Accommodation: 45 singles, 15 doubles, 1 family room, 1 suite, all with private baths or showers. B&B £33 single, £40 double Monday-Thursday. Weekend £15 single per night, £20 double. Children welcome, terms by arrangement. Credit cards: Access, Amex, Diners, Visa.

**Ferryhill House**
Bon Accord Street

Licensee: Douglas Snowie
Tel: 0224 590867

The Ferryhill is a small, cheerful and attractive Georgian hotel with a large choice of cask beers for the area, some served by traditional tall founts. The other main plus point is that the hotel has no juke box, pool table or television in the bar. 'It is a pub where the art of conversation has not died,' according to one enthusiast. The main bar has large bow windows that overlook the hotel's spacious grounds. There is a hall with more seating and a plush cocktail bar. Bar food offers soup, jacket potatoes, ploughman's and curries. There is a separate restaurant, too. In warm weather there are tables and chairs on the lawn.

Beer: Broughton Greenmantle Ale and Merlin's Ale, McEwan 80 shilling and Younger No 3 and regular guest beers on handpumps and air pressure.

Accommodation: 4 singles, 6 doubles. B&B £20-£25 single, £36-£38 double.

# FINDHORN

**Crown & Anchor Inn**
Off A96, 6 miles from Forres

Proprietors: Roy & Peta Liddle
Tel: 0309 30243

An 18th-century inn on the edge of Findhorn bay and jetty. The bar is packed with old photos and prints of the area. Darts, dominoes, cribbage and backgammon are played and there is a large fireplace with welcoming fires in winter. There are more pictures in the comfortable lounge which also stages folk music on Sunday evenings. Bar food includes soup, ploughman's, sandwiches and toasties, fish and chips and chicken, and there are children's portions. Residents have the use of the inn's boats on the sandy beach. As well as the excellent draught beers, there is a collection of more than 100 international beers and 100 or so different whiskies.

Beer: Brakspear Bitter, Maclay 80 shilling, Tennent 80 shilling on handpumps plus 3 regular guest beers and draught cider.

Accommodation: 5 doubles/twins. 1 family room, all with private showers. B&B £14 single, £25 double. Children welcome, half price under 12 when sharing.

# FORRES

Red Lion Hotel
2 Tolbooth Street, A96

Licensee: James Storrier
Tel: 0309 72716

The Red Lion, known locally as the 'Red Beastie', is an old hotel rebuilt in 1838 with small cosy bedrooms, including attic rooms. The public bar has darts, dominoes and cribbage and there is a quieter, wood-panelled lounge bar. The hotel owns a rare Campbell's Brewery mirror. Forres is a delightful town that takes a vigorous part in the annual 'Britain in Bloom' competition and is a good base for taking the Whisky Trail or visiting Loch Ness. Forres, known as the Riviera of the North as a result of its mild climate, has a first-class golf course.

Beer: McEwan 80 shilling and Younger No 3 on air pressure.

Accommodation: 2 singles, 2 doubles. B&B £11.50.

Royal Hotel
Tytler Street

Proprietor: B Teasdale
Tel: 0309 72617

The Royal is an imposing, three-storey hotel on the west side of the Royal Burgh. The exterior has impressive balconies, dormer windows and sheltering trees. Inside is a comfortable lounge and a public bar has a cheery log and peat fire. Lunch, high tea and dinner are served. All the guest rooms have colour TVs and tea and coffee making facilities.

Beer: Younger No 3 on air pressure.

Accommodation: 5 singles, 10 doubles, 4 family rooms, 6 with en suite facilities. B&B £20 per person, Weekend £40, Week £140. Off-season Weekend 2 people for the price of 1. Children welcome, charged for meals only under 15 years.

# INVERURIE

Thainstone House Hotel
2 miles outside town on A96

Proprietors: Edith & Michael Lovie
Tel: 0467 21643

Thainstone House is a palladian mansion in meadows and woodlands of old Aberdeenshire's Don Valley. The house was designed by the famous local architect, Archibald Simpson, as a medieval manor house and then rebuilt, in 1820, after a disastrous fire. It was once the ancestral home of James Wilson, a signatory to the American Declaration of Independence. Close by are the ruins of the fortifications where Robert the Bruce's troops rested before the Battle of Barra in 1308. The interior of the hotel is sumptuous, with elegant dining room, lounges and beautifully appointed guest rooms, including two four-posters, all with private baths, TVs and tea and coffee making facilities. The bar menu offers soup, frog's legs in batter, lasagne, chilli, curry, trout and grills. The restaurant has such delights as melon filled with prawns and smoked salmon, vegetable terrine, game broth, king scallops, baked rainbow trout, supreme of chicken and escalope of salmon in pastry.

Beer: Tennent 80 shilling on handpump.

Accommodation: 6 doubles, 3 family rooms. B&B £33 single, £44 double. Weekend £35 per person, Week £165. Children welcome, charged for meals only if sharing.

# KINCARDINE O'NEIL

Gordon Arms Hotel
North Deeside Road, A93

Licensee: David Bell
Tel: 033 984 236

The Gordon Arms is an hospitable old inn built around 1810 in one of the oldest villages in Royal Deeside, close to Balmoral Castle. Outside, there are impressive chimneys and steeply sloping tiled roofs: inside, carefully restored lounges and guest rooms with hand-picked antique furniture that reflects the inn's early 19th-century origins. Food is based on local produce and home cooking and includes soup, scampi carbonara, spaghetti bolognaise, haddock and halibut, poacher's pie, chicken and grills. The village has a 13th-century church and there are many castles in the area, plus golf, fishing, gliding and water skiing.

Beer: Theakston Best Bitter on handpump.

Accommodation: 1 single, 4 doubles, 1 family room, 3 en suite. B&B from £11 per person. Off-season Weekends 10% reductions. Children welcome, no reductions.

# STONEHAVEN

Marine Hotel
Shorehead, off A92

Licensee: Philip Duncan
Tel: 0569 62155

A popular harbour hotel where you can sit outside in summer and watch the boats while you eat and drink. The hotel is more than 200 years old and most of the guest rooms overlook the harbour. There is a games room with darts, pool and bar billiards, plus a lounge bar and dining room. The hotel uses fresh local produce and offers morning coffee, lunch, high tea and evening meals. Fresh fish is the high spot of the menus. There is no specific children's room but they can use an upstairs room when the weather is bad.

Beer: McEwan 80 shilling, Tennent 80 shilling, Theakston Best Bitter on handpumps.

Accommodation: 4 singles, 4 doubles. B&B £18 single, £25.50 double. Children welcome, half price (some of the doubles also used as family rooms). Credit cards: Access, Amex, Visa.

# FORT WILLIAM

Nevis Bank Hotel
Belford Road, A82

Licensee: Jim Lee
Tel: 0397 5721

A cheerful and welcoming hotel on the outskirts of Fort William, a braw, sea-swept and historic old Highlands town. The hotel is conveniently placed at the start of the road up Ben Nevis and on the Road to the Isles. Climbers tackling the famous peak are strongly advised to have a pint in the bar first: better still, have two pints and forget the climb. The hotel has two bars offering a wide range of bar snacks, lunches and suppers. The separate Country Kitchen restaurant offers soup, country pâté, local salmon, Scottish lamb, Aberdeen Angus steaks, salads and a local delicacy called Cranachan — raspberries blended with oatmeal, cream and malt whisky. The Ceilidh Bar has weekend live Scottish and Country and Western music.

Beer: McEwan 80 shilling and Younger No 3 on air pressure.

Accommodation: 30 doubles, 2 family rooms, all with private bath. B&B £22 per person. Weekend £45, Week £170. Off-season Weekend £22.50 B&B + evening meal. Children welcome, half price.

# GLENCOE

Clachaig Inn
Off A82 on old riverside Glencoe road; near Ballachulish

Proprietors: Eileen & Peter Daynes
Tel: 085 52 252

The Clachaig Inn has one of the most spectacular settings in Britain in the heart of Glencoe, scene of the appalling massacre of the MacDonald clan by the combined forces of the Campbells and English troops. Wooded hillsides give way to the bare, bleak and awesome peak of Aonach Dubh. The inn has stood in its remote setting for some 300 years but the Daynes have carefully modernised it: the accommodation is of a high standard and there is now a self-catering lodge as well as the guest rooms in the inn. The dining room seats 50 and serves good Scottish home-cooked food. There are two bars and the lounge has fine views of the west face of the mountain. The Clachaig is open all year and has folk music most Saturday nights. The inn is the ideal base for climbing and walking and there are also seasonal opportunities for fishing and skiing.

Beer: McEwan 80 shilling and Younger Scotch Bitter and IPA on air pressure.

Accommodation: 2 singles, 17 doubles/twins/family rooms, all with private bath or shower. B&B from £10 per person. Weekly rates: 1 night in 7 free. Children welcome, half price under 12. There are also 4 self-catering chalets; terms on application.

# INVERNESS

Glen Mhor Hotel
Ness Bank, off A9 & A82

Licensee: J Nicol Manson
Tel: 0463 234308

The Glen Mhor is a large and imposing stone built hotel in a lovely setting by the banks of the Ness and at the foot of Inverness Castle. It offers the best of all winter welcomes: a blazing log fire in the entrance hall. There are two bars —

Nicky Tams in converted stables, and Nico's Bar and Bistro. There are bar lunches and the acclaimed restaurant offers à la carte and table d'hôte menus, with such specialities as grilled Ness salmon, fresh local fish and seafood, lamb, beef and game in season. Bar meals include haggis, local salmon, mussels stew, vegetarian dishes, jacket potatoes and salads. All the splendid guest rooms, 11 of which are in an adjacent riverside cottage, have colour TVs and tea and coffee making facilities. Inverness is the historic capital of the Highlands with fine Georgian and Victorian buildings, a museum and art gallery, two golf courses, fishing, sailing, mountaineering, riding and Loch Ness.

Beer: Burton Ale on handpump.

Accommodation: 6 singles, 23 doubles, 1 family room, 22 rooms with private baths. B&B from £16.50 per person. Children welcome, free if sharing with 2 adults.

Lochardhil House Hotel
Stratherrick Road, 1½ miles from town centre

Licensee: Richard Green
Tel: 0463 235995

Lochardhil House, on the outskirts of Inverness, is a splendid old mansion house set in five acres of grounds with a sunken garden. It has a partly castellated frontage, sweeping staircases, a quiet cocktail lounge and a genuine locals' bar in the courtyard. The stunning dining room has Gobelin tapestries depicting the biblical story of Esther. Excellent food ranges from home-made soup and sandwiches to lasagne, roast chicken with bacon and oatmeal stuffing, curry, grills,

salads, omelettes, and jacket potatoes with choice of fillings. The delightful guest rooms all have colour TVs and tea and coffee making equipment.

Beer: Younger No 3 on air pressure.

Accommodation: 3 singles, 5 doubles, 3 family rooms, all en suite. B&B £39 single, £49 double. Children welcome, £10 per night.

# LOTHIAN

# DIRLETON

Castle Inn
½ mile off A198

Licensee: Douglas Stewart
Tel: 062 085 221

The Castle Inn was once an important coaching stop on the old Dunbar road to Edinburgh. Now it stands in a quiet old Berwickshire village, still offering good ale and victuals to travellers. It has a long, low stucco frontage with tall chimneys and little windowless dormers, like raised eyebrows above the first storey windows. There is a free standing inn sign and two porches. The inn looks across the village green to the castle built in 1225 and the scene of a major battle during the 'English' Civil War, when it was taken by Cromwell's forces. The village grew around the castle in the 17th century when the sea engulfed the area of the original village and the people moved towards the safety of the battlements. The Castle Inn offers two bars — a public one with fine engraved mirrors and an open fire, and a comfortable lounge with another blazing welcome on chilly days. There is lunchtime food and service every day, including Sunday afternoons.

Beer: McEwan 80 shilling on air pressure.

Accommodation: 3 singles, 5 doubles, 4 rooms en suite. B&B from £14 per person. Week from £91. Children welcome, half price. Credit cards: Access, Amex.

# EDINBURGH

Navaar House Hotel
12 Mayfield Gardens, A7, 1 mile from city centre

Licensee: Mrs J McLay
Tel: 031 667 2828

Mayfield is a late 19th-century suburb in the south of Edinburgh. Its houses are big, stately and elegant and many of the main road ones have been converted into hotels. The Navaar has plasterwork in many of the rooms that suggests how ornate the interior must have been originally before it was modernised. It is now a comfortable, urbane, roadside hotel conveniently placed for the centre of Old Reekie with its snooty elegance, magnificent buildings and some of the finest and most ornate bars in Britain: the *Good Beer Guide* is even more essential than usual when in the Athens of the North. The bars in the Navaar House are popular with local football, hockey and even cricket teams and there is live jazz every Tuesday. The bars are open every day and all day until midnight and food is served both lunchtime and evening. Guest rooms have TVs and tea and coffee makers.

Beer: Caledonian 80 shilling, Maclay 70 shilling and 80 shilling, McEwan 80 shilling and guest beers on air pressure.

Accommodation: 2 doubles, 3 family rooms, 4 rooms with showers. B&B £15-£18 per person. Half and full board available. Children welcome, half price. Credit cards: Access, Amex, Diners, Visa.

# KIRKLISTON

Newliston Arms Hotel
76 Main Street, B8000, 2 miles off A1 & M8

Licensee: Alexander Nicol
Tel: 031 333 3214

The Newliston is a lively village local two miles from the Forth bridges. It has a thriving and boisterous bar with a panelled ceiling, popular with local folk. Watch for the splendid old tall founts that serve the beer. There is a cheering open fire in winter and bar food lunchtime and evening. Hopetoun House is close by.

Beer: McEwan 70 shilling and 80 shilling on air pressure.

Accommodation: 2 singles, 3 doubles. B&B £12.50 per person. Half and full board available. Week B&B £75. Children welcome, half price.

# AIRDRIE

Tudor Hotel
39 Alexander Street, off A89

Licensee: Nigel Foster
Tel: 023 64144

The Tudor is a bright and cheerful hotel 13 miles from Glasgow. It has two lounge bars: cask beer is available in the Elizabethan Bar, which has attractive wood panelling. The grill room offers both à la carte and fixed menus. There are two suites for functions and all the bedrooms have TVs and tea and coffee making facilities. Airdrie is a good base for visiting Glasgow, Edinburgh and Strathclyde Park.

<u>Beer</u>: Burton Ale on handpump.

<u>Accommodation</u>: 13 singles, 7 doubles, 1 twin, 10 rooms with private baths. B&B £26-£30 single, £39-£45 double. Children welcome. Weekends (3 nights) 50% discounts.

# AYR

Old Racecourse Hotel
2 Victoria Park, off Racecourse Road, A719

Licensee: John Nicol
Tel: 0292 262873

The hotel is a fine sandstone Georgian town house next to the beach and golf courses and a mile from the town centre and new racecourse. The lounge bar has a vast circular open fire in the centre of the room with a copper canopy fashioned like a whisky still. The hotel serves lunch, high tea and supper and offers local salmon and game when available. Other dishes include guacomole with crudités, smoked trout, soups, lobster and crab salads, and home-made apple pie. The hotel is a good base for visiting Burns country, the Burns cottage and the haunted Alloway church. Families are welcome.

<u>Beer</u>: McEwan 70 shilling and Younger No 3 on handpumps.

<u>Accommodation</u>: 2 singles, 7 doubles, 3 family rooms, 2 rooms en suite. B&B £15.50-£22.50 per person. Children's room; children welcome to stay, half price when sharing.

# BIGGAR

Hartree Country House Hotel
1 mile off A702

Proprietors: Brian & Margaret Quinn
Tel: 0899 20215

Hartree House is a handsome old building dating back to the 14th century, with a striking, partially castellated tower that is half mock-Norman and half mock-French château. The interior includes delightful lounges, dining room and a superb bar that was built in 1885 as a billiard room: its fittings and atmosphere stand in sharp contrast to the modern 'pool room'. There are open fires, splendid lunches and dinners lovingly prepared by Mrs Quinn, who also welcomes families. Biggar is a charming old market town with the fascinating Gladstone Court Museum that houses old traditional shops and workshops, and Greenhill Covenanters House with relics of the Covenanters.

<u>Beer</u>: Broughton Greenmantle Ale on air pressure.

<u>Accommodation</u>: 10 doubles, 1 family room, all with private bathrooms, colour TVs and tea and coffee making equipment. B&B £33 per person. Weekend £59, Week £189. Children's room; children welcome to stay, no charge if sharing with parents. Credit cards: Access, Amex.

# BRODICK (ISLE OF ARRAN)

Ormidale Hotel
Knowe Road, near the castle

Licensee: Tom Gilmore
Tel: 0770 2293

The hotel is a fine Victorian building with superb views over Brodick Bay to the Sleeping Warrior and Goatfell, 2,866 feet above sea level. It has a large, licensed conservatory with handsome brass beer founts. In summer there are live music events most nights, including discos and jug bands. Good bar meals, with local seafood as a speciality, are served lunchtime and evening between Easter and September. There is a children's menu and a large beer garden with a play area, and also a residents' TV lounge. The island is a delight, with deer roaming through the heather and opportunities for fishing, walking, pony trekking and golf: there are seven courses on the island and the first tee of one is just a few yards from the Ormidale. There are car ferries from Ardrossan to Brodick (booking essential in summer) and a smaller car ferry in summer only between Kintyre to Lochranza in the north of the island.

Beer: McEwan 70 shilling on air pressure.

Accommodation: (*Easter-September only; bar open all year*) 4 singles, 3 doubles, 1 family room. B&B £12.50 per person, Weekend £37.50. Children welcome, half price.

# CASTLECARY

Castlecary House Hotel
Main Street, A80, off M73

Tel: 0324 840233

A small village hotel close to Glasgow, with a quiet lounge, busy bar and snugs and a range of cask beers that constitutes a mini, regular beer festival. It is open all day, including Sundays, and serves both lunch and evening bar meals. Food includes lentil and potato soup, grills, salads, trout, home-made steak and kidney pie, and haddock in beer batter. Accommodation comprises rooms in the hotel and three cottages, one of which has a jacuzzi in the bathroom.

Beer: Belhaven 80 shilling, Broughton Greenmantle Ale and Merlin's Ale, Harviestoun 80 shilling, Theakston Best Bitter, XB and Old Peculier on handpumps and air pressure.

Accommodation: 8 singles, 9 doubles, 13 rooms with en suite facilities. B&B £14-£25 single, £30-£40 double, terms depend on type of room and facilities: some cottage accommodation includes private lounge and own TV and tea and coffee makers.

# EAGLESHAM

Eglinton Arms Hotel
Gilmour Street, off A77

Licensee: T Paterson
Tel: 03553 2631

The Eglinton Arms is a popular village local in old Renfrewshire. It dates back to the 16th century when it was an important coaching inn. There are reminders of the past in the Stables Bar and the Postillion Restaurant. Darts and dominoes are played in the snug, which has a cheery fire in winter. Good bar food includes home-made soups and pâté, grills, chicken, seafood and poached cod. Cask beer in the lounge bar only.

Beer: McEwan 80 shilling, Younger No 3 on air pressure.

Accommodation: 6 singles, 3 doubles, 5 twins, all with private baths. B&B £38 single, £48 double/twin. Weekend £25 single, £35 double/twin per day.

## GLASGOW

Babbity Bowster
16-18 Blackfriars Street, east of the city centre

Proprietor: Fraser Laurie
Tel: 041 552 5055

A brilliant new creation in the centre of Glasgow that is bar, café and restaurant rolled into one in an elegant Robert Adam town house on the site of an ancient monastery. The fine recreation of a medieval inn sign is repeated inside as a wall plaque. There are tall windows, pastel walls, a mass of drawings and photographs of Glasgow and Glaswegians and a restaurant that also doubles as an art gallery for Glasgow painters. Food ranges from light snacks to full meals, starts with breakfast and goes on until the wee small hours. Try soup, vegetarian casserole, haggis, neeps and tatties, Bowster potted hough, cabbage and bacon, beef sausage and mixed bean casserole, jacket potatoes with choice of fillings, Orkney oatcakes and Scottish cheeses such as Arran truckle and Lanark blue. There are open fires, outside seating in pleasant weather and live music, including traditional fiddlers. The enterprise is named after a Scots kissing dance.

Hats off to Fraser Laurie for a stylish and innovative hostelry.

Beer: Maclay 70 shilling, 80 shilling and Porter on air pressure.

Accommodation: 3 singles, 3 doubles, all en suite. B&B £22.50 per person. Full board available. Children welcome to stay. Credit cards: Access, Amex, Visa.

## GOUROCK

Spinnaker Hotel
121 Albert Road, A78, south of town

Licensee: Ann McCartney
Tel: 0475 33107

A friendly family-run hotel on the sea front with sweeping views over the Clyde to Dunoon and the distant Highlands. The hotel is a haven of peace with no juke boxes or gambling machines. There is a downstairs bar and dining room and a cocktail bar on the first floor. A wide range of bar meals are served daily. Sailing, fishing, hill climbing and golf are all available in the area.

Beer: Belhaven 80 shilling on air pressure.

Accommodation: 2 singles, 2 doubles. B&B £12.50 per person, £12 for more than 1 night. Children welcome.

## HOUSTON

Houston Inn
North Street, off A761

Licensee: Thomas McKean
Tel: 0505 614315

The inn is the oldest pub in Houston and offers a warm welcome at the centre of the village. Near the Clyde, it is just ten minutes from Glasgow airport and 15 minutes from Loch Lomond. There is a pleasant garden for warm weather, a residents' lounge for families and lunchtime snacks. It is a good base for walking in the lovely countryside and for visiting Glasgow.

Beer: McEwan 80 shilling on air pressure.

Accommodation: 2 family rooms. B&B £10-£15 per person. Credit cards: Amex.

# INVERBEG

Inverbeg Inn
On A82 near Luss, by Loch Lomond

Licensee: Jack Bisset
Tel: 043 686 678

The inn, once the Ferry Inn, stands in breathtaking countryside on the west bank of the loch opposite the craggy slopes of Ben Lomond. The loch ferry calls at the inn's own jetty three times a day in summer. The Inverbeg was once a drovers' ale house and is still a genuine local, with shepherds and fishermen playing dominoes and cribbage in the bar. The lounge bar has sofas and armchairs and a host of prints including one of the Monarch of the Glen. There is an evening restaurant while bar meals are served lunchtime and evening and include home-made soups, meat and fish grills, jacket spuds with choice of fillings, ploughman's, pizzas, quiche, sandwiches, toasties and salads. The children's menu includes hoops, bangers, beans and fish fingers and chips. As well as the accommodation at the inn, Mr Bisset owns cruisers for hire on the loch with sleeping

quarters. There are also day trips in season to Dunoon, Oban, Fort William and Glencoe, and the Trossachs.

Beer: McEwan 70 shilling on air pressure.

Accommodation: 2 singles, 11 doubles, 1 family room, 7 rooms with private baths. B&B £20 single, with off-season reductions. Children welcome. Facilities for the disabled. Credit cards: Access, Amex, Carte Blanche, Diners, Visa.

# JOHNSTONE

Lynnhurst Hotel
Park Road, A737

Licensee: D McIntyre
Tel: 0505 24331

The Lynnhurst is a comfortable, family-owned hotel with a large lounge bar. It is in a quiet and pleasant position overlooking a park, away from the town centre. It has a residents' lounge and a snooker room, facilities for families and meals lunchtime and evening.

Beer: Younger No 3 on air pressure.

Accommodation: 14 singles, 8 doubles, 2 family rooms, 16 rooms with en suite facilities. B&B £15-£25 per person. Credit cards: Access, Diners, Visa.

# KILMUN

Coylet Inn
Loch Eck, A815

Licensees: R & H Addis
Tel: 036 984 426

A small roadside hotel with imposing dormer windows and superb views of the loch amid the lovely forests of Argyll and the idyllic Cowal peninsula. The Coylet was formerly a coaching inn and parts of the building date back to the 18th century. It offers excellent hospitality with open log fires in winter, two bars, food lunchtime and evening and a good base for fishing, walking or visiting nearby Dunoon.

Beer: McEwan 80 shilling and Younger No 3 on air pressure.

Accommodation: 1 single, 2 doubles. B&B £12 per person. Children welcome, half price.

# WHITING BAY (ISLE OF ARRAN)

Cameronia Hotel
Shore Road, A841

Licensee: Bob Fisher
Tel: 0770 7254

The Cameronia is a small and lively family-run hotel overlooking Holy Isle and close to Brodick Castle. There is a comfortable snug, and a steak and wine bar, with a high priority placed on home cooking for both bar and restaurant meals. The hotel is the home of the Cameronia darts team who play badly but with great enthusiasm and raise large amounts of money for charity. There is folk singing every weekend in summer and ceilidhs and beer and malt whisky tastings in winter.

Beer: Broughton Greenmantle Ale on handpump.

Accommodation: 2 singles, 5 doubles, 1 family room, 1 room with private bath. B&B + evening meal £22 per person. Half board weekends and weeks available, with golf, fishing and pony trekking

holidays by arrangement. Children welcome, terms by arrangement.

# PERTH

Hunters Lodge
Bankfoot, off A9, A93 & A94

Licensee: Michael Anderson
Tel: 0738 87325

The lodge is an old coaching inn ideally placed for visiting the imposing city of Perth and as a base for the Highlands. Bar meals are a speciality and the restaurant serves traditional high tea and dinner seven days a week. There is a children's games room and a skittle alley and there are opportunities in the area for golf and fishing.

Beer: Tennent 80 shilling on air pressure.

Accommodation: 10 doubles. B&B from £20 per person. Children welcome. Credit cards: Access, Amex, Diners.

# The Maps

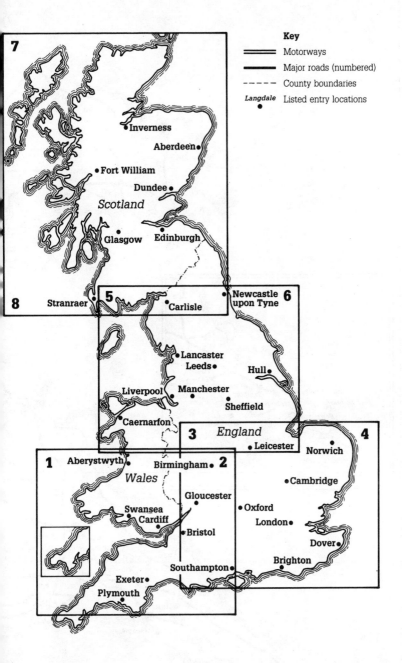

**Key**

═══ Motorways

━━━ Major roads (numbered)

----- County boundaries

*Langdale* • Listed entry locations

7

• Inverness

Aberdeen •

• Fort William

Dundee •

*Scotland*

Glasgow • Edinburgh •

8 | Stranraer • | 5 | • Carlisle | • Newcastle upon Tyne | 6

• Lancaster
Leeds •

Hull •

Liverpool • Manchester •

Sheffield •

Caernarfon •

3 | *England*

• Leicester | Norwich • | 4

1 | Aberystwyth • | Birmingham • | 2

*Wales*

Gloucester •

• Cambridge

Swansea •
Cardiff •

• Oxford
London •

• Bristol

Dover •

Southampton •

Brighton •

Exeter •
Plymouth •

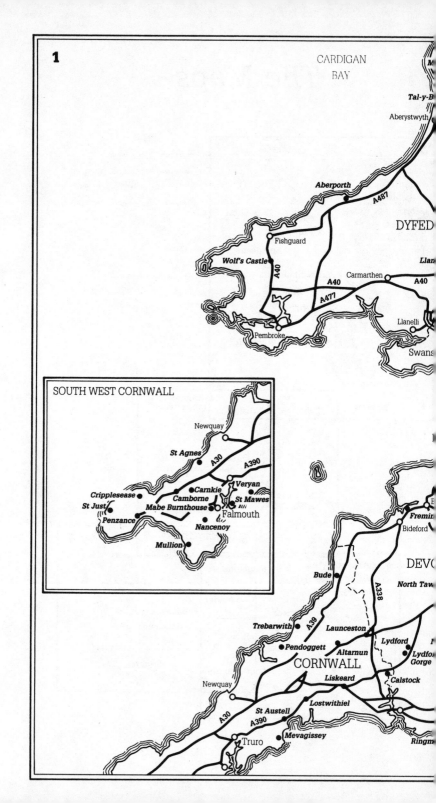

**1**

CARDIGAN
BAY

Tal-y-B

Aberystwyth

Aberporth ● A487

DYFED

Fishguard

Wolf's Castle

Llan

A40

Carmarthen ○ A40

A477

Llanelli

Pembroke ○

Swans

SOUTH WEST CORNWALL

Newquay

St Agnes ●

A30

A390

Veryan ●

Carnkie ●

Camborne ● St Mawes

Cripplesease ●

St Just ● Mabe Burnthouse ● Falmouth

Penzance ○

Nancenoy

Mullion ●

E

Fremin

Bideford

DEVO

Bude ● North Taw

A39

A338

Trebarwith ● A39 Launceston

Lydford

Pendoggett ● Altarnun Lydfo
Gorge

CORNWALL

Liskeard Calstock

Newquay ○

Lostwithiel

A30 St Austell

A390

Truro ○ Mevagissey Ringm

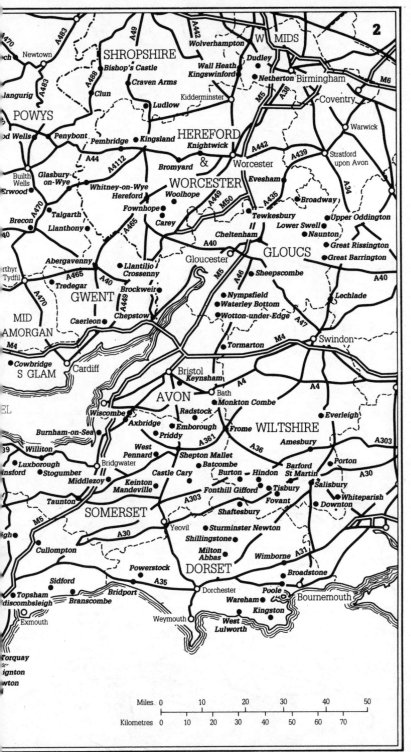

**2**

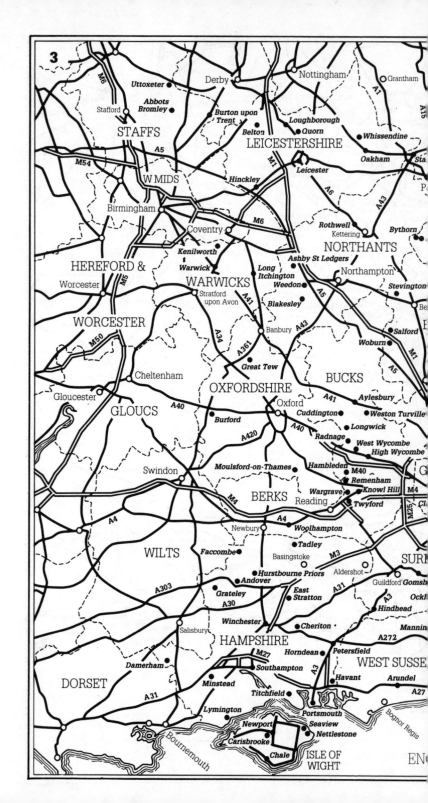

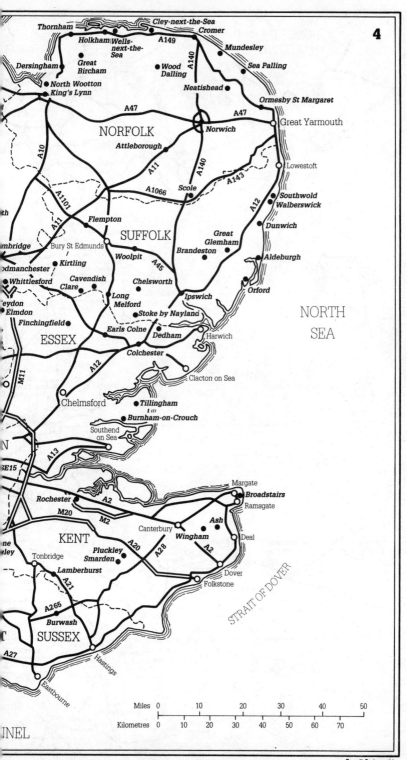

4

Thornham
Cley-next-the-Sea
Cromer
Holkham
Wells-next-the-Sea
A149
A140
Mundesley
Great Bircham
Sea Palling
Dersingham
Wood Dalling
North Wootton
King's Lynn
Neatishead
Ormesby St Margaret
A47
A47
Great Yarmouth
NORFOLK
Norwich
A10
Attleborough
A11
Lowestoft
A140
A1066
Scole
Southwold
A143
Walberswick
A1101
A11
Flempton
Dunwich
SUFFOLK
Great Glemham
Aldeburgh
mbridge
Bury St Edmunds
A12
Brandeston
odmanchester
Kirtling
Woolpit
A45
Whittlesford
Cavendish
Chelsworth
Orford
Clare
eydon
Long Melford
Ipswich
Elmdon
Stoke by Nayland
NORTH SEA
Finchingfield
Earls Colne
Dedham
ESSEX
Harwich
Colchester
A12
Clacton on Sea
M11
Chelmsford
Tillingham
Burnham-on-Crouch
Southend on Sea
A13
E15
Margate
Broadstairs
Rochester
A2
Ramsgate
M20
M2
Ash
Canterbury
Wingham
Deal
KENT
A20
A28
ne
Pluckley
A2
ley
Tonbridge
Smarden
Lamberhurst
Dover
A21
Folkstone
STRAIT OF DOVER
A265
Burwash
SUSSEX
A27
Hastings
Eastbourne

| Miles | 0 | | 10 | | 20 | | 30 | | 40 | | 50 |
|---|---|---|---|---|---|---|---|---|---|---|---|
| Kilometres | 0 | 10 | 20 | 30 | 40 | 50 | 60 | 70 | | | |

NEL

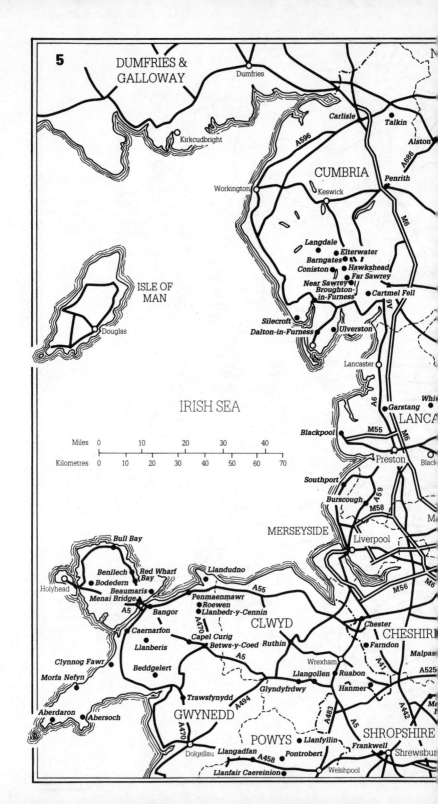

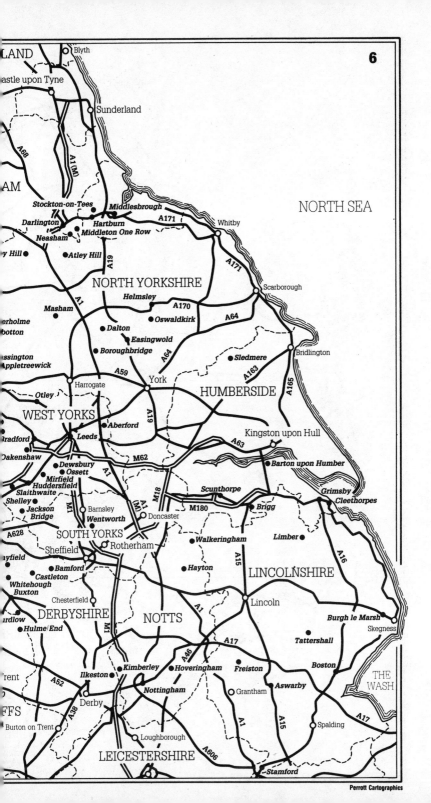

LAND

Blyth

astle upon Tyne

Sunderland

A68

A1(M)

AM

NORTH SEA

Stockton-on-Tees   Middlesbrough

Darlington   Hartburn   A171   Whitby

Neasham   Middleton One Row

y Hill   Atley Hill

A19

NORTH YORKSHIRE

A171

Masham   Helmsley   A170   Scarborough

erholme   Oswaldkirk   A64

botton   Dalton   Easingwold

ssington   Boroughbridge   A64   Sledmere   Bridlington

ppletreewick

A59   York   A163

Harrogate   HUMBERSIDE   A165

Otley

WEST YORKS   A19

Bradford   Aberford   Kingston upon Hull

Leeds   A63

Oakenshaw   M62   Barton upon Humber

Dewsbury   Ossett   Scunthorpe   Grimsby

Mirfield   Huddersfield   M18   M180   Cleethorpes

Slaithwaite   A1(M)   Brigg

Shelley   Jackson   Barnsley   Doncaster

Bridge   M1   Wentworth   A16

A628   SOUTH YORKS   Walkeringham   Limber

ayfield   Sheffield   Rotherham

Bamford   Hayton   LINCOLNSHIRE

Castleton   A15

Whitehough

Buxton   Chesterfield   Lincoln

rdlow   DERBYSHIRE   NOTTS   Burgh le Marsh

Hulme End   A1   Skegness

M1   A17   Tattershall

rent   A52   Ilkeston   Kimberley   Hoveringham   Freiston   Boston

Derby   A46   Nottingham   Grantham   Aswarby   THE WASH

FFS   A38   A15

Burton on Trent   Loughborough   Spalding   A17

LEICESTERSHIRE   A606   Stamford

**Perrott Cartographics**

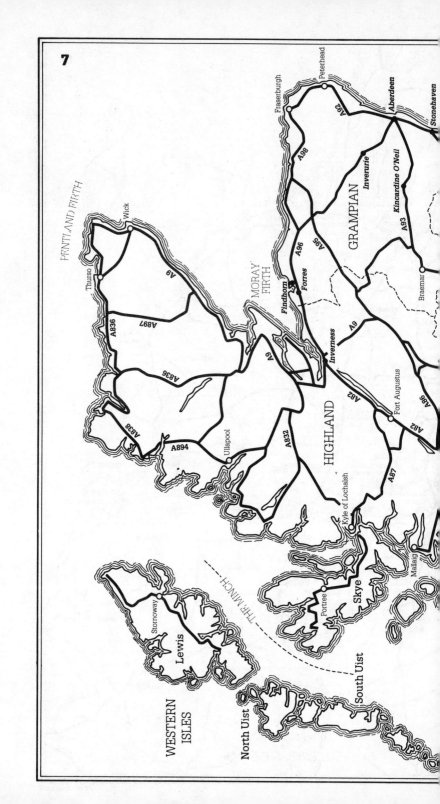

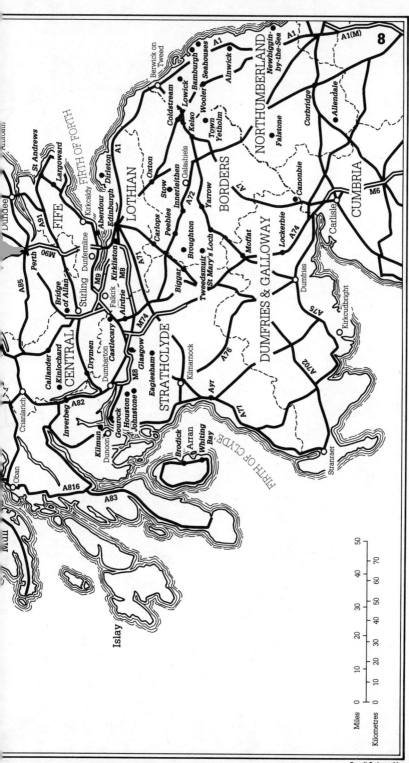

**8**

Perrott Cartographics

er and pub lovers will enjoy the following books available
om CAMRA:

**assic Country Pubs** and **Classic Town Pubs** by Neil Hanson,
vilion Books, are handsome books with full colour photographs that lovingly
rtray some of the finest ale houses and inns in Britain, many of them with
cinating histories and architecture. **Classic Country** costs £10.95, **Classic
wn**, £11.95.

**e Great British Beer Book** by Roger Protz, Impact Books, is a
·man's history of ale and beer from pre-Roman times to the present day. En
ite it covers the arrival of the hop from Holland, the rise of porter and the
mmercial brewers, the advent of Burton beers that tickled the palate of the
ıssian Czars as well as British drinkers, the growth of the tied house and keg
er in the 20th century, and the present-day battles between real-ale lovers and
e giant brewing battalions. Illustrated with cartoons, songs, poems and original
ints, it costs £5.95.

ıe **Good Cider Guide** by David Kitton is the appleholic version of the
**ood Beer Guide**, listing every known outlet and producer of real draught
ler. £4.95. Both are published by CAMRA.

ıe **CAMRA Dictionary of Beer**, compiled by Brian Glover, Longman,
vital for all serious beer connoisseurs with definitions of all beer types and
les, malts, hops and methods of fermentation and serving. £2.95.

receive these books send a cheque for the appropriate amount to
AMRA, 34 Alma Road, St Albans, Herts AL1 3BW.

# REPORT FORM

County _____

Town or village _____

Name of pub/hotel _____

Address _____

Location (A or B road) _____

Tel no _____ Name of licensee _____

Description of pub (including bars, food, guest rooms and any special
facilities) _____

_____

_____

_____

Draught beers (including method of dispense) _____

_____

_____

## Accommodation:

No of single rooms _____ doubles/twins _____ family rooms _____

Cost of B & B per person per day_____ cost for double/twin if price

based on room _____ cost for family room _____

No of rooms with en suite baths or showers_____

Can children stay ☐ yes ☐ no Children's reductions _____

Cost of any special 'breaks', eg off-season, weekend,

mid-week _____

Name and address of person recommending _____

_____

_____

**Send to**
**Roger Protz, CAMRA, 34 Alma Road, St Albans, Herts AL1 3BW**

# DELETION FORM

County _____

Town or village _____

Name of pub/hotel _____

Address _____

_____

_____

The entry should be deleted for the following reasons:

_____

_____

_____

_____

_____

_____

_____

Name and address of person recommending deletion

_____

_____

_____

Send to
Roger Protz, CAMRA, 34 Alma Road, St Albans, Herts AL1 3BW

# PUBS FOR FAMILIES

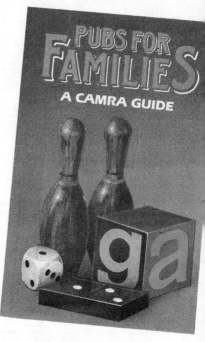

How often have you been to a pub with a 'family room' that had all the warmth and atmosphere of a railway waiting room. . . and none of the facilities? Pubs for Families brings you pubs that don't just tolerate families but positively welcome them. CAMRA has searched the lowlands of England and the Highlands of Scotland to come up with a selection that makes pub-going a treat for all the family. There are pubs with gardens and play areas for the summer, pubs with games, books and videos, and properly equipped family rooms with changing facilities. There is also vital information about enclosed play areas and children's menus. Don't have any more ruined days out. . . take Pubs for Families on your next trip.

Edited by Jill Adam and Neil Hanson.
Published by Alma Books, £4.95.

Available direct from
CAMRA, 34 Alma Road, St Albans, Herts AL1 3BW.